justinguitar.com
Pop Songbook

Published by
Wise Publications
14-15 Berners Street, London W1T 3LJ, UK.

Exclusive Distributors:
Music Sales Limited
Distribution Centre, Newmarket Road,
Bury St Edmunds, Suffolk IP33 3YB, UK.
Music Sales Corporation
180 Madison Avenue, 24th Floor,
New York NY 10016, USA.
Music Sales Pty Limited
Units 3-4, 17 Willfox Street, Condell Park
NSW 2200, Australia.

Order No. AM1005158
ISBN: 978-1-78038-685-0

Written, compiled and arranged by Justin Sandercoe.
Edited by Toby Knowles.
Design by Fresh Lemon.
Cover design by Paul Agar.
Cover photographs by Nick Delaney.
With thanks to Dario Cortese.
Printed in the EU.

justinguitar.com
Pop Songbook

Wise Publications
part of The Music Sales Group
London / New York / Paris / Sydney / Copenhagen / Berlin / Madrid / Hong Kong / Tokyo

Your Guarantee of Quality
As publishers, we strive to produce every book to the highest commercial standards.
This book has been carefully designed to minimise awkward page turns and to make playing from it a real pleasure.
Particular care has been given to specifying acid-free, neutral-sized paper made from pulps which have not been elemental chlorine bleached.
This pulp is from farmed sustainable forests and was produced with special regard for the environment.
Throughout, the printing and binding have been planned to ensure a sturdy, attractive publication which should give years of enjoyment.
If your copy fails to meet our high standards, please inform us and we will gladly replace it.

www.musicsales.com

www.justinguitar.com

Contents

STARTED LEARNED PERFORMED

PERFORMED LEARNED STARTED

INTRODUCTION

Welcome to my Pop Songbook!

This book is for guitar players who have worked through the basics of playing, and are now aiming to progress beyond beginner level. I expect many of you will have completed my free online Beginner's Guitar Course and perhaps learned songs from the *Justinguitar.com Beginner's Songbook*. This book continues on from there and introduces material used in the Intermediate Method (also free on the website), including barre chords and sixteenth-note strumming.

There are four sections to the book, starting with a 'Beginner' section, and ending with a section of full TAB transcriptions. The Beginner section mainly uses chords, rhythms and techniques covered in my Beginner's Guitar Course, with a few new tricks thrown in to keep things interesting. It's a great selection of tunes, which are fun to play, not too tricky to master, and which will help you consolidate your knowledge.

The 'Intermediate' section introduces barre chords. Playing barre chords is probably the most important skill to learn after you've become confident with all your beginner techniques. Some songs use only barre chords, while others mix them with open chords—you'll need to master both approaches. If you are uncertain about how to play barre chords, please check out the relevant lessons on the website.

Next up we have 'Intermediate Plus' which, as the name suggests, uses many of the skills and techniques covered in the Intermediate Method but adds some other interesting elements, such as new chords, more complex rhythm patterns and riffs.

Lastly, we have five full guitar TAB transcriptions, which should prove a little more challenging and give you something to work towards! These songs differ quite a lot in terms of style and technique, but they're all pop classics.

I'd like to thank Toby and Tom at Music Sales for their help and suggestions, and also the many users that offered song suggestions. Thanks also to Jed Wardley for helping get this book to you, Dario Cortese for proofreading and to the forum moderators (Tom, Lieven, Jonathan and Richard) for their massive contribution to our community.

If you enjoy this book then you might like to keep an eye out for others in this series, which will include a range of styles including rock, acoustic and vintage. I hope you enjoy playing the songs in this book and wish you a lot of joy on your musical journey.

Justin Sandercoe
February 2013, London

If you get stuck with anything in this songbook then your first port of call should be my website where there are many hundreds of completely free lessons that will take you from complete novice level to wherever you want to go!

www.justinguitar.com

If you enjoy online interaction there is a great forum where there are many thousands of students helping each other every day! It really is a passionate, supportive and active community, and you are welcome to join it.

www.justinguitarcommunity.com

PRACTICE GUIDE

Top 10 Practice Tips

1. Practise what you can't do, not what you can.
2. Practice makes permanent (not perfect). So get it right!
3. Start slowly and get it right before you speed up.
4. Using a timer saves time.
5. Focus on one element of a song at a time.
6. Try to practise a little every day, rather than a lot all on one day.
7. Keep track of your practice: use a practice schedule.
8. If it sounds good, it is good!
9. Playing and Practising are very different—don't confuse them.
10. The more you think, the more you stink! Practise until the part becomes instinctive.

Using Software

I would strongly suggest getting some software that will allow you to change the speed of a recording but not the pitch. I use one called Transcribe! but there are many others available, including Audacity, Capo and the Amazing Slow Downer.

Set the software to play the song at 50%, or at whatever speed you can practise in time with. Play along with the recording; use the 'cycle' feature to repeat one section (or the whole song) over and over. Once you are confident that you can play this section precisely, speed the track up, a little bit at a time. This may happen over the course of a few weeks, or in one practice session, depending on your ability and on the difficulty of the song.

Take time to learn how to use the software, in particular how to use the key commands (keyboard shortcuts). This will save you countless hours!

Practising Harder Material

When approaching a more complex song, start by having a mess around—play through the song a few times as well as you can, working out where the tricky bits are, and which sections will require the most attention. Pick one section and play it very slowly and accurately—I usually start with the main riff or theme, or perhaps the introduction. Make sure that you get it right. Every time you play something wrong you are entering 'bad code' into your brain.

Try to play this section with the correct rhythm, even if it is very slow. I recommend that you count out the beats while you're practising, as this will help a lot. Don't worry about the groove just yet, but concentrate on precision, making sure that your timing is mathematically correct.

Try to get this first 'chunk' into your memory as soon as you can. Your goal should be to play while looking at your guitar (or closing your eyes), rather than following the music on the page. After you have memorised this first 'chunk', you should build upon it. Learn the next section, slowly and carefully, and once you can play this new section in time (no matter how slowly), join it on to the first section. Work on creating a flow between the two sections, and practise both sections 'joined-up' until you can play them at 70-80% of the actual speed of the song.

Continue this process until you can play through the whole song at a slower tempo, and then start to speed the tempo up, until you can play at full speed. It's much better to play correctly at a slower tempo than to play at full speed, with mistakes. If there are one or two extra hard bits, extract them and work on them on their own. When they are sounding good enough, put them back into the whole song.

BEGINNER STAGE

Introduction

This first chapter mainly uses the chords, rhythms and techniques covered in my Beginner's Course. The layout is the same as in my Beginner's Songbook, with chords and lyrics on one page and tips and rhythms on the facing page.

Chords

For the most part, the chords used in this section are the eight essential open chords:

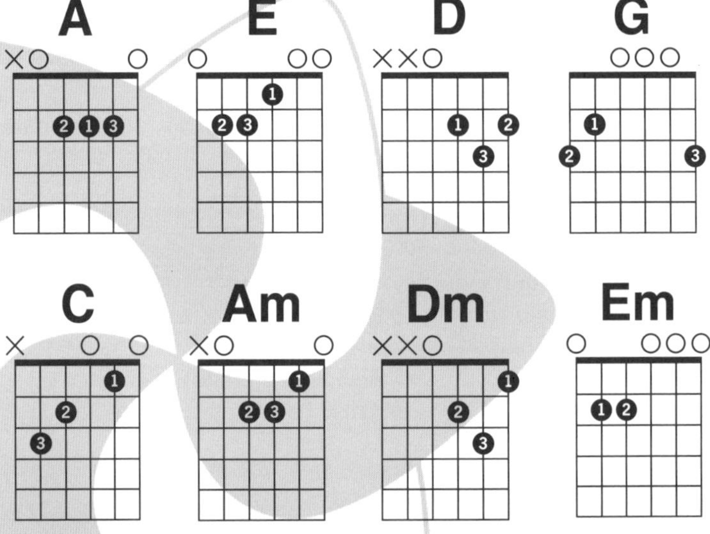

You'll also find a few variations of these and some basic slash chords.

F Chord

I assume that you are also familiar with the F chord. Below left is the full barre version of the chord, and on the right is the smaller, simpler version of the chord.

7th Chords

We'll also be using these (dominant) 7th chords, which are also open chords, as shown below.

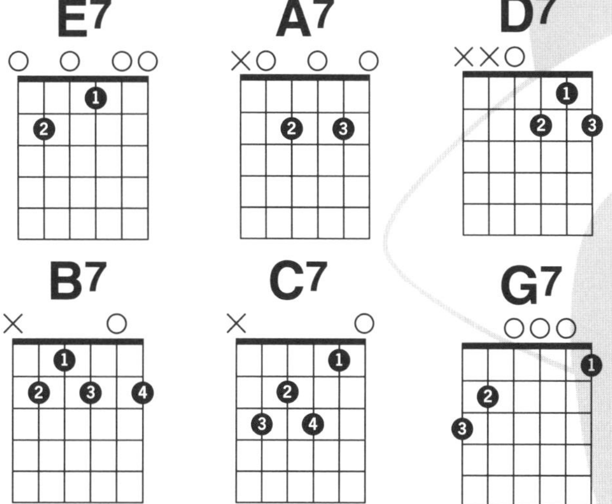

Sus Chords

Lastly, we'll be playing a few sus chords, which again are nice, friendly open chords.

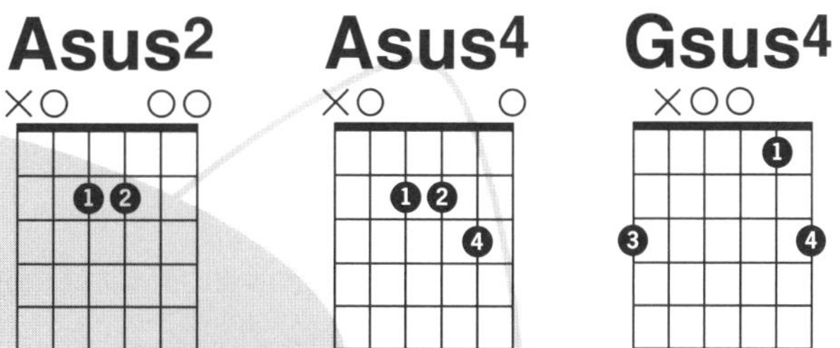

Chord Glossary

Any chords not featured here, or in the song's tutorial, will be found in the Chord Glossary at the back of this book.

Breakeven

Words & Music by Andrew Frampton, Stephen Kipner, Mark Sheehan & Daniel O'Donoghue

Beginner

Intermediate

Intermediate +

TAB

Intro

```
|: C     | G     | D     | Em    :|  Play x 4
 | Em    | D     | G     | Am    |
```

Verse 1

```
Em                    D                   G   Am
I'm still alive but I'm barely breathing,
     Em                    D                 G   Am
Just prayed to a God that I don't believe in.
         Em         D                       G   Am
'Cause I got time while she got freedom,
         Em                  D                          G   Am
'Cause when a heart breaks, no, it don't break even.
```

Verse 2

Her best days were some of my worst,
She finally met a man that's gonna put her first.
While I'm wide awake she's no trouble sleeping,
'Cause when a heart breaks no it don't break even, even, no.

Chorus 1

```
C               G
   What am I supposed to do
           D                          Em
When the best part of me was always you?
     C              G
And    what am I supposed to say
            D                      Em
When I'm all choked up and you're ok?
C        G          D      Em        C
    I'm falling to pie - ces, yeah,
     G           D    Em
I'm falling to pie - ces.
```

Link 1

```
| Em    | D     | G     | Am    |
```

Verse 3

They say bad things happen for a reason,
But no wise words gonna stop the bleeding.
'Cause she's moved on while I'm still grieving,
And when a heart breaks no it don't break even, even, no.

Chorus 2

What am I gonna do
When the best part of me was always you?
And what am I supposed to say
When I'm all choked up and you're ok?
I'm falling to pieces, yeah.
I'm falling to pieces, yeah.
I'm falling to pieces. I'm falling to pieces.

Link 2 ‖: Em | D/F# | G | C :‖

Bridge

```
(C)            Em                                D/F#
Oh, you got his heart and my heart and none of the pain,
G                           C
You took your suitcase, I took the blame.
          Em                                  D/F#     G       C
Now I'm trying to make sense of what little re - mains, oh,
            C                          C           C          C
'Cause you left me with no love,   with no love to my name.
```

Verse 4

I'm still alive but I'm barely breathing,
Just prayed to a God that I don't believe in.
'Cause I got time while she got freedom,
'Cause when a heart breaks, no, it don't break,
No, it don't break, no, it don't break even, no

Chorus 3 As Chorus 2

Outro Repeat Chorus chords to fade *(vocals ad lib.)*

Introduction

Dublin's The Script struck gold with this heartfelt ballad, released in 2008.

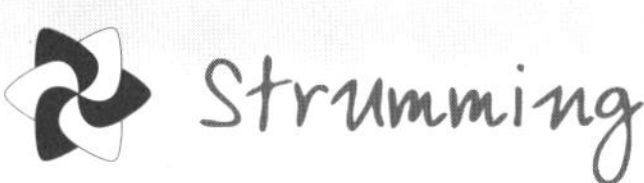

Strumming

The guitar part to this song is based on a repeated riff, but it will also sound great if you strum the chords, which is what we're going to focus on here. I've added a capo (at the 3rd fret) and simplified the chords a little to suit a strummed guitar part. There is no set strumming pattern for this song, so pick a pattern that you are already comfortable with and try it out. Even using a very simple eighth-note pattern—playing all down-strums—will sound cool, but experiment with a few alternatives.

cont...

usic by Andrew Frampton, Stephen Kipner, Mark Sheehan
'Donoghue

The Riffs

If you want to copy the actual guitar part played on the recording, I have tabbed out arrangements of the two riffs—these will match up with the chords, and will also require a capo on the 3rd fret. For the intro riff, the left-hand fingering is shown above the stave. There is no set fingering for the second riff, so for this, please use whichever fingers feel comfortable. Neither riff is hard to play but you must watch out for the rhythm, which is by far the most challenging element.

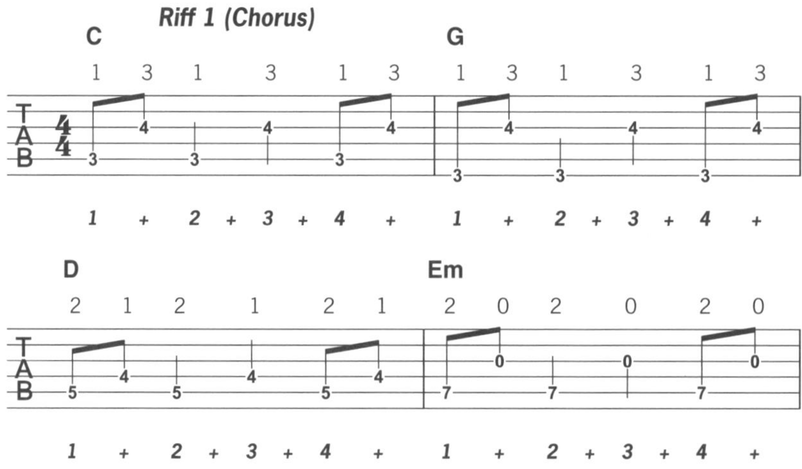

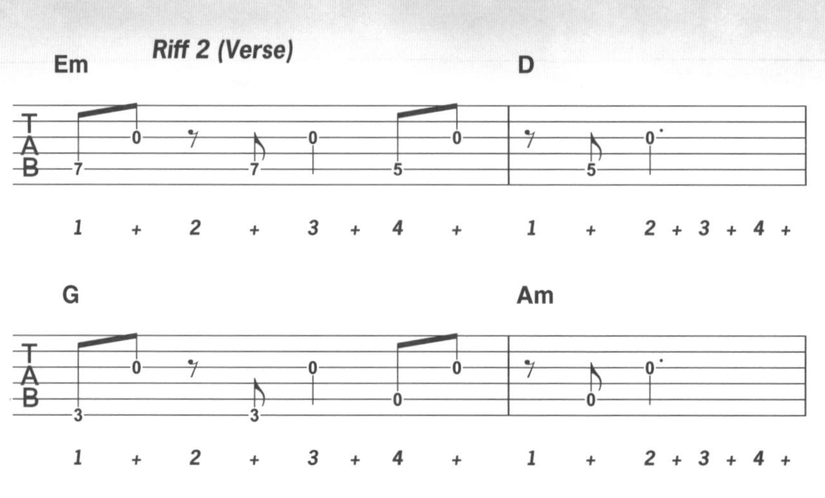

I Gotta Feeling

Words & Music by Will Adams, Jaime Gomez, Allan Pineda, Stacy Ferguson, David Guetta & Frederic Riesterer

Introduction

This collaboration between the Black Eyed Peas and David Guetta is great fun to play (and has a wicked video too!).

Main Riff

The song starts with a repeated synth riff which is simple to play, so I have written it out for you too. There are many options when it comes to left-hand fingering, so experiment a little and choose a logical and comfortable fingering that works for you.

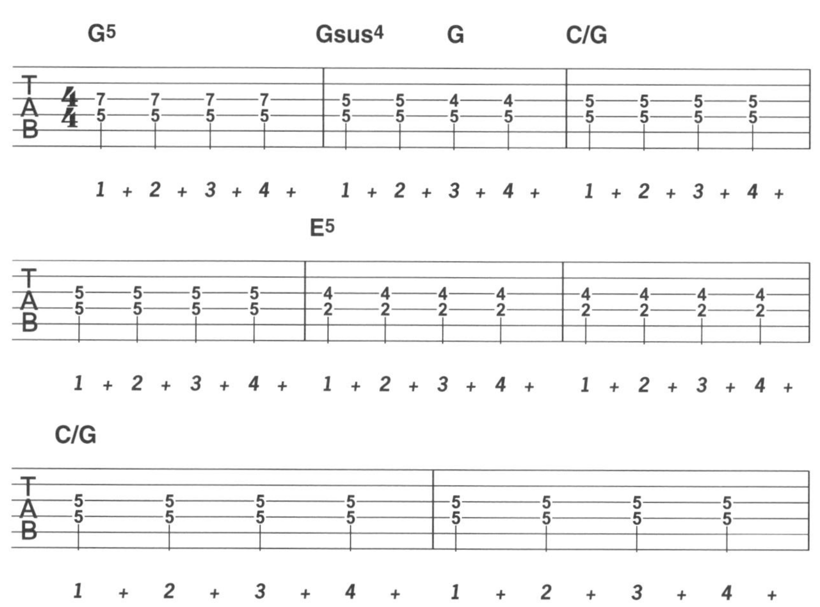

I Gotta Feeling

Words & Music by Will Adams, Jaime Gomez, Allan Pineda, Stacy Ferguson, David Guetta & Frederic Riesterer

Beginner

Intermediate

Intermediate +

TAB

Chord sequence throughout:

Intro

G	Gsus4 G	C	C
Em	Em	C	C

Chorus 1

I gotta feeling that tonight's gonna be a good night,
That tonight's gonna be a good night,
That tonight's gonna be a good, good night.
A feeling that tonight's gonna be a good night,
That tonight's gonna be a good night,
That tonight's gonna be a good, good night.

Chorus 2

A feeling, whoo hoo, that tonight's gonna be a good night,
That tonight's gonna be a good night,
That tonight's gonna be a good, good night.
A feeling, whoo hoo, that tonight's gonna be a good night,
That tonight's gonna be a good night,
That tonight's gonna be a good, good night.

Verse 1

Tonight's the night, let's live it up,
I got my money, let's spend it up.
Go out and smash it like oh my God,
Jump off that sofa, let's get, get off.
I know that we'll have a ball
If we get down and go out and just lose it all.
I feel stressed out, I wanna let it go,
Let's go way out spaced out and losing all control.
Fill up my cup, mazel tov!
Look at her dancing, just take it off.
Let's paint the town, we'll shut it down,
Let's burn the roof and then we'll do it again.

Pre-chorus 1

Let's do it, let's do it, let's do it, let's do it,
And do it and do it, let's live it up.
And do it and do it and do it, do it, do it,
Let's do it, let's do it, let's do it. ('Cause I gotta...)

Chorus 3

As Chorus 2

Verse 2

Tonight's the night, (Hey!) let's live it up, (Let's live it up)
I got my money, (My pay) let's spend it up. (Let's spend it up)
Go out and smash it (Smash it) like oh my God, (Like oh my God)
Jump off that sofa, (Come on!) let's get, get off
Fill up my cup, (Drink) mazel tov, (L'chaim!)
Look at her dancing, (Move it, move it) just take it off.
Let's paint the town, (Paint the town)
We'll shut it down, (shut it down)
Let's burn the roof and then we'll do it again.

Pre-chorus 2

As Pre-chorus 1

Bridge

Here we come, here we go, we gotta rock,
Easy come, easy go, now we on top.
Feel the shot, body rock, rock it, don't stop,
Round and round, up and down, around the clock.
Monday, Tuesday, Wednesday and Thursday (Do it!)
Friday, Saturday, Saturday to Sunday (Do it!)
Get, get, get, get, get with us, you know what we say, say
Party every day, p-p-p-party every day. (And I'm...)

Chorus 4

As Chorus 2

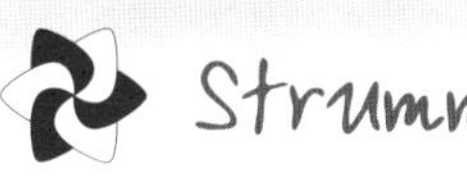

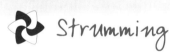

Strumming

The first thing to note about this song is that it repeats the same chord sequence all the way through. I'd recommend strumming the chords on this song—there are lots of strumming patterns that will fit the groove, and as there is no strumming on the original recording you have a lot of freedom to experiment. 'Old Faithful' (BC-165) will work pretty well, as will playing regular eighth-note down-strums.

The most important thing here is to remember to use dynamics (loud and soft) to add variety and a bit of drama to the music, because repeating the same chord sequence and strumming pattern for a whole song could get mighty boring for the listener. My tip would be to play the main synth riff for the verses and then strum during the choruses. But try a few options and see what feels good for you!

Crazy

Words & Music by Thomas Callaway, Brian Burton, Gianfranco Reverberi & Gian Piero Reverberi

Beginner

Intermediate

Intermediate +

TAB

Verse 1

```
Am                    Am                                      Cmaj7
  I remember when, I remember, I remember when I lost my mind,
        Cmaj7                               Fmaj7
There was something so pleasant about that place.
                         Fmaj7              E7sus4  E7
Even your emotions had an echo, in so much space.
Am                                  Am                 Cmaj7
  And when you're out there, without care, yeah, I was out of touch.
     Cmaj7                                  Fmaj7   Fmaj7
But it wasn't because I didn't know enough,
               E7sus4  E7
I just knew too much.
```

Chorus 1

```
                     Am     Am
Does that make me cra - zy?
                     Cmaj7  Cmaj7
Does that make me cra - zy?
                     F      F        E7sus4  E7
Does that make me cra - zy?   Possi - bly.
```

Bridge 1

```
A                             A                       F   F
   And I hope that you are having the time of your life.
           C     C                   E7sus4 E7
But think twice,    that's my only ad - vice.
```

Verse 2

Come on now, who do you, who do you, who do you,
Who do you think you are?
Ha ha ha bless your soul,
You really think you're in control.

Chorus 2

Well, I think you're crazy, I think you're crazy,
I think you're crazy, just like me.

Bridge 2

My heroes had the heart to lose their lives out on a limb.
And all I remember is thinking, I want to be like them.

Verse 3

Ever since I was little, ever since I was little,
It looked like fun.
And it's no coincidence I've come,
And I can die when I'm done.

Chorus 3

But maybe I'm crazy? Maybe you're crazy?
Maybe we're crazy, probably.

Bridge 4

Mm, ooh, ooh, ooh, ooh,
Ooh, ooh, mm.

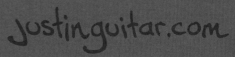

Introduction

Gnarls Barkley, which comprises two of the biggest talents in the world of R&B (Cee-Lo Green and Dangermouse) released their debut single, 'Crazy' in 2006.

Major Change

The chord sequence to this song is pretty much the same the whole way through. The main chord sequence is basically (2 bars each of) Am, C, F and E7, with the only substantial change coming in the Bridge. Just to summarize it, I've arranged the chords a little to:

Verse	Am	Cmaj7	Fmaj7	E7sus4 E7
Chorus	Am	Cmaj7	F	E7sus4 E7
Bridge	A	F	C	E7sus4 E7

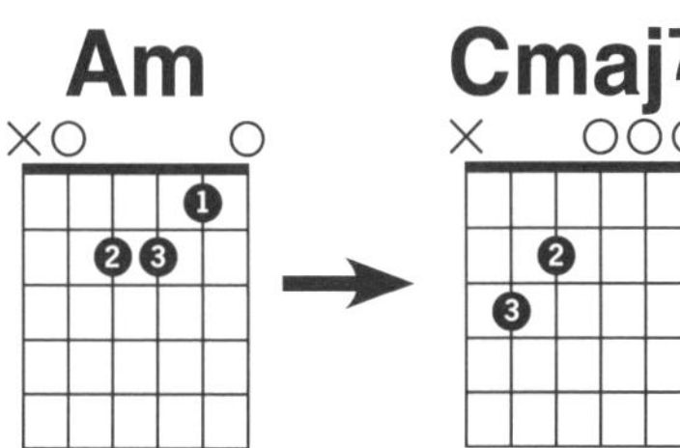

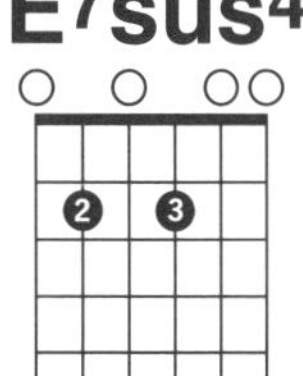

E7sus4

Rhythm

The rhythm is pretty consistent on the recording, just 'pumping' along on the bass strings, very simply. If you play this song solo, I would advise experimenting a bit to build in some dynamics. You should add in more strums and more volume for the choruses and bring the volume down for the verses, in order to create a sense of movement and contrast.

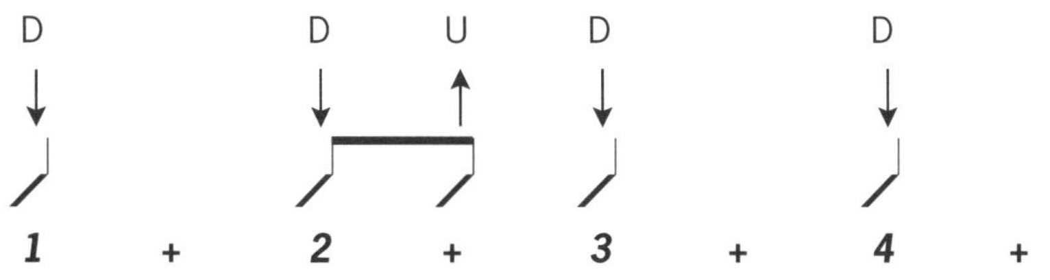

Dreams

Words & Music by Stevie Nicks


```
Intro          |: F      | G      | F      | G      :|  (Play x4)

Verse 1        F                 G                    F                   G
                  Now here you go again, you say   you want your free - dom,
               F               G                F        G
                  Well who am I to keep you down?
               F           G                        F                  G
                  It's only right that you should play the way you feel it,
                   F               G          F                 G
               But listen carefu - lly to the sound, of your loneliness...

                     Fmaj7                G7
Pre-chorus 1   Like a heartbeat drives you mad,
                    Fadd9          G7                    Fmaj7
               In the stillness of re - membering what you had,
               G7                  Fadd9     G7
                  And what you lost...
                           Fmaj7     G7
               And what you had...
                           Fadd9     G7
               And what you lost.

                  F          G                   F       G
Chorus 1       Oh thunder only happens when it's raining,
               F          G                    F       G
               Players only love you when they're playing,
                   F              G                  F    G
               Say, women they will come and they will go,
                   F                 G                   F      G      (F)
               When the rain wash - es you clean, you'll know,   you'll know.

Instrumental   | F      | G      | G      | F      | Am     | G      | G      | F      |

Verse 3        Now here I go again I see the crystal vision,
               I keep my visions to myself.
               It's only me, who wants to wrap around your dreams and...
               Have you any dreams you'd like to sell? Dreams of loneliness...

Pre-chorus 2   As Pre-chorus 1

Chorus 2       As Chorus 1   (Play x2)
                 F                   G                   F       G
               ...When the rain wash - es you clean, you'll know,
                     F    G                F    G                Fmaj7
               You'll know,   you will know,    oh____ you'll know.
```

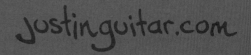

Introduction

This is Fleetwood Mac's classic ballad, released on the album *Rumours* (1977).

Less Is More

The guitar part during the verses is very minimal, and just involves picking individual notes from the chords. This will sound great in a band setting but a bit empty if you're performing solo, in which case I would recommend strumming during the verses. When performing with a band, try picking just a note or two from each chord and letting them ring out. You could even try to work out the exact guitar part from the record.

The pre-chorus features a nice melodic movement on the thinnest string. You can strum it or pick the thinnest three strings individually, as per the recording—just start on string 3 and pick upwards to string 1 (playing one note per beat) and then move back down again. If you're stumming, I've added an optional bass note on the F chords, played with the thumb.

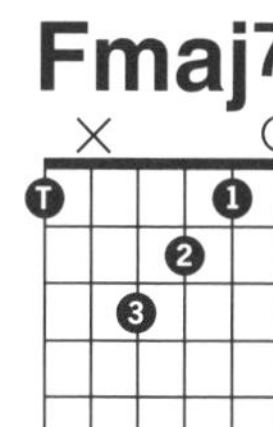

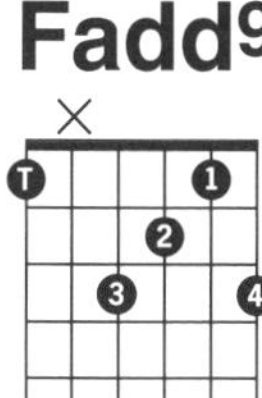

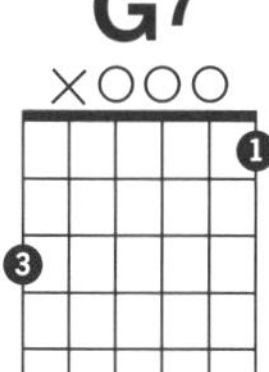

Rhythm

The only time you will hear a regular strumming pattern on the recording is during the chorus. It's a 2-bar pattern where the first bar seems consistent but the second bar alternates between the pattern shown below and continuous eighth-notes. If you are performing solo, I'd suggest using 'Old Faithful' for the verse and pre-chorus and then using the pattern below for the chorus. Having said that, I would encourage you to experiment with these patterns, particularly during the verses.

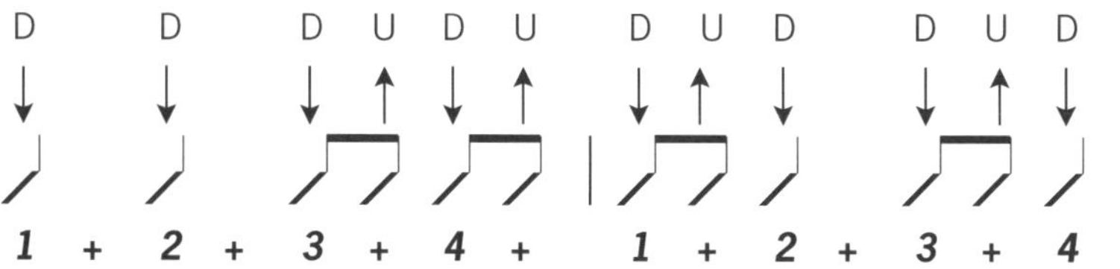

(Everything I Do) I Do It For You

Written by Michael Kamen, Bryan Adams & Robert John Lange

Intro

```
| C        | C/G      | F        | G        |
```

Verse 1

```
C                      G/C              F                      G/C
   Look into my eyes,    you will see, what you mean to me.
             C                   G/C
Search your heart, search your soul
                F                    |C/G       G    |
And when you find me there you'll search no more.
    |Dm                      C    |Dm
Don't tell me it's not worth trying for,
C        |Dm                       C    |Dm
   You can't tell me it's not worth dying for.
              C/G              G          C      C
You know it's true: everything I do, I do it for you.
```

Verse 2

```
C                       G/C
   Look into your heart,   and you will find,
       F                 G
there's nothing there to hide.
              C          G/C
Take me as I am, take my life,
       F                  |C     G   |
I would give it all, I would sacri - fice.

    |Dm                      C    |Dm
Don't tell me it's not worth fighting for,
    |Dm                       C    |Dm
I can't help it, there's nothing I want more.
              C                G          C      C
You know it's true, everything I do: I do it for you.
```

Bridge

```
       B♭         E♭                 B♭                F
There's no love like your love, and no other could give more love.
       C                G
There's nowhere unless you're there,
      D            |G   Gsus4 |Gsus4
All the time, all the way.
```

Solo

```
||: F      | F      | C      | C      :||
```

Verse 3

```
                Dm                         G
Oh, you can't tell me it's not worth trying for,
           Dm                          G
I can't help it, there's nothing I want more.
               C            G
Yeah, I would fight for you, I'd lie for you,
         F               Fm
Walk the wire for you, yeah I'd die for you.
N.C.           C/G              G    | F  Dm |        C
You know it's true, everything I do. Oh,          I do it for you.
```

Introduction

This song is Bryan Adam's biggest hit, written for the soundtrack to *Robin Hood: Prince Of Thieves* (1991).

Interesting Chord

A lot of pop songs are written on the keyboard instead of guitar, and consequently there are certain chords and riffs that are a lot easier (and sound better) on the piano. A good example of this is the G/C chord found in this song. Changing the bass note to a chord is easy on the piano as the bass is played with left hand and the chord with the right hand, but on the guitar there is less separation between bass notes and chords, so the G/C 'clashes' a bit more—it doesn't sound bad, but it is a little unusual.

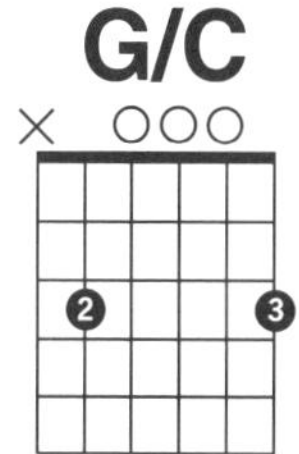

Look out for the barre chords in the Bridge section. If you have not learned your full barre chords yet, you can easily substitute them with power chords (BC-172), even for the Fm at the end, which you can substitute with an F5 power chord. Please also note that where you see a Dm and C in the same bar (e.g. in Verse 1), the C chord is played on beat 4.

cont...

Rhythm

This song is lead by the piano part, which gives you some freedom to create your own guitar accompaniment. You could try strumming the chords, but I think that fingerstyle guitar will work better. In the Bridge you can play the big power chords on a 'crunchy' electric guitar, playing all the chords with down-strums.

When playing a piano-based song I often pick the thumb and fingers separately to emulate the piano, as shown below. You might like to use this type of fingerstyle pattern throughout the song. Remember though that you will have to adapt this pattern to fit whichever chord you are playing.

Intro

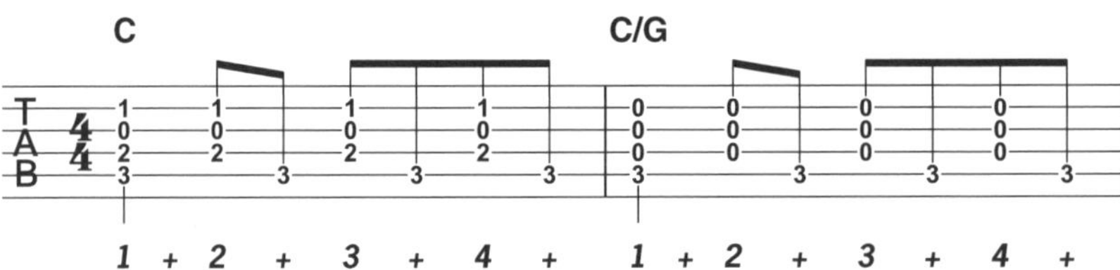

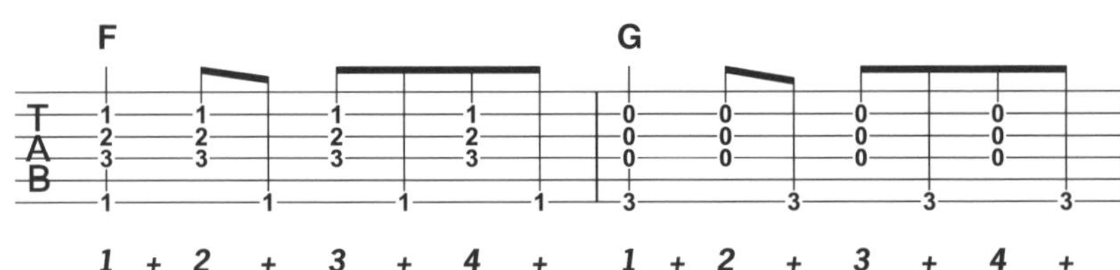

Super Trouper

Words & Music by Benny Andersson & Björn Ulvaeus

Introduction

This classic ABBA song doesn't feature a lot of guitar, but it's a lot of fun to play, especially on acoustic guitar.

Variations On C And More...

ABBA's music is often a little more complex than it first appears, and this song features quite a few interesting chords. In the Intro we have a Csus4, which involves muting the thinnest string (see below).

The Link section uses a host of sus chords—some are familiar and some are new, including Csus2 and Gadd9, both of which are shown below.

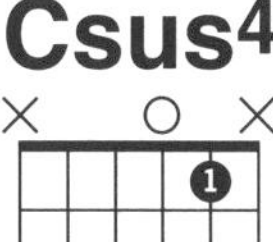

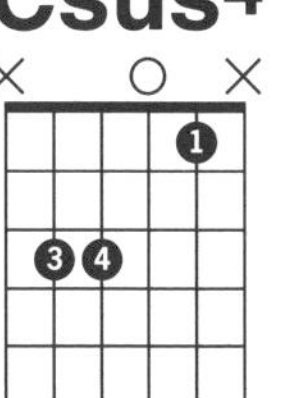

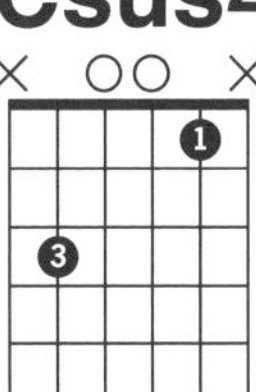

Gadd9

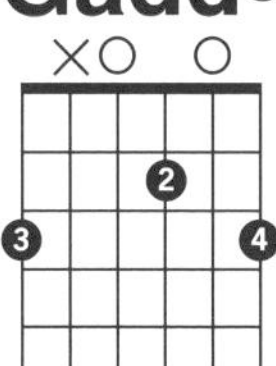

The verse has a nice C/G grip and also uses C/E, for which you should remember to take off your 3rd finger and mute the fifth string with your 2nd finger. If you leave your 3rd finger down, it makes the chord sound muddy. Also, don't be alarmed that the resulting chord will look more like an Am7!

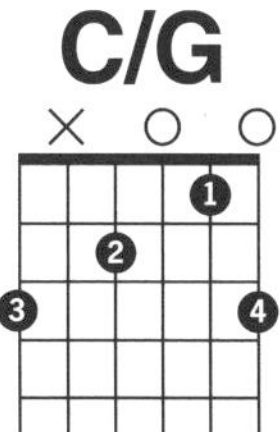

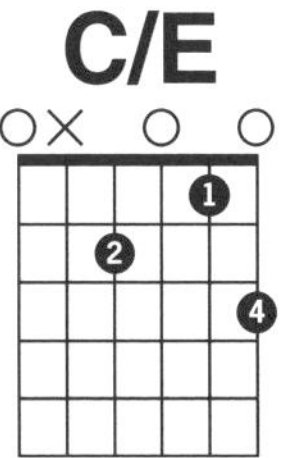

Super Trouper

Words & Music by Benny Andersson & Björn Ulvaeus

Intro

| C Csus4 | C Csus4 C | G
Super Trouper beams are gonna blind me, but I won't feel blue
Dm G G (C)
Like I always do, 'cause somewhere in the crowd there's you.

Link 1

| C Csus2 | C Csus2 | Am Asus2 | Am Asus2 |
| Dm Dsus2 | Dm Dsus2 | G Gadd9 | G Gadd9 |

Verse 1

C Em
I was sick and tired of every - thing
Dm | C/G G |
When I called you last night from Glas - gow.
C Em
All I do is eat and sleep and sing,
Dm | C/G G |
Wishing ev'ry show was the last show.
F C/E
So imagine I was glad to hear you're coming,
F C/E
Suddenly I feel al - right
F C Gsus4 G
And it's gonna be so different, When I'm on the stage to - night.

Chorus 1

(G) | C Csus4 | C
Tonight the Super Trouper lights are gonna find me,
| Csus4 C | G Dm G
Shining like the sun, Smiling, having fun,
G C
Feeling like a number one.
| C Csus4 | C
Tonight the Super Trouper beams are gonna blind me,
| Csus4 C | G Dm G
But I won't feel blue, Like I always do,
G (C)
'Cause somewhere in the crowd there's you.

Link 2

As Link 1

Verse 2

Facing twenty thousand of your friends,
How can anyone be so lonely?
Part of a success that never ends,
Still I'm thinking about you only.
There are moments when I think I'm going crazy,
But it's gonna be alright,
Ev'rything will be so different, when I'm on the stage tonight.

Chorus 2 As Chorus 1

```
         G                                        C     C
...'Cause somewhere in the crowd there's you.
```

Bridge

```
          F                  Am
So I'll be there when you arrive,
            |Dm                 G              |C
The sight of you will prove to me I'm still a - live,
                     G         |F
And when you take me in your arms
              |Dm     A7 |
And hold me tight,
  Dm                             G        G
I know it's gonna mean so much tonight.
```

Chorus 3 As Chorus 1 *(Play x2)*

There are quite a few possibilities for rhythms to strum in this song. You could use 'Old Faithful' (shown below) quite successfully, or you could use 'pumping 8ths' (continuous eighth-note down-strums) to drive the song along, or a mixture of both. Remember that when there is no set strumming pattern, you should explore your options and feel out which pattern works best for you. It all depends on the context—in a band situation, I'd suggest keeping it very simple with pumping 8th strumming, but if you are on your own, you can mix things up a bit more!

Lastly, you will often be playing two chords per bar—in almost every case, you should play the second chord on the third beat of the bar. The only exception comes in the Bridge, where the lyrics are 'And when you take me in your arms...' Here, you need to play the G chord on the fourth beat of the bar.

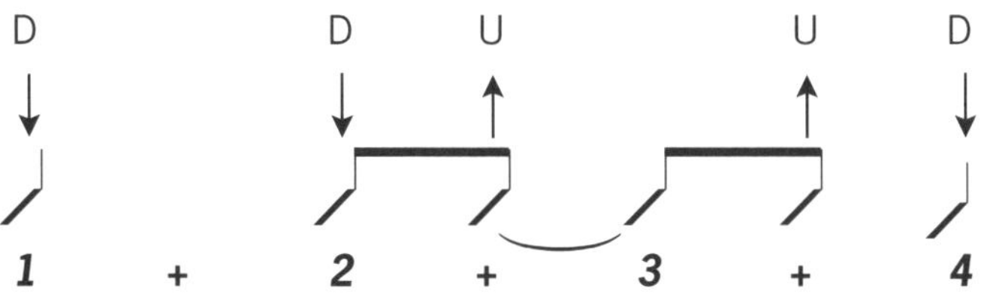

Realize

Words & Music by Colbie Caillat, Jason Reeves & Mikal Blue

Verse 1

G
Take time to realize

Dsus4/F♯ | C(add9) Em7 | Dsus4
That your warmth is crashing down on in.

G
Take time to realize

Dsus4/F♯ | C(add9) Em7 | Dsus4
That I am on your side, didn't I, didn't I tell you?

Pre-chorus 1

| C(add9) Em7 |
But I can't spell it out for you,

Dsus4
No, it's never gonna be that simple.

| C(add9) Em7 | Dsus4/F♯
No, I can't spell it out for you.

Chorus 1

| G D/F♯
If you just realize what I just realized,

| Em7 C(add9)
Then we'd be perfect for each other and we'll never find another.

| G D/F♯
Just realize what I just realized,

| Em7 C(add9) |
We'd never have to wonder if we missed out on each other now.

Link 1

| G D/F♯ | Em7 C(add9) |

Verse 2

Take time to realize, oh, oh, I'm on your side,
Didn't I, didn't I tell you?
Take time to realize, this all can pass you by, didn't I tell you?

Pre-chorus 2 As Pre-chorus 1

Chorus 2 As Chorus 1

Bridge

| Em7 D/F♯ | C D
But, it's not all the same, no, it's never the same.

| Em7 Dsus4/F♯ G G/B | C(add9)
If you don't feel it too.

| Em7 D | C D
If you meet me half way, if you would meet me half way,

| Em7 Dsus4/F♯ G G/B | C(add9)
It could be the same for you.

Chorus 2 As Chorus 1 *(Play x4)* *Vocals ad lib. on repeats*

Outro

| G | G/F♯ | C(add9) Em7 | G/F♯ |

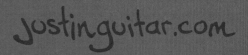

Introduction

This lovely acoustic song is by singer-songwriter Colbie Caillat. The chords are pretty simple, but make sure you look up the Dsus4/F♯ in the Chord Glossary.

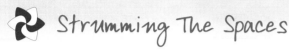

Strumming The Spaces

Up until the first chorus, there is a lot of space in the rhythm guitar part. For this minimal style of playing, you will find it a lot easier to keep your strumming hand moving even when you are not making contact with the strings, so in effect you are 'strumming' the spaces. If you have a very strong sense of time then you may get away with just tapping your foot, but the majority of players will keep their strumming hand moving all the time, especially when there isn't a consistent pattern to follow—as is the case here. The pattern for the first verse involves just 4 strums per bar but your hand will make 16 movements per bar!

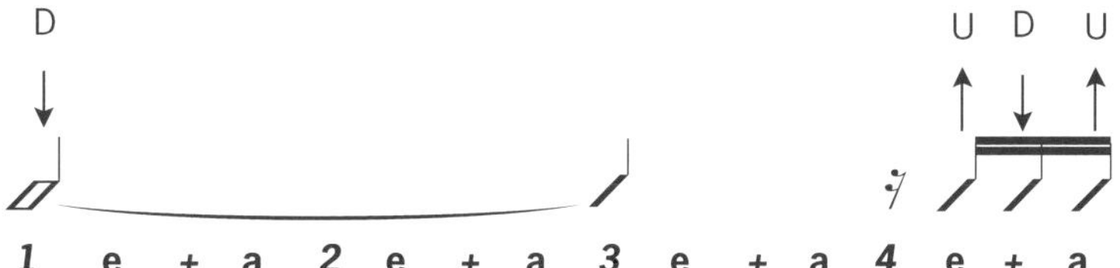

As the song develops, more strums are added. Feeling where these extra strums are played is really important, but don't worry—as long as you keep your strumming hand moving in time you will be fine. Where there are 2 chords per bar, the change will come on the 'a' after beat 2. This next pattern is a 'summary' of the strumming during the pre-chorus:

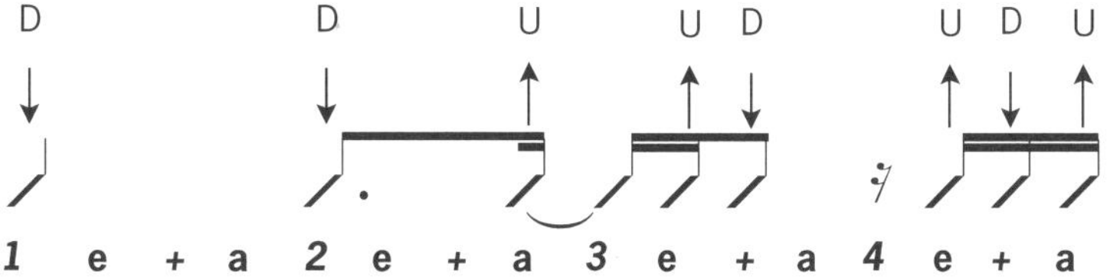

Once we reach the chorus, the strumming pattern is much more involved:

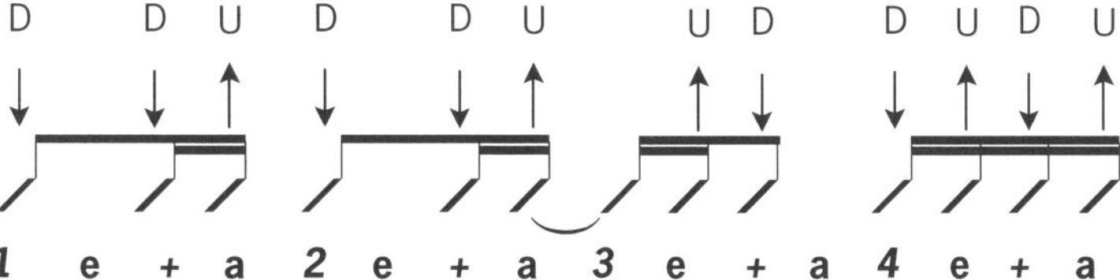

In this song you should focus on how to develop your strumming to build the dynamics in the song. It will take a bit of practice but stick with it.

Rise

Words & Music by Bob Dylan, Gabrielle, Ferdy Unger-Hamilton & Ollie Dagois

Chord Sequence Throughout:

| **G** | **D** | **Am** | **Am7** |

Intro Play Sequence *x 2*

Verse 1
I know that it's over, but I can't believe we're through.
They say that time's a healer, yeah, and I'm better without you.
It's gonna take time I know, but I'll get over you.

Chorus 1
Look at my life, look at my heart, I have seen them fall apart,
Now I'm ready, to rise again.
Just look at my hopes, look at my dreams,
I'm building bridges from these scenes,
Now I'm ready, to rise again.

Link Play Sequence *x 1*

Verse 2
Caught up in my thinking, yeah,
Like a prisoner in my mind.
You pose so many questions,
But the truth was hard to find.
I better think twice, I know that I'll get over you.

Chorus 2 As Chorus 1

Much time has passed between us,
Do you still think of me at all?
My world of broken promises,
Now you won't catch me when I fall.

Chorus 3 As Chorus 1

I'm gonna make it all right.
Yes, I'm gonna rise, gonna make it all right,
I'm gonna be who I wanna be, yeah, baby.
Yeah, yeah. I'm gonna make it all right.
I'm gonna make it all right. I'm gonna make it all right.

Beginner | Intermediate | Intermediate + | TAB

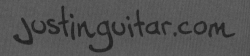

Introduction

Gabrielle sampled Bob Dylan's guitar from 'Knockin' On Heavens Door' and turned it into a hit single, back in 2000.

Super-Easy Or Super-Hard?

This song is both! On the surface, the chord sequence is just G, D, Am, Am7, which couldn't be much simpler. You can use any simple strumming pattern and it will sound great.

But if you want to emulate the recording precisely, you are in for some fun. The guitar part is a sample from Bob Dylan's 'Knockin' On Heaven's Door' and there are lots of subtleties to capture. It features continuous eighth-note strumming but with enough 'ghost notes' (notes played very quietly) that it doesn't seem that way. Also, the last bars of Am and Am7 feature some very interesting accents.

To master the details of a guitar part, I always listen to the recording and find a section where the guitar part is more exposed, and then listen to this section over and over until I have the notes 'in my ears', before trying to play them. It's a lot more effective to learn a song this way than from a written example. Nevertheless, I have written the guitar part below in a way that will get you very close to the recording. I have left out the 'ghost notes' and added accents (>) but you'll need to listen and make sure you are performing the accents correctly, as sometimes the accent is on the bass strings, and sometimes on the thin strings. The good news is that once you have done a few detailed listens, and put in enough practice, you will get better and quicker at copying guitar parts from recordings.

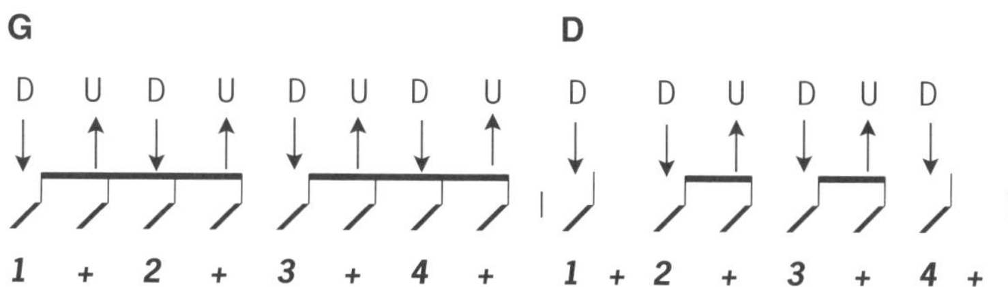

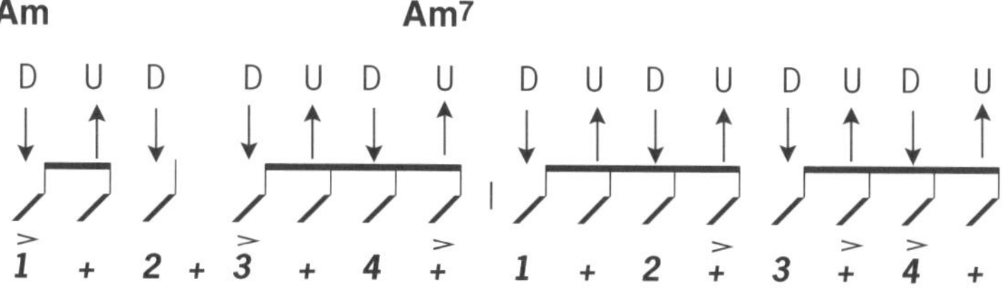

Sing

Words & Music by Fran Healy

Capo Fret 2

Intro ||: Em | Am | Am7 | Em :||

Verse 1

```
Em                           Am
Baby, you've been going so crazy,
Am7                          Em
Lately, nothing seems to be going right.
Em                               Am
So low, why do you have to get so low?
Am7                                    Em
You're so, you've been waiting in the sun too long.
```

Chorus 1

```
(Em)        | G    D  | Am
But if you sing, sing,
Am              G
Sing, sing, sing, sing.
                 | G    D            | Am
For the love you bring won't mean a thing
             Am               G
Unless you sing, sing, sing, sing.
```

Verse 2

Colder, crying over your shoulder,
Hold her, tell her everything's gonna be fine.
Surely, you've been going too hurry,
Hurry, 'cause no one's gonna be stopped, na, na, na, na, na,

Chorus 2

But if you sing, sing, sing, sing, sing.
For the love you bring won't mean a thing
Unless you sing, sing, sing, sing, sing, sing, sing.

Link ||: G D | Am | Am | G :||

Verse 3

Baby, there's something going on today
But I say nothing, nothing, nothing,
Nothing, nothing, nothing, nothing …
Na, na, na, na, na,

Chorus 3 As Chorus 1

Chorus 4 As Chorus 1 *(Vocals ad lib.)*

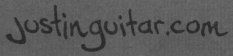

Introduction

'Sing' was the first single from Travis' third album, *The Invisible Band* (2001).

Banjo-tastic

Although the chords for this song are very simple and fairly repetitive, there is a distinctive feature in the form of the banjo part. If you have a loop pedal or another guitarist to jam along with, try to combine the chords and the banjo part, which will sound ace. It will be easiest to play this banjo part fingerstyle, using just the thumb and the first two fingers in the picking hand.

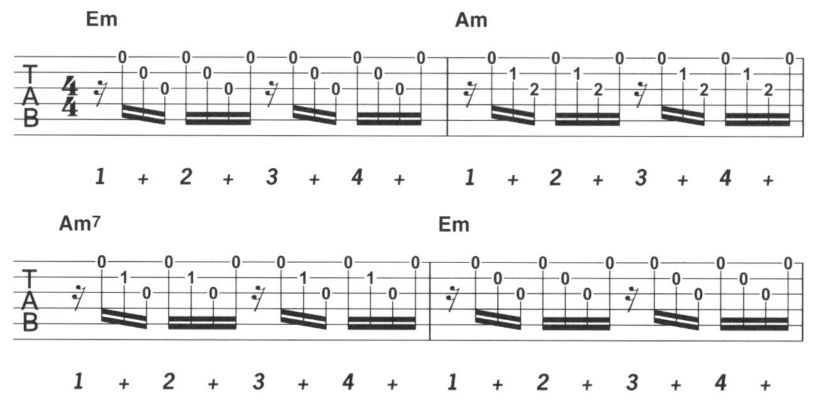

Rhythm

The rhythm part to this song is all about accents. The rhythm guitar is strummed as continuous sixteenth-notes, so it's the accent pattern that gives colour and shape to the rhythm. Check out the pattern below, and observe which up- and down-strokes have an accent—these notes need to be a little louder. If you struggle to make the accents louder then you need to make the other strums softer! Although there are changes to the pattern throughout the song, this is a good place to start.

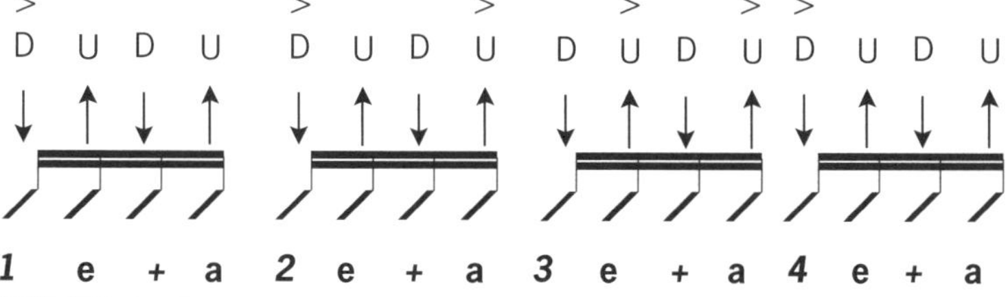

Teardrops On My Guitar

Words & Music by Taylor Swift & Liz Rose

Capo Fret 3

Beginner

Intermediate

Intermediate +

TAB

Intro | G | Em7 | C(add9) | D/F# |

Verse 1
G Em7 C(add9) D/F# G
Drew looks at me, I fake a smile so he won't see
Em7 C(add9) D/F#
That I want and I need him, everything that we should be.

Pre-chorus 1
Em7 C(add9)
I'll bet she's beautiful, that girl he talks about.
G D/F#
And she's got everything that I have to live without.

Verse 2
Drew talks to me, I laugh 'cause it's just so funny
That I can't even see, anyone when he's with me.

Pre-chorus 2
He says he's so in love, he's finally got it right.
I wonder if he knows he's all I think about at night.

Chorus 1
G D/F#
He's the reason for the teardrops on my guitar,
Em7 C(add9)
The only thing that keeps me wishing on a wishing star.
G D/F#
He's the song in the car I keep singing,
Em7 C(add9)
Don't know why I do.

Verse 3
Drew walks by me, can he tell that I can't breathe?
And there he goes, so perfectly, the kind of flawless I wish I could be.

Pre-chorus 3
She better hold him tight, give him all her love.
Look in those beautiful eyes and know she's lucky 'cause

Chorus 2
As Chorus 1

Instrumental | G | Em7 | C(add9) | D/F# |

Pre-chorus 4
So I drive home alone as I turn out the light.
I'll put his picture down and maybe get some sleep tonight,

Chorus 3
'Cause he's the reason for the teardrops on my guitar,
The only one who's got enough of me to break my heart.
He's the song in the car I keep singing, don't know why I do.
He's the time taken up but there's never enough,
And he's all that I need to fall into.

Outro
G Em7 C(add9) Dsus4 G
Drew looks at me, I fake a smile so he won't see.

Introduction

This is country-pop starlet Taylor Swift's hit single from 2006.

The Magic Four Chords

It's amazing what you can do with just four chords, and these particular four chords are responsible for many pop songs. The grips have many common notes, which tie the chord sequence together very nicely. They also sound great when overdubbed on to different layers.

Listen closely to the arrangement of this song to hear the layers of acoustic guitar: layer 1 is strumming very even eighth-notes, layer 2 is playing arpeggios of the chords and layer 3 is playing spread chords on beat 1 (starting in the pre-chorus). Add some banjo and pedal steel guitar to that and you've got a country-pop hit!

G(5)

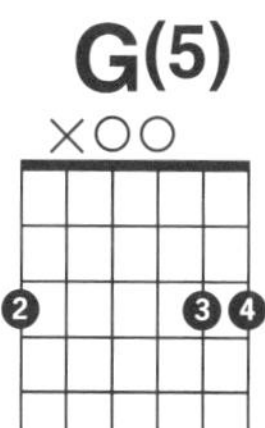

Em7

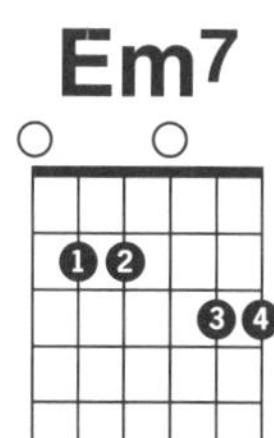

Cadd9

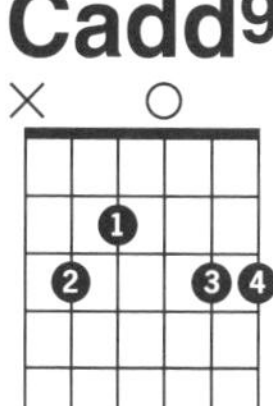

Dsus4/F♯

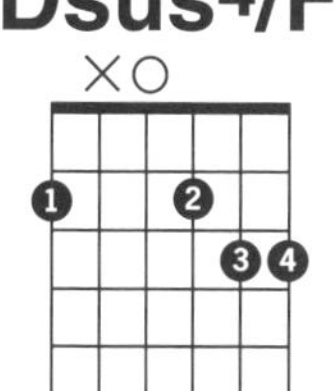

Rhythm

The main acoustic guitar part uses even eighth-note strumming. It's quite unusual to strum without accenting any notes, so make sure that you can play your strums perfectly even, and all at the same volume! Of course you can experiment with different strumming patterns and accents.

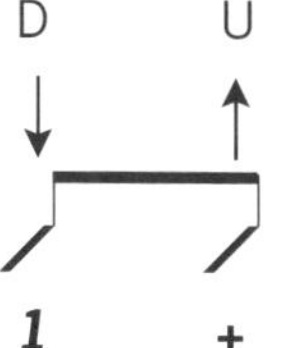

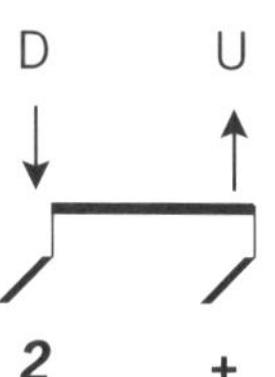

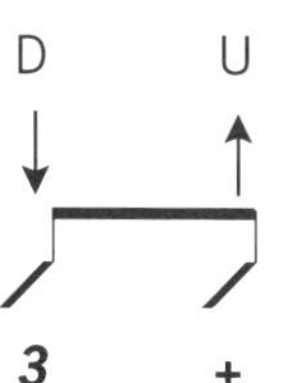

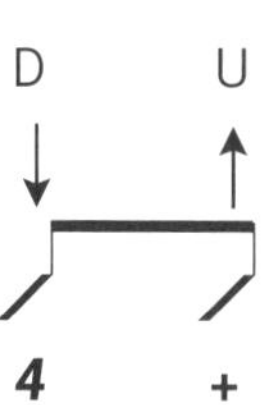

The Passenger

Words & Music by Iggy Pop & Ricky Gardiner

Beginner

Intermediate

Intermediate +

TAB

Chord Sequence throughout

| Am F | C G | Am F | C E |

Verse 1

I am the passenger
And I ride and I ride:
I ride through the city's backsides,
I see the stars come out of the sky.
Yeah, the bright the hollow sky,
You know it looks so good tonight.

Verse 2

I am the passenger,
I stay under glass,
I look through my window so bright,
I see the stars come out tonight,
I see the bright and hollow sky
Over the city's ripped-back sky,
And everything looks good tonight.

Chorus 1

Singing la la, la la, la-la-la-la, la la, la la, la-la-la-la,
La la, la la, la-la-la-la, la la la.

Verse 3

Get into the car,
We'll be the passenger:
We'll ride through the city tonight,
We'll see the city's ripped backsides,
We'll see the bright and hollow sky,
We'll see the stars that shine so bright,
Stars made for us tonight.

Verse 4

Oh, the passenger how, how he rides.
Oh, the passenger he rides and he rides.
He looks through his window,
What does he see?
He sees the bright and hollow sky,
He sees the stars come out tonight,
He sees the city's ripped backsides,
He sees the winding ocean drive.
And everything was made for you and me,
All of it was made for you and me,
'Cause it just belongs to you and me,
So let's take a ride and see what's mine.

Chorus 2

As Chorus 1

Verse 5

Oh, the passenger he rides and he rides:
He sees things from under glass,
He looks through his window side,
He sees the things he knows are his.
He sees the bright and hollow sky,
He sees the city sleep at night,
He sees the stars are out tonight.
And all of it is yours and mine,
And all of it is yours and mine,
So let's ride and ride and ride and ride.

Chorus 3 As Chorus 1 *(Repeat to fade)*

Introduction

This is one of Iggy Pop's best known songs, produced by David Bowie and released on Iggy Pop's second solo album, *Lust For Life* (1977).

Chord Grip Variations

The chord sequence in this song is the same all the way through. You might like to start by using all open chords (except for F) although I'm pretty sure that on the recording, the F, C and G chords are all barre chords—the C using an 'A-shape' and the F and G using an 'E-shape'. Don't feel you have to use barre chords just yet—it sounds great using open chords, but I'm sure those barre chords are in there so thought I'd let you know! I recommend coming back to this song once you have started working with barre chords. You can use the barre chords until your hand gets tired and then go back to using open chords for a while to recover!

Rhythm

The rhythm used in this song is instantly recognisable, so I'd advise that you listen to the original recording and play along with it to pick up the right feel. It's pretty easy—you just miss out the down-strums on beats 1 and 3 and play the remaining strums with a light swing feel.

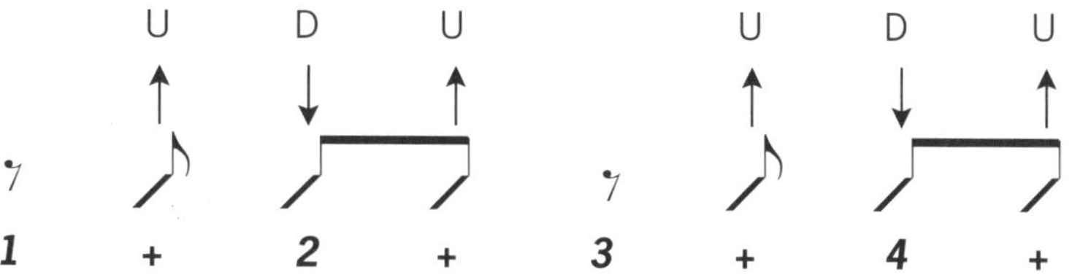

What Took You So Long?

Words & Music by Emma Bunton, Richard Stannard,
Julian Gallagher, David Morgan, Martin Harrington & John Themis

Intro |: Fmaj7 | Am | G | G :|
(*2nd Time*) Yeah, yeah, yeah.

Verse 1
Fmaj7 Am G G
Oh, talk to me, can't you see, I'll help you work things out.
Fmaj7 Am G G
Oh, don't wanna be your enemy, and I don't want to scream and shout

Pre-chorus 1
Dm7 Fmaj7 Am G
'Cause baby, I believe in honesty, and then be strong and true.
Dm7 Fmaj7 Am G (N.C.)
I shouldn't have to say now, baby, that I believe in you.

Chorus 1
N.C. Dm7 Am
What took you so long, what took you all night,
G G
What took you for - ever to see I'm right?
Dm7 Am
You know I treat you so good, I make you feel fine,
G N.C.
You know I'll never give it up this time. No, no, no.

Link | Dm7 | Am | G | (N.C.) |

Verse 2
Oh, you touched my heart right from the start,
You didn't know what to say.
But honey, I understand,
When you take my hand everything's O.K.

Pre-chorus 2
'Cause baby, I believe reality, Is never far away.
I've had enough, so listen baby, I've got something to say.

Chorus 2 As Chorus 1 (*Play x2*)
G G
...You know I'll never give it up this time. No, no, no.

Bridge |: D7sus4 | Fadd9 | Am7 | G :|

Pre-chorus 3 As Pre-chorus 1

Chorus 4 As Chorus 1 (*Play x3*)
Am Am Am G
...No, no, no.

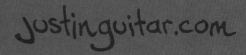

Introduction

Emma Bunton, the sweetest Spice Girl, launched her solo career with this poptastic tune in 2001.

Perfect Pop

This tune is a great example of pop songwriting—it's simple harmonically, simply lyrically, very catchy and uses a song structure that is very common in pop music. It starts with a nice, short Intro, involving a catchy guitar melody (which you might like to work out yourself), followed by a chorus starting around the 1-minute mark. It even uses a 'pop stop'—the one bar stop at the end of the pre-chorus to bring in the chorus. The song also features a Dm7 chord, which is not covered in the Beginners Course, but it's a useful chord and not hard to play.

Dm7

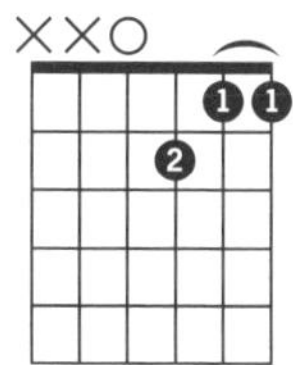

D7sus4

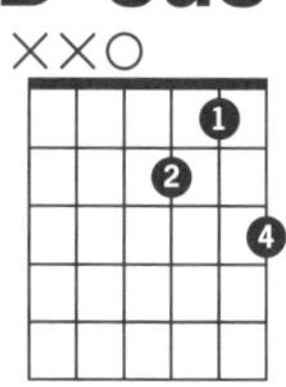

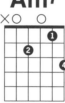

Fadd9

Am7

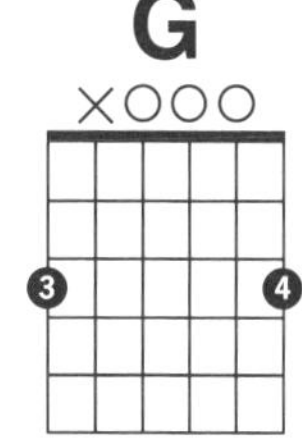

G

Play these in the pre-chorus and in the Bridge, keeping the high G note on the thinnest string.

Rhythm

The dominant acoustic guitar part plays the pattern shown below, but it's been double-tracked, so there are some variations along the way. You can (and should!) experiment with the strumming pattern in this tune.

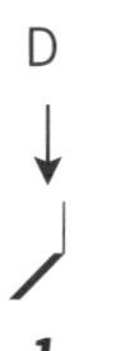

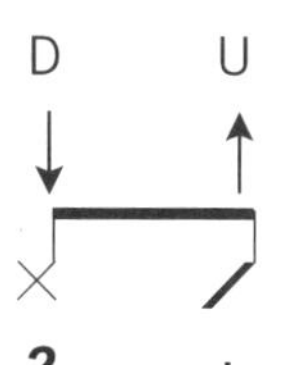

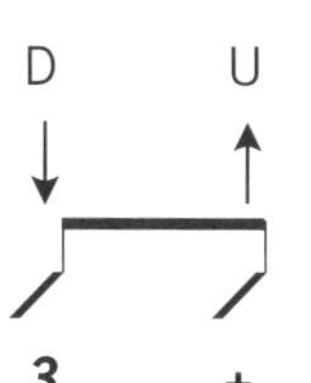

You're Still The One

Words & Music by Shania Twain & R.J. Lange

Intro

| C | C/E | F | G |

Verse 1

```
C                 C/E
  Looks like we made it,
F                   G
Look how far we've come my baby,
C                         C/E
  We might have took the long way,
F                G
  We knew we'd get there some day.
C            C/E    F              G
  They said,   'I bet  they'll never make it',
           C          F       G     G
But just look at us holding on.
                C           F     G      F
We're still to - gether, still going strong
```

Chorus 1

```
C                       F
  You're still the one I run to,
Dm                     G
  The one that I be - long to.
C                       F        G     F
  You're still the one I want for life.
C                            F
  You're still the one that I love,
Dm                G
  The only one I dream of.
C                       F           G      G
  You're still the one I kiss good - night.
```

Verse 2

Ain't nothing better,
We beat the odds together.
I'm glad we didn't listen,
Look at what we would be missing.
They said, 'I bet they'll never make it',
But just look at us holding on.
We're still together, still going strong.

Chorus 2 As Chorus 1

Instrumental ||: C | F | G | G :||

Chorus 3 As Chorus 1

Outro

```
C                   C/E       F                     G
  I'm so glad we made it, look how far we've come my baby.
```

Introduction

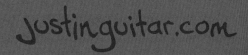

This is Shania Twain's Grammy Award-winning single, which featured on her hugely successful album *Come On Over* (1997).

Strumming Fill

It is quite common for a drummer to play a drum 'fill' before a chorus or a change of section in a song. A 'fill' is simply a change to the main groove, usually with some interesting accents, and which often links two sections together. Here, the whole band join in on the fill, both at the end of each verse and halfway through each chorus. Remember that the off-beats will all be up-strums and that the last 3 strums will build (get louder) into the chorus.

It will sound really impressive if you add in this fill when performing the song. Also, listen out for fills in other songs—imitating these fills will add a 'pro' touch to your rhythm playing.

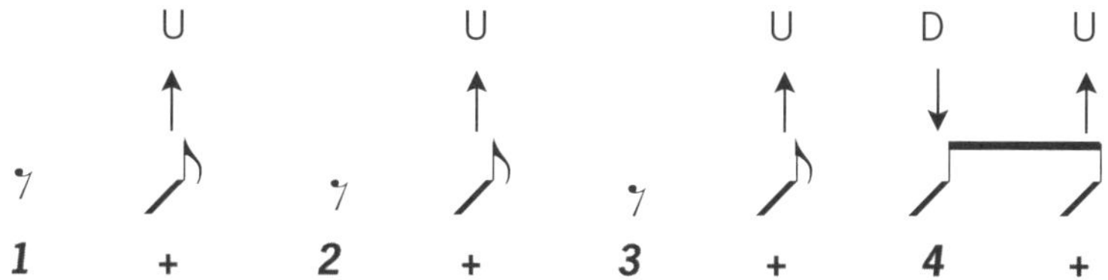

Rhythm

The predominant strumming pattern here is two bars long, although there are many variations throughout the course of the song. The best way to recreate the strumming on the recording is to play accents in the 2nd bar on the + after 1 and on beat 3. The chord in the second bar is delayed by half a beat, changing on the + after 1, which really asserts the groove of the song.

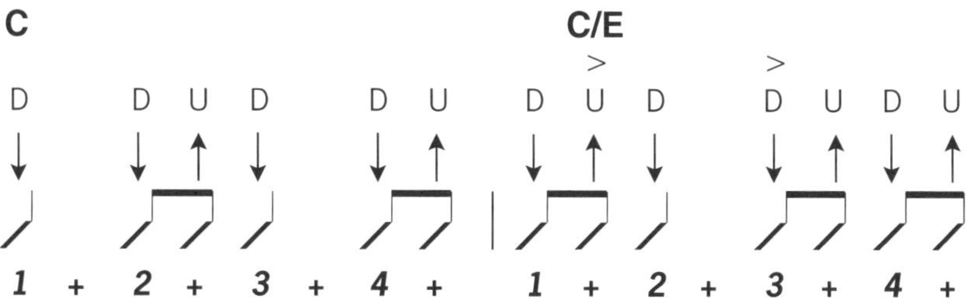

Beginner

Intermediate

Intermediate +

TAB

Love The Way You Lie

Words & Music by Marshall Mathers, Alexander Grant & H. Hafferman

Beginner

Intermediate

Intermediate +

TAB

Chord progression throughout:

| Em | C(add9) | G | Dsus4/F♯ |

Chorus 1

Just gonna stand there and watch me burn,
But that's all right because I like the way it hurts.
Just gonna stand there and hear me cry,
But that's all right because I love the way you lie,
I love the way you lie.

Verse 1 (Rap)

I can't tell you what it really is, I can only tell you what it feels like.
And right now there's a steel knife in my windpipe
I can't breathe, but I still fight while I can fight,
As long as the wrong feels right, it's like I'm in flight.
High off of love, drunk from my hate,
It's like I'm huffing paint and I love it the more I suffer, I suffocate.
And right before I'm about to drown, she resuscitates me,
She f***ing hates me and I love it. Wait, where you going?
I'm leaving you, no you ain't, come back, we're running right back.
Here we go again, it's so insane,
'Cause when it's going good, it's going great,
I'm Superman with the wind at his back, she's Lois Lane.
But when it's bad, it's awful, I feel so ashamed, I snap
Who's that dude? I don't even know his name.
I laid hands on her, I'll never stoop so low again,
I guess I don't know my own strength.

Chorus 2

Just gonna stand there and watch me burn,
But that's all right because I like the way it hurts.
Just gonna stand there and hear me cry,
But that's all right because I love the way you lie,
I love the way you lie; I love the way you lie.

Verse 2

You ever love somebody so much, you can barely breathe,
When you're with them, you meet and neither one of you
Even know what hit 'em got that warm fuzzy feeling,
Yeah them, chills, used to get 'em,
Now you're getting f***ing sick of looking at 'em.
You swore you've never hit 'em, never do nothing to hurt 'em,
Now you're in each other's face, spewing venom
And these words when you spit 'em.
You push, pull each other's hair,

(cont.)

Scratch, claw, bit 'em, throw 'em down, pin 'em,
So lost in the moments when you're in 'em.
It's the rage that took over, it controls you both,
So they say it's best to go your separate ways,
Guess that they don't know ya 'cause today
That was yesterday, yesterday is over, it's a different day,
Sound like broken records playin' over.
But you promised her next time you'll show restraint,
You don't get another chance.
Life is no Nintendo game, but you lied again,
Now you get to watch her leave out the window,
Guess that's why they call it window pane.

Chorus 3 As Chorus 2

Verse 3

Now I know we said things, did things that we didn't mean,
And we fall back into the same patterns, same routine.
But your temper's just as bad as mine is,
You're the same as me, when it comes to love you're just as blinded.
Baby please come back, it wasn't you, baby it was me,
Maybe our relationship isn't as crazy as it seems.
Maybe that's what happens when a tornado meets a volcano,
All I know is I love you too much to walk away though.
Come inside, pick up your bags off the sidewalk,
Don't you hear sincerity in my voice when I talk.
Told you this is my fault, look me in the eyeball,
Next time I'm pissed I'll aim my fist at the dry wall
Next time, there will be no next time.
I apologize even though I know it's lies,
I'm tired of the games, I just want her back, I know I'm a liar
If she ever tries to f***ing leave again,
I'm-a tie her to the bed and set this house on fire.

Chorus 4 As Chorus 2

Introduction

This is Eminem and Rihanna's hugely successful duet, released in 2010.

Chord Variations

You can simplify this song down to just Em, C, G and D/F♯ but the recorded version is slightly more distinctive. Bar 2 in each sequence starts with half a bar of Cadd9, and the second half of the bar adds in a high G note on the thinnest string. The last chord in the sequence is somewhere between a D/F♯ and a G/F♯, and is best described as a Dsus4/F♯.

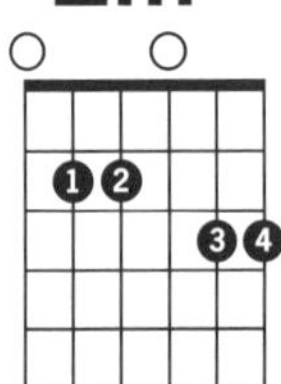

Cadd9

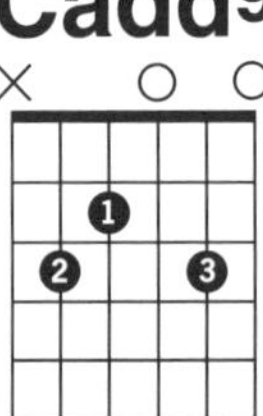

Cadd9

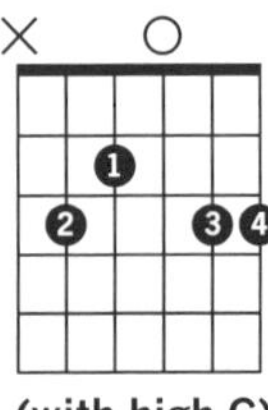

(with high G)

G(5)

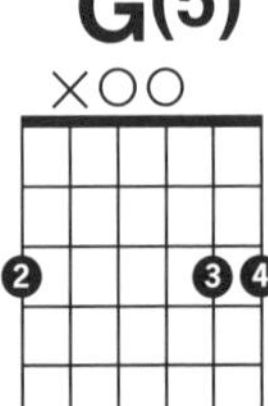

Dsus4/F♯

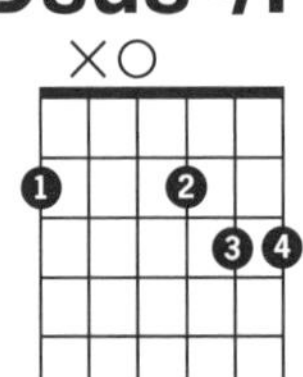

Rhythm

There is a pretty consistent rhythm part for this song (it's probably the same 4-bar loop sampled and repeated), which uses sixteenth-notes. Beginner or early Intermediate players might like to stick to playing constant down-strums on the beats and on the 'ands', just pumping it along. The pattern opposite isn't easy and you will probably have to give it some attention to get it right, especially if you plan to rap complex rhythms over it!

Rhythm (cont.)

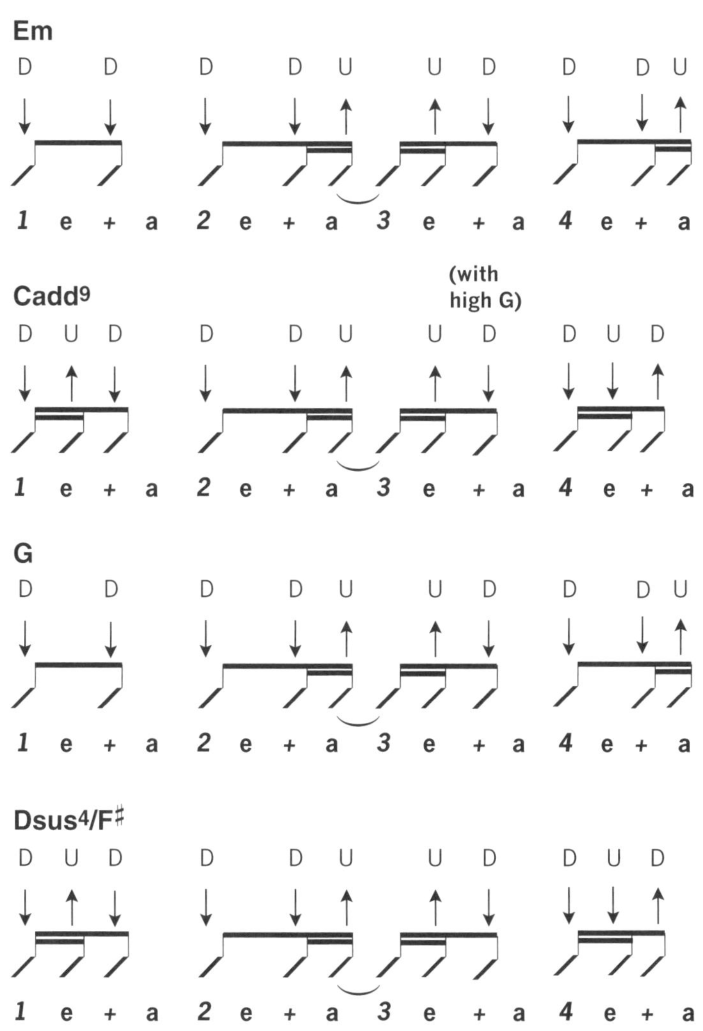
Em
D D D D U U D D D U
1 e + a 2 e + a 3 e + a 4 e + a
Cadd9
(with
high G)
D U D D D U U D D U D
1 e + a 2 e + a 3 e + a 4 e + a
G
D D D D U U D D D U
1 e + a 2 e + a 3 e + a 4 e + a
Dsus4/F♯
D U D D D U U D D U D
1 e + a 2 e + a 3 e + a 4 e + a

You're So Vain

Words & Music by Carly Simon

Verse 1

```
     Am                  Am
You walked into the party
                F                       Am
Like you were walking onto a yacht,
         Am                                Am
Your hat strategically dipped be - low one eye,
     F                      Am
Your scarf it was apri - cot.
         |F          G      |Em    Am   |
You had one eye in the mirror as
     F                     C
You watched yourself ga - votte.
           2/4|G                 4/4|F
And all the girls dreamed that they'd be your partner,
F
They'd be your partner and...
```

Chorus 1

```
C             C
   You're so vain,
    Dm                                   C
You probably think this song is a - bout you.
           Am
You're so vain  (you're so vain)
 F                                  G
I bet you think this song is a - bout you,
           G
Don't you, don't you?
```

Verse 2

Oh, you had me several years ago
When I was still quite naïve;
Well you said that we made such a pretty pair,
And that you would never leave.
But you gave away the things you loved
And one of them was me.
I had some dreams, they were clouds in my coffee,
Clouds in my coffee, and...

Chorus 2

As Chorus 1

Guitar solo

```
|: Am     | Am      | F      | Am     :|
|  F   G  | Em  Am  | F      | (C)     |
```

Bridge

I had some dreams, they were clouds in my coffee,
Clouds in my coffee and...

Chorus 3

As Chorus 1

Verse 3

Well I hear you went up to Saratoga
And your horse naturally won,
Then you flew your Lear jet up to Nova Scotia
To see the total eclipse of the sun.
Well, you're where you should be all the time,
And when you're not you're with
Some underworld spy or the wife of a close friend,
Wife of a close friend and...

Chorus 4

As Chorus 1

Coda

| C | C | Dm | C |

```
   C          C
|: You're so vain,
     Dm                              C
You probably think this song is a - bout you. :|  (Repeat to fade)
```

Introduction

Carly Simon stuck it to her ex in her 1972 pop hit. But which ex was she talking about?

Rhythm

The strumming for most of the song is based around the pattern shown below but there are quite a few variations, so feel free to experiment, and add in extra strums once you feel confident.

Also, listen out for 'pushes', where the chord changes half a beat earlier than you might expect. I would write some examples out for you, but it's easier and more effective to learn by listening to the song!

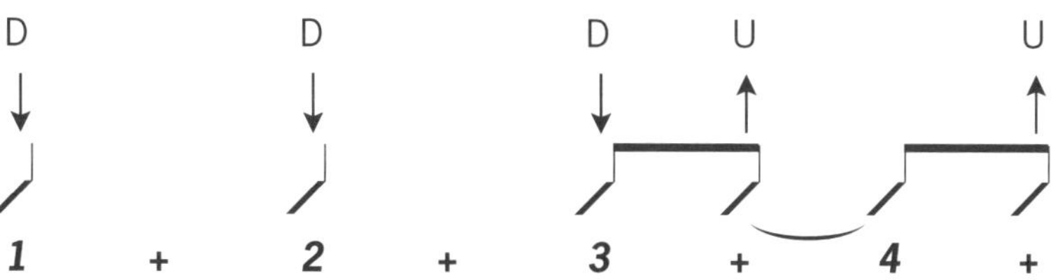

cont...

Beginner

Intermediate

Intermediate +

TAB

Fun Time

By far the trickiest part of this song is the 2/4 bar at the end of the verses. It's not hard, just unusual—but follow these simple instructions and you'll have no problem.

Count along with the original recording, counting 4 beats for the C chord, 2 for the G and then 2 bars of 4 beats on the F (see below). Notice that on the C there is a break at the beginning of the bar (beat 2 isn't played)—this often seems to throw people off.

Start by strumming down on beat 1 of the C chord and letting it ring out for 2 beats. The next strum (still on C) will be another down-strum on beat 3, falling on the word 'and', followed by one more down-strum on beat 4. Then move to the G for two more down-strums before we go back to 4/4 for the F chord, where there is a bar of down-strums, followed by a bar of 'build-up'. Do it slowly, then play along with the recording, and once you feel confident with it you can start to embellish as you wish.

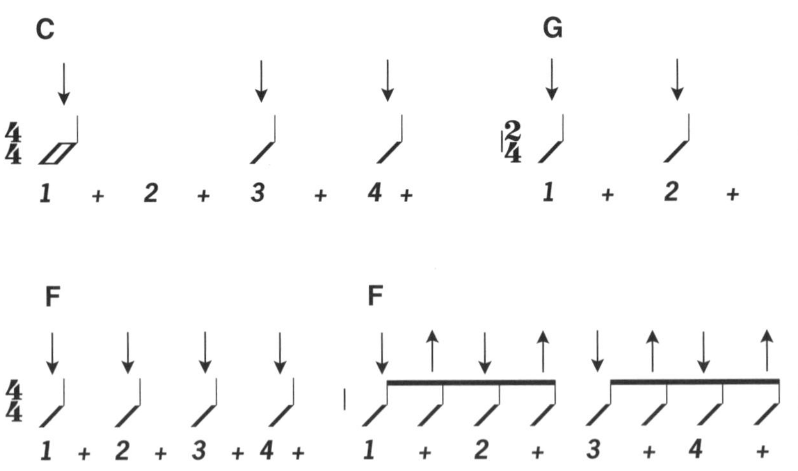

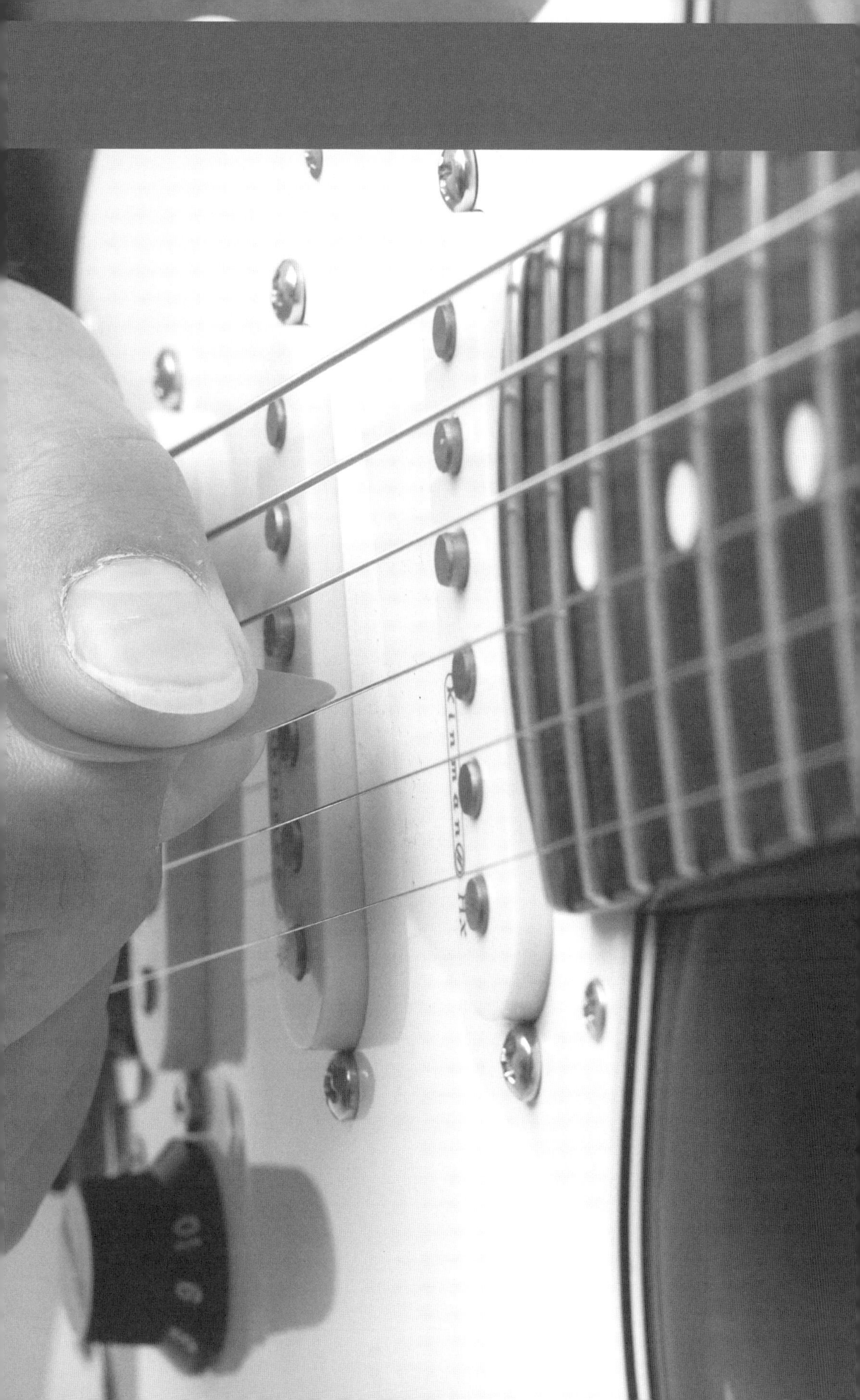

Introduction

Now that you're not a beginner any more (congratulations, by the way!) we're going to learn some more advanced songs and skills. Above all, these Intermediate songs will help you develop your ability to play barre chords. I spent many years avoiding barre chords and worrying that I wasn't ready, but my advice to you is to get stuck into them as soon as you are confident with all your beginner techniques.

At this stage, a big part of your studies will be learning to recognise which chords to play as barre chords, and which to play 'open'. The matter is made more interesting by the fact that many chords can be played both as open chords and as barre chords. You must decide which voicings to use in each situation. There is often no right or wrong, although there may be creative or practical reasons that lead you to choose one voicing over another.

Over the page, you will find a guide on playing the eight main barre chord shapes. When you start learning how to play barre chords, it is likely that you will find the E-shape chords (with the root on the 6th string) easiest to play, and will prefer to play them, rather than the A-shape chords. This is absolutely fine. As you get used to the A-shape barre chords, your options will increase and you will choose your voicings accordingly.

You may find that a song sounds better if all the chords are played as barre chords. At other times you will play most of the chords open, and only barre when you have to. Do what you feel most comfortable with to start with, and as your playing develops, choose the voicing that sounds best!

Also in this section I will be focusing more on sixteenth-note strumming patterns. Remember that the trick to playing them is to practise them slowly and carefully and repeat them many times. 'Practice makes permanent' (not 'perfect' as is so often quoted!), and you should be aiming to practise a pattern until it feels completely natural and instinctive. A good test is to keep playing a pattern while having a conversation with someone. If you can do that then you'll have the pattern well and truly 'in the bag'.

Intermediate Stage: Your Notes

BARRE CHORDS

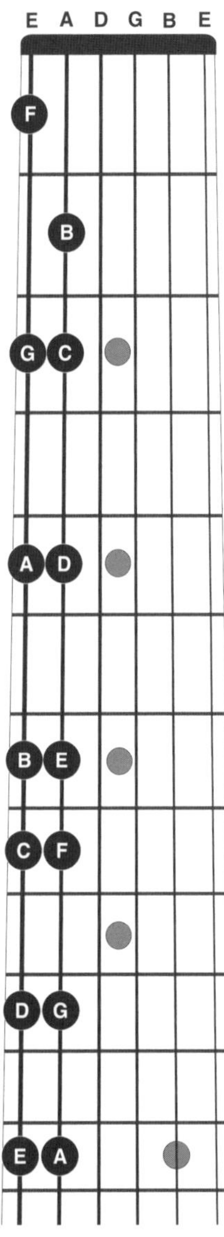

Getting Started

On the facing page are the eight essential barre chord grips. You must memorise these grips, along with the corresponding bass notes on the thickest two strings.

To find a chord, first locate the root note. If the root note is a sharp or a flat (e.g. F♯ or B♭), then move up or down one fret accordingly (sharp—move towards the bridge, flat—move towards the nut). Then use the appropriate chord shape (major, minor, 7th or minor 7th), using E-shape grips when the root note is on the 6th string, and A-shape grips when the root is on the 5th string.

You will notice that I often use the terms 'R5' and 'R6' to refer to a Root 5 or Root 6 barre chord. It's quite a common shorthand, which you'll see cropping up throughout the book, and in plenty of other publications.

If you have any problems playing any of these chords, please check out the relevant lessons in the Intermediate Method section of the website (starting with IM-111 and IM-131).

E-Shape Barre Chords

Major

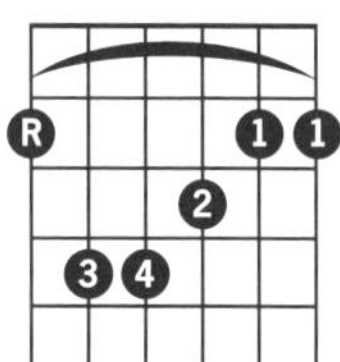

Minor

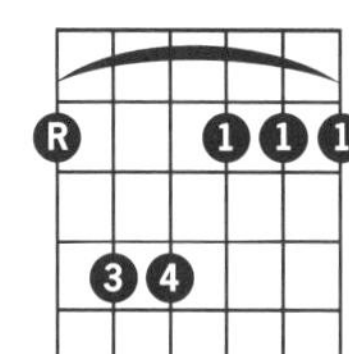

7

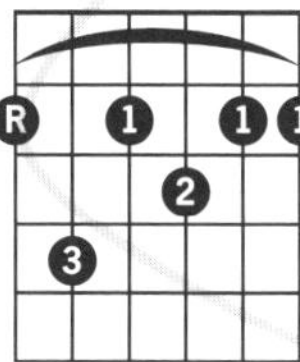

Minor 7

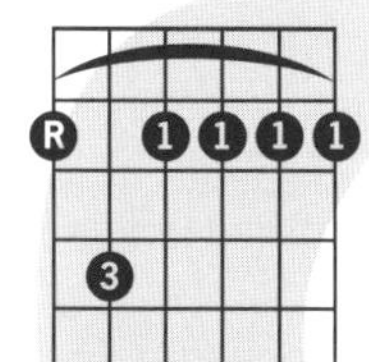

A-Shape Barre Chords

Major

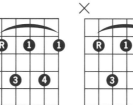

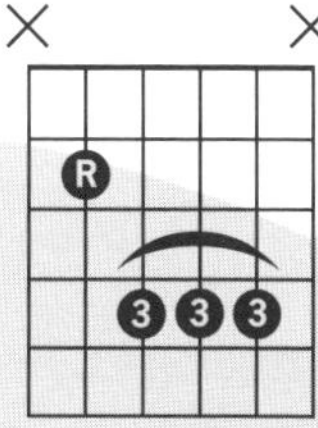

Minor

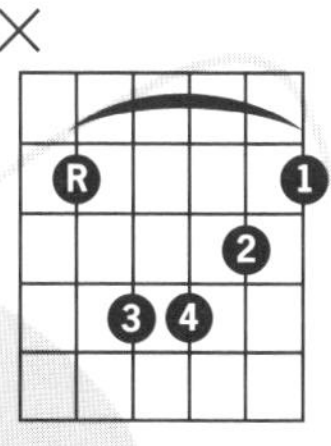

7

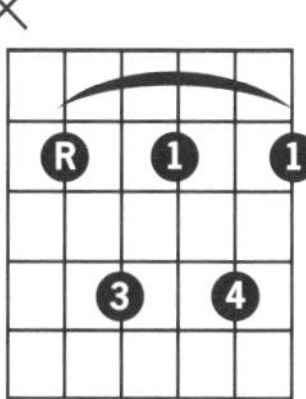

Minor 7

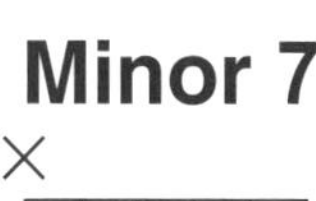

(R = Root note)

Angels

Words & Music by Robbie Williams & Guy Chambers

Intro

| E | E |

Verse 1

E
I sit and wait,
E A B
Does an angel contem - plate my fate?
E E
And do they know, the places where we go
A B F♯m
When we're grey and old? 'Cause I have been told
A C♯m A
That sal - vation lets their wings unfold.

Pre-chorus 1

D
So when I'm lying in my bed,
A/C♯
Thoughts running through my head
E | D A/C♯ | E
And I feel that love is dead, I'm loving angels instead.

Chorus 1

B C♯m
And through it all, she offers me pro - tection,
A E
A lot of love and af - fection, whether I'm right or wrong.
B C♯m
And down the water - fall, wherever it may take me,
A E/G♯
I know that life won't break me, when I come to call.
F♯m
She won't for - sake me,
| Dsus2 A/C♯ | E
I'm loving angels in - stead.

Verse 2

When I'm feeling weak,
And my pain walks down a one way street,
I look above, and I know I'll always be blessed with love.

Pre-chorus 2

And as the feeling grows, she brings flesh to my bones,
And when love is dead, I'm loving angels instead.

Chorus 2

As Chorus 1

Guitar solo

| Bm | A | E | E |
| Bm | F♯m | E/G♯ |

Chorus 3

As Chorus 1

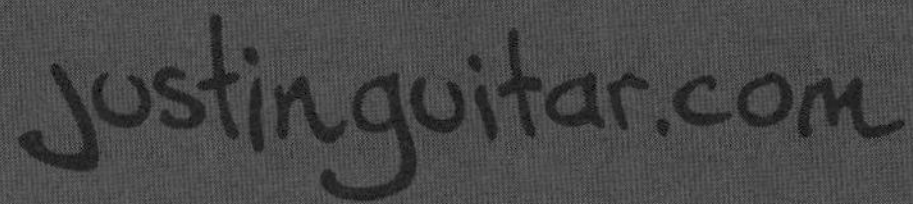

Introduction

This is Robbie Williams' breakthrough single from 1997, which certified him as a star outside Take That, and a respected songwriter.

Chord Additions

There are some very cool and clever chord grips used in the acoustic guitar part during this song, and also some nice bits that we can borrow from the piano part. The first thing to try out is using an Esus4 chord in the intro and for parts of the verse. This Esus4 chord is a variation on the E chord, and appears on the 'and' after beat 4, before going back to a standard E at the start of the next bar—you can hear this clearly played by the piano during the intro.

In the verse (after the words 'fate' and 'old') you will notice an Amaj7 chord sneaks in on beat 4 before changing to the B chord. This is another very nice little trick that we can steal from the pianist!

In the chorus there are a couple of interesting chords to borrow. Firstly, you can replace the B with a Badd4—just leave the thinnest string open, which does mean you have to play the B barre chord in an unconventional way, but it sounds cool. Similarly, you can play the C♯m as a C♯m7 by leaving the two thinnest strings open—this adds a really cool, resonant quality to the chords.

Badd4

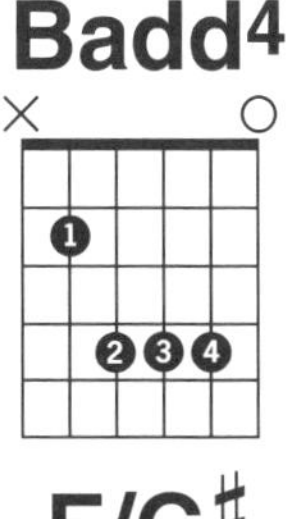

C♯m7

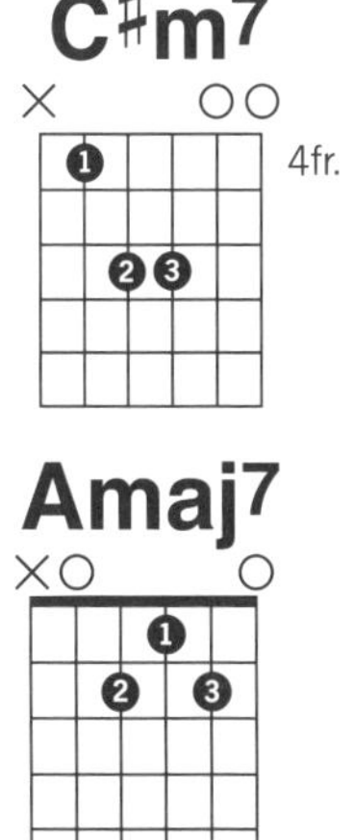

Esus4

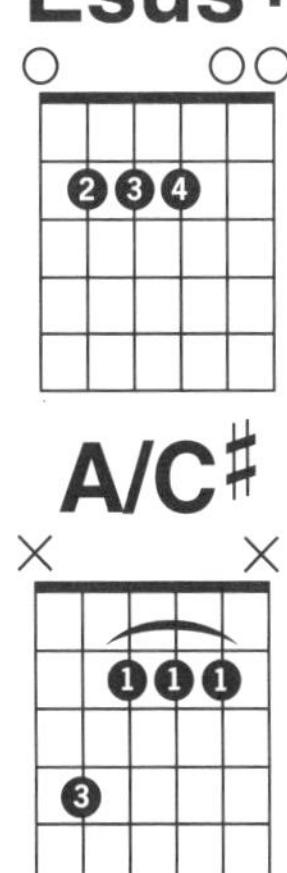

E/G♯

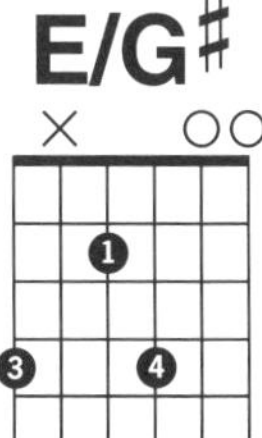

Amaj7

A/C♯

cont...

The main groove of this song is an eighth-note, all down-strum pattern. To imitate the sound of the piano part, play the on-beats (1,2,3,4) a little louder, and just touch the strings lightly for the off- beats. Of course, you will probably want to build up to full volume for the chorus!

I have heard this song played many ways—it sounds great played fingerstyle, and there are many strumming patterns that will work. I like playing in a way that emulates the piano, using the thumb for the bass notes and fingers 1/2/3 for playing the chord as a block. You have a lot of freedom in this song to try things out!

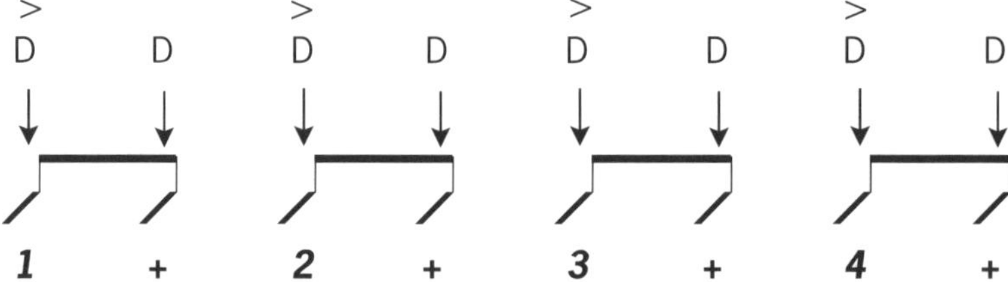

Here It Goes Again

Words & Music by Damian Kulash

Introduction

Finding fame through a YouTube video...where have I heard that before? OK Go made it big with an awesome video for this song, while the song itself has some really enjoyable guitar parts in it.

Barre Chord Riffs

Have you been practising your barre chords? They are fundamental to playing this song, as is listening to the tune itself a few times to get familiar with the various rhythmic variations. It's often a lot easier to learn a song by listening to it, rather than by relying solely on TAB. I recommend that you treat the TAB extracts as building blocks and then use your ears to help you put the whole song together.

Check out the riffs below and practise them until they are 'under your fingers'. I've deliberately not tabbed out the Intro, because if you have mastered the other riffs you'll be able to play it with no difficulty, but it will force you to listen closely to the song!

The first riff to learn is the main hook, which has a very distinct rhythm. The reason that I suggest you learn it first is that parts of it are used in the Intro (the C to G lick) and it appears at various points in the song. You will hear it clearly just before and after the first verse.

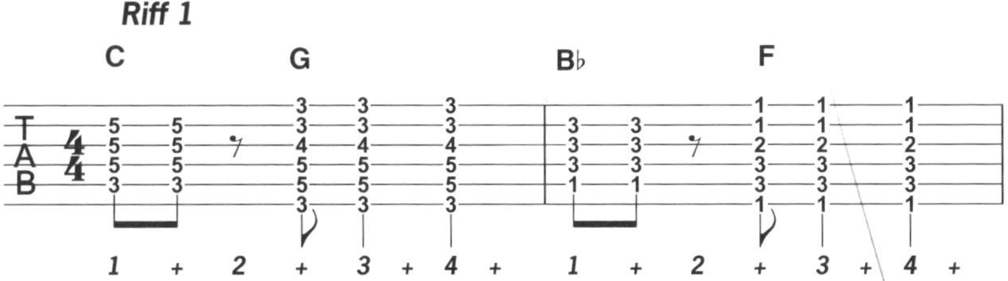

During the verses, one guitar is playing even eighth-notes (all down-picks) while the other guitar plays short 'chips' on the chords, as shown below.

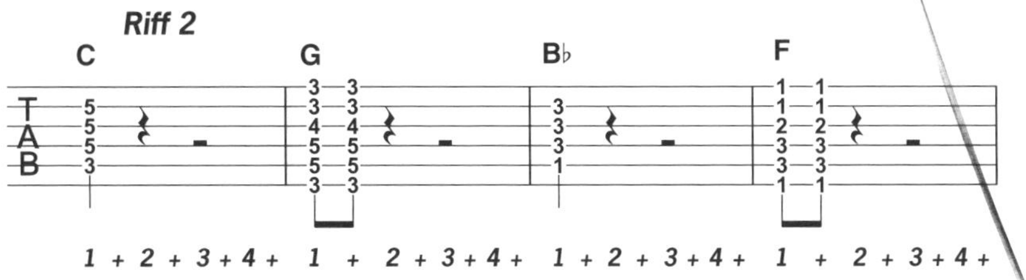

Here It Goes Again

Words & Music by Damian Kulash

Beginner

Intermediate

Intermediate +

TAB

Intro

| C | C | C G |

(riff 1)

| C | C | C G | B♭ F |

Verse 1
(with riff 2)

C G
It could be ten, but then a - gain I can't remember
B♭ F
Half an hour since a quarter to four
C G
Throw on your clothes, the second side of *Surfer Rosa*
B♭ F
And you leave me with my jaw on the floor.
| C G | B♭ F |
Hey!

Pre-chorus 1

Em Am
Ah,__ just when you think you're in control
Em
Just when you think you've got a hold
| Am G |
Just when you get on a roll.

Chorus 1
(with riff 3)

| C G | B♭ F |
Oh, here it goes, here it goes, here it goes again
| Am G | C
Oh, here it goes a - gain
G | B♭ F |
I should have known, should have known, should have known again
| Am G | A♭
But here it goes a - gain
| A♭ G | C | C |
Ah,__ oh, here it goes again.

Verse 2

C G/B
It starts out easy, something simple, something sleazy
B♭ F/A
Something inching past the edge of the re - serve
C G/B
Now through lines of the cheap Venetian blinds
B♭ F/A
Your car is pulling off of the curb. Hey!

Pre-chorus 2

As Pre-chorus 1

Chorus 2

| C G | B♭ F |
Oh, here it goes, here it goes, here it goes again
| Am G | C
Oh, here it goes a - gain

(cont.)

```
                   G                          |B♭                       F               |
I should have known, should have known, should have known again
|Am    G                  |C
    But here it goes a - gain
               G    |B♭                F      |
Oh here it goes,     oh, here it goes
|Am    G                   |A♭                    B♭            |
    Oh, here it goes a - gain   Oh, here it goes again.
```

Solo

```
|: E♭      | E♭      | B♭      | B♭      | Cm      | G   A♭  :|

| C    G   | B♭   F  | Am   G  |
```

Verse 3

I guess there's got to be a break in the monotony
But Jesus, when it rains how it pours
Throw on your clothes, the second side of *Surfer Rosa*
And you leave me, yeah, you leave me. Ah!

Outro-chorus

Repeat Riff 3 *(Play x 7)*
(vocals ad lib.)

```
(Am    G)                 A♭
   Oh, here it goes a - gain
   |A♭                 B♭          |E♭
Oh,___ oh, here it goes again.
```

Riff 3

This riff forms the main chorus hook and is very unusual because it's a 3-bar riff. It feels a little unusual but it works brilliantly in the track. After this riff both guitars switch to even eighth-note strumming, so follow the chart for the chords here.

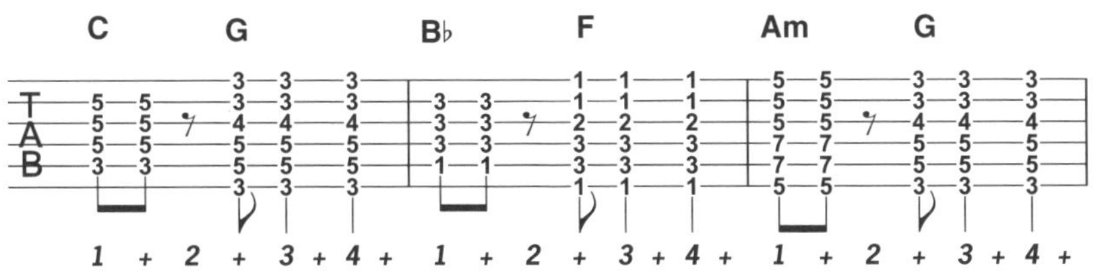

Beginner

Intermediate

Intermediate +

TAB

Chasing Cars

Words & Music by Paul Wilson, Gary Lightbody, Jonathan Quinn, Nathan Connolly & Tom Simpson

Intro

```
| A5     | A5     |
```

Verse 1

```
A5      A5       E/G#  E/G#       Dsus2 Dsus2    A5  A5
   We'll do it all,      everything       on our own.
A5 A5              E/G#  E/G#      Dsus2  Dsus2  A5  A5
   We don't need           anything      or anyone.
```

Chorus 1

```
           A    A          E/G#        E/G#
If I lay here,    if I just lay here,
                  Dsus2       Dsus2                    A   A
Would you lie with me and just forget the world?
```

Verse 2

I don't quite know how to say how I feel.
Those three words are said too much, they're not enough.

Chorus 2

```
If I lay here, if I just lay here,
Would you lie with me and just forget the world?
Forget what we're told before we get too old,
               Dsus2        Dsus2                A
Show me a garden that's bursting into life.
```

Verse 3

Let's waste time chasing cars around our heads.
I need your grace to remind me to find my own.

Chorus 3

If I lay here, if I just lay here,
Would you lie with me and just forget the world?
Forget what we're told before we get too old,
Show me a garden that's bursting into life.

Chorus 4

All that I am, all that I ever was
Is here in your perfect eyes, they're all I can see.
I don't know where, confused about how as well,
Just know that these things will never change for us at all.

Chorus 5

If I lay here, if I just lay here,
Would you lie with me and just forget the world?

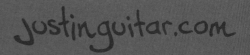

Introduction

This is Snow Patrol's huge hit, released in 2006, and which became the most widely played song of the entire decade in the UK.

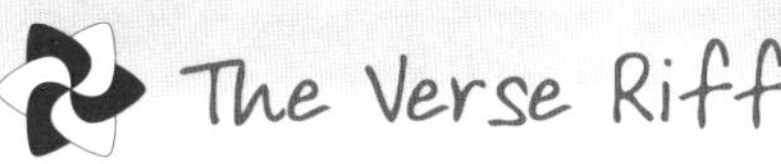

The Verse Riff

This song will sound fine if you just strum the chords, but you'll add a lot more to your playing by including the verse riff. It's not hard to play, other than the fret 5-9 stretch (which just takes a little practice), and if you can keep the riff going while you sing, it will sound beautiful (look up one of the live acoustic versions of the band playing it). The song will sound even better with another guitar playing the chords too.

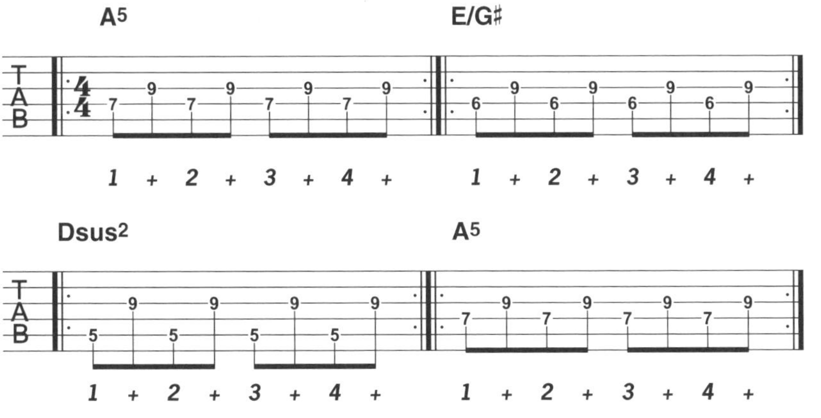

Rhythm

The real core of this song is a continuous eighth-note rhythm, all played as down-strums, which keeps the song moving along. A strong arrangement for this song would be to play the riff for the verses, and then break into the full chords for the chorus to give it a 'lift'.

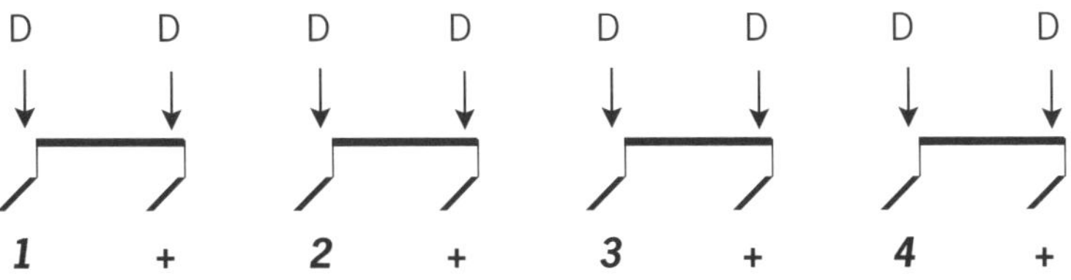

In My Place

Words & Music by Guy Berryman, Chris Martin,
Jon Buckland & Will Champion

Beginner

Intermediate

Intermediate +

TAB

```
|: G      G/F#  | Bm     D      | G      Em     | Bm     D     :|
```

Verse 1

```
 |G          G/F#        |Bm            D                   |G
   In my place, in my place were lines that I couldn't change
       Em7   |Bm      D   |
 I was lost, oh yeah.
 |G               G/F#     |Bm            D                   |G
   And I was lost, I was lost, crossed lines I shouldn't have crossed
       Em    |Bm      D   |
 I was lost, oh yeah.
```

Chorus 1

```
 C                |G                 D/F#   |C
   Yeah, how long must you wait for it?
               |G                D/F#   |C
 Yeah, how long must you pay for it?
               |G                D/F#   |C           D
 Yeah, how long must you wait for it?   Ah, for it?
```

Link

```
| G      G/F#  | Bm     D      | G      Em     | Bm     D      |
```

Verse 2

I was scared, I was scared, tired and under-prepared,
But I'll wait for it.
And if you go, if you go and leave me down here on my own,
Then I'll wait for you, yeah.

Chorus 2

As Chorus 1

Instrumental

```
|: G      G/F#  | Bm     D      | G      Em     | Bm     D     :|
```

Bridge

```
              |G       G/F#   |Bm
 Singing: 'Please, please, please,
       D                |G       Em     |Bm
 Come back and sing to me, to me, ah me.
       D              |G   G/F#  |Bm
 Come on and sing it out, now,  now
       D              |G      Em      |Bm          D          |
 Come on and sing it out, to me, ah me, come back and sing it.'
```

Outro

```
 |G          G/F#        |Bm            D                   |G
   In my place, in my place were lines that I couldn't change
       Em       D        G
 I was lost, oh yeah. Oh yeah.
```

Introduction

Kicking off Coldplay's massive international success, this was the first single off their second album, *A Rush Of Blood To The Head* (2002).

Melody Line

A lot of Coldplay guitar parts are based around quite short, melodic guitar lines. On the song page we have the rhythm guitar part, kept simple by using a capo, and below we have the lead line, played during the Intro. It seems that Jon Buckland plays it in a non-standard tuning, but I've written it out for you here in regular tuning. Since you don't need a capo to play the lead line, I've written the chords below at sounding pitch (in bold), with the capo version of the chord in brackets.

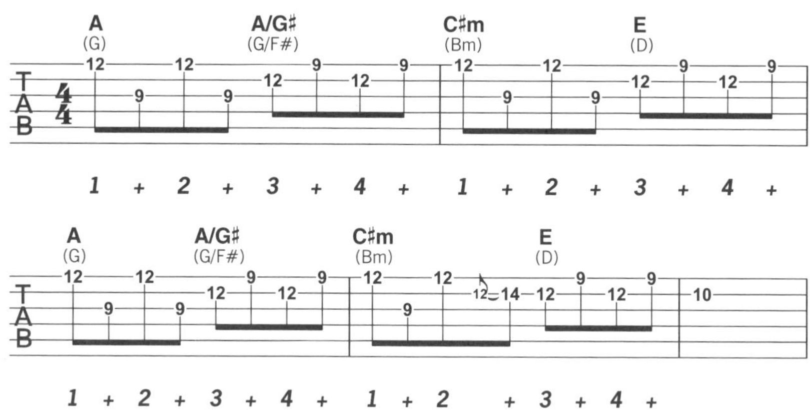

Rhythm

There is not a strong rhythm pattern on the album recording, so the pattern below is based on the way that Chris Martin plays the song for live acoustic performances. However, the strumming pattern varies quite a lot on these performances, so explore it yourself and don't feel that it should be too rigidly stuck to.

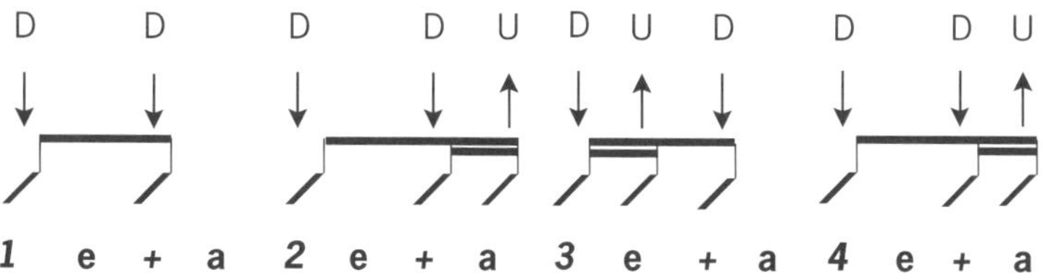

Just Like Heaven

Words & Music by Robert Smith, Simon Gallup, Porl Thompson, Boris Williams & Laurence Tolhurst

Intro |: A | E | Bm | D :|

Verse 1

A E
'Show me, show me, show me how you do that trick,
Bm D
The one that makes me scream' she said,
A E
'The one that makes me laugh' she said,
Bm D A E
And threw her arms a - round my neck, 'Show me how you do it,
Bm D A E
And I'll promise you, I'll promise that I'll run a - way with you,
Bm D
I'll run a - way with you.'

Instr. 1 |: A | E | Bm | D :|

Verse 2

Spinning on that dizzy edge, I kissed her face, I kissed her head
And dreamed of all the different ways I had to make her glow.
'Why are you so far away?' she said,
'And won't you ever know, that I'm in love with you,
That I'm in love with you.'

Chorus 1

F♯m G F♯m G
You, soft and only, you, lost and lonely
F♯m G
You, strange as angels,
D D
Dancing in the deepest oceans, twisting in the water
A E Bm D
You're just like a dream, you're just like a dream.

Instr. 2 |: A | E | Bm | D :| *(Play x3)*

Verse 3

Daylight licked me into shape, I must have been asleep for days,
And moving lips to breathe her name, I opened up my eyes,
And found myself alone, alone, alone, above a raging sea
That stole the only girl I loved, and drowned her deep inside of me.

Chorus 2

F♯m G F♯m G
You, soft and only , you, lost and lonely.
F♯m G D
You, just like Heaven.

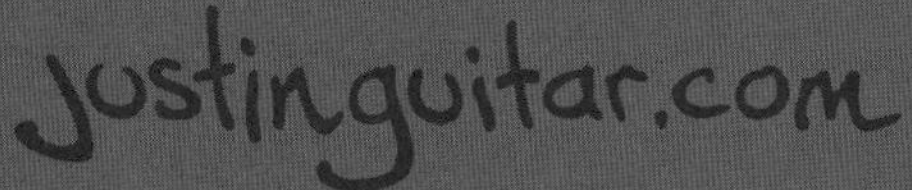

Introduction

One of singer Robert Smith's favourite Cure songs, this was a hit in 1987, and was included on the album *Kiss Me, Kiss Me, Kiss Me*.

Mixing Options

Once again, it's up to you to decide which of the chords in this song you should play as barre chords. I often ask students to study 'Just Like Heaven', since it's a good song for mixing in a barred Bm chord with open chords—this combination is probably the best option for easy strumming, especially if you plan to sing too. However, if you are playing an electric guitar, it makes sense to play most of the chords as barre chords, focusing a little more on the thicker strings when you strum, and letting the song rock out a little more.

Rhythm

This song uses 'pushes' on every other chord, meaning that for every second chord, the change comes half a beat early. To keep it simple I have written out the strumming pattern for the main chord sequence—practise it slowly until you get the hang of it and then run it at full speed. 'Pushes' are a very common rhythm guitar technique and once you can use them properly you will find yourself noticing them all over the place!

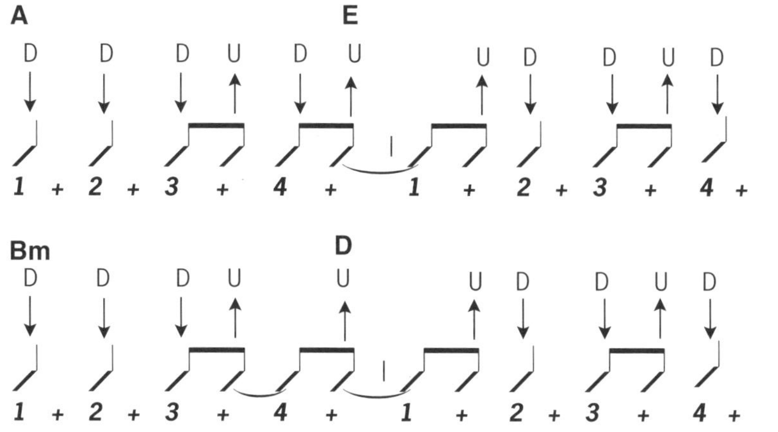

La Bamba

Trad Arr. by Ritchie Valens

Intro

(riff)
| (G) (A) (B) | C F | G | C F | G |

Verse 1

N.C. | C F |
Para bailar La Bamba,
G | C F | G | C F |
Para bailar La Bamba, se necess - ita una poca de gracia
G | C F | G
Una poca de gracia, para mi, para ti,
| C F | G
Ay arriba ar - riba
| C F | G | C F | G (N.C)
Ay arriba ar - riba, por ti se - re, por ti se - re, por ti se - re.

Verse 2

Yo no soy marinero, yo no soy marinero, soy capitan
Soy capitan, soy capitan,

Chorus 1

| C F | G
Bam - ba, Bamba
| C F | G
Bam - ba, Bamba
| C F | G | C F | G (N.C)
Bam - ba, Bamba.

Verse 2

Para bailar La Bamba, para bailar La Bamba, se necessita
Una poca de gracia, una poca de gracia,
Para mi, para ti, ay arriba (arriba)

Instrumental

| C F | G | C F | G |
ar - riba
| C F | G | C F | G |
C F | G | C F | G |
| C F | G | C F | G | C (N.C)

Verse 4

As Verse 1

Outro

||: C F | G :|| *(Repeat to fade)*
Bam - ba, Bamba

Introduction

A great rock 'n' roll tune based on a Mexican folk song, this song was first recorded by Ritchie Valens in 1958.

Opening / Main Riff

'La Bamba' features one of the all-time great guitar riffs, which is a lot of fun to play. The riff on the Ritchie Valens recording is quite loose, so the version below is closer to the other famous version, recorded by Los Lobos. There are a couple of places where the nearby strings are unintentionally hit, so I would recommend holding down the chord shapes as you play the riff. It seems to work best with all down-strums, but you can use alternate picking if you prefer. Fingering is easy because the fret and finger number are the same (e.g. notes on the 2nd fret are played by finger 2).

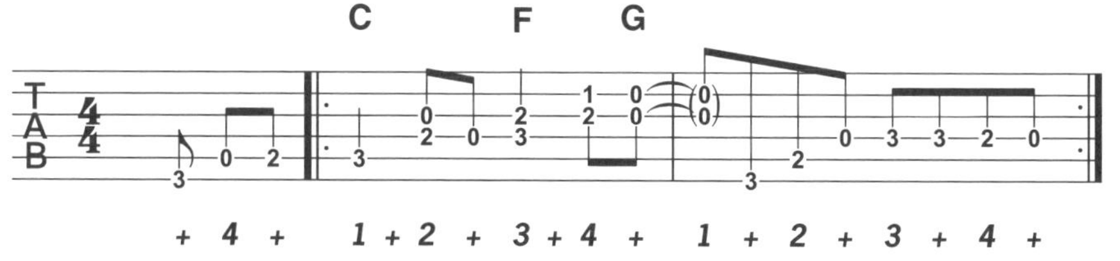

Strumming

After the riff, you will be strumming the chords, and the pattern on the record is a two bar pattern. However, it should be played loosely—add a few extra strums, and don't adhere too strictly to the pattern. The pattern below is just a starting point, which will hopefully develop as you get more familiar with the song.

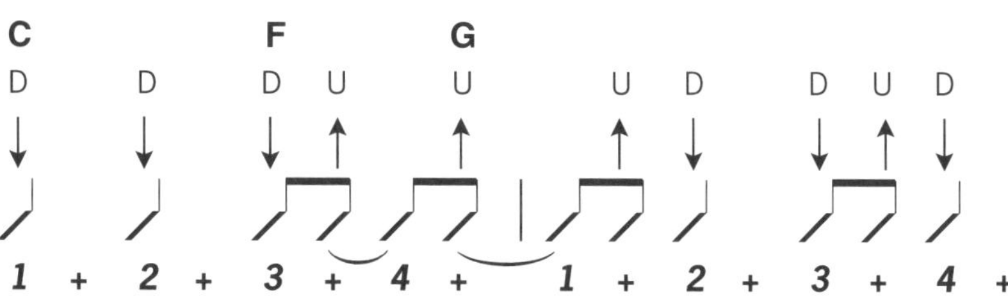

The Lazy Song

Words & Music by Ari Levine, Philip Lawrence, Peter Hernandez
& Keinan Abdi Warsame

Chorus 1

```
     B                F♯          E          E
To - day I don't feel like doing anything,
B              F♯          E         E
I just wanna lay in my bed.
    B                 F♯
Don't feel like picking up my phone,
  E                    E
So leave a message at the tone,
             B                D♯7        E          E
'Cause to - day I swear I'm not doing anything.
```

Verse 1

```
N.C.       B                       F♯
I'm gonna kick my feet up then stare at the fan,
E                            E
Turn the TV on, throw my hand in my pants,
B                F♯      E
Nobody's gonna tell me I can't.
E        B                               F♯
  No, I'll be lounging on the couch, just chillin' in my snuggie,
E                              E
Click to M.T.V., so they can teach me how to Dougie,
        B              F♯             E          E
'Cause in my castle I'm the freak - ing man.
    C♯m          D♯m           E            F♯
Oh, yes I said it,      I said it, I said it 'cause I can.
```

Chorus 2

As Chorus 1

```
N.C.              B            F♯            E
Nothing at all,   ooh, hoo,    ooh, hoo, ooh, ooh, ooh.
                  B            F♯            E
Nothing at all,   ooh, hoo,    ooh, hoo, ooh, ooh, ooh.
```

Verse 2

Tomorrow I'll wake up, do some P90X
Meet a really nice girl, have some really nice sex
And she's gonna scream out: 'This is great.'
(*Oh my God, this is great.*) Yeah.
I might mess around and get my college degree,
I bet my old man will be so proud of me.
But sorry pops, you'll just have to wait.
Oh, yes I said it, I said it, I said it 'cause I can.

Chorus 3

As Chorus 1

Bridge

```
N.C.  C♯m                      F♯
No, I ain't gonna comb my hair,
         G♯m               G♯m
'Cause I ain't going any - where,
C♯m            F♯                  G♯m      G♯m
No, no, no, no, no, no, no, no, no.____
       C♯m                     F♯
I'll just strut in my birthday suit
        G♯m               G♯m
And let everything hang loose,
C♯m                        F♯                                  G♯m  N.C.
Yeah, yeah, yeah, yeah, yeah, yeah, yeah, yeah, yeah, yeah.
```

Chorus 3 As Chorus 2

Introduction

This pop-reggae hit was the third single from Bruno Mars' debut album, *Doo-Wops & Hooligans* (2010).

Tight Chords

The chords in this song are played very short (staccato). To achieve this technique, you have to release the chord (with the fretting hand) immediately after it is played, only don't let your fingers leave the strings—just release the pressure. Try this with the B chord a few times—play the chord with a fairly hard down-strum, and then immediately release the pressure and the chord should stop sounding. You should only press down at the instant when you strum, and then release the chord right away. This will keep the rhythm tight.

Beginner

Intermediate

Intermediate +

TAB

This funky rhythm pattern involves playing chords on beats 2 and 4, using down-strums and the technique mentioned on the previous page. There are a few points where the chords are held, and there are some breaks and extra strums added in, but you will easily identify them once you have listened to the recording a few times.

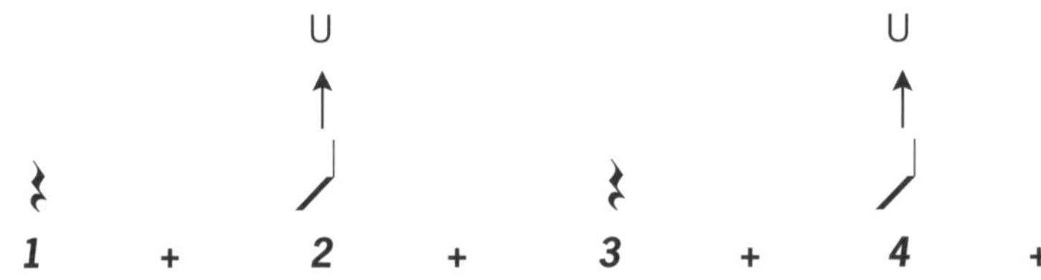

Fingerstyle

This same pattern could be played fingerstyle, with the bass note played (with the thumb) on beat 1 of each bar and the 3 fingers plucking the chord. Remember that you will need to adapt the pattern as the chords change throughout the song.

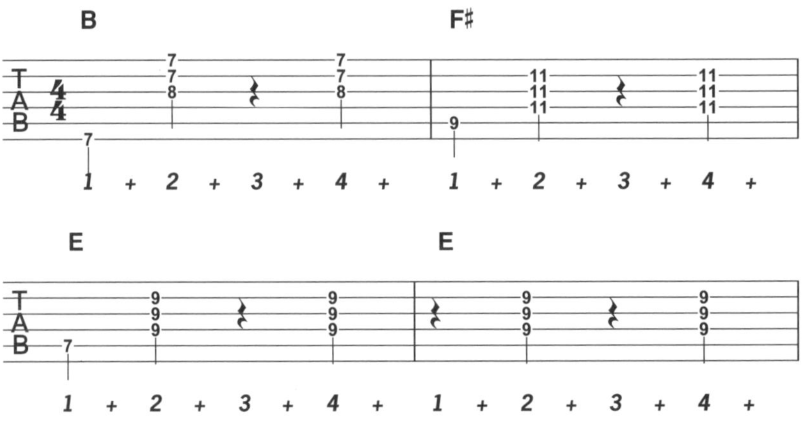

Price Tag

Words & Music by Lukasz Gottwald, Claude Kelly, Bobby Ray Simmons & Jessica Cornish

Introduction

This feel-good pop song established Jessie J as an international star, and works beautifully both as an up-tempo pop tune and as an acoustic ballad.

To Barre Or Not To Barre?

There a quite a few options when choosing your chord voicings in this song, which you can use some or all of. As the song uses the same chord sequence throughout, you should introduce some variety to the guitar part to keep the listener (and you!) interested. Moreover, this song really needs to be performed with a lead vocal part, otherwise your audience will start glazing over pretty quickly. I would suggest checking out the live version on *Later... with Jools Holland*, which was performed with just acoustic guitar accompanying the lead vocal.

I recommend starting off using all barre chords—R5 (F chord), R6 (C chord), R5 (Dm chord), R6 (B♭ chord). Check out the album version and you will hear the electric guitar playing some very funky rhythms. To achieve this style you need to use a strumming pattern like the one over the page. However, when you are strumming, you should intermittently press the chord down (to make the chord sound) and lift it up again (to mute the chord). This will create a funky groove. There are clear chords played on beats 2 and 4, while the other strums in the pattern are played very lightly or are just percussive clicks that you can create by lightly strumming, with the chord relaxed, not pressed hard enough for the notes to ring out.

To increase the dynamics in the chorus, you might choose to play the chord sequence in open position—of course the F and B♭ will have to be barre chords, but playing the Am and Dm as open chords should lift the dynamics up. This trick will work best on acoustic guitar, although you can try it out on electric guitar too.

Price Tag

Words & Music by Lukasz Gottwald, Claude Kelly,
Bobby Ray Simmons & Jessica Cornish

Chord sequence throughout

| F | Am | Dm | B♭ |

Verse 1

Seems like everybody's got a price,
I wonder how they sleep at night.
When the sale comes first and the truth comes second,
Just stop for a minute and smile.
Why is everybody so serious?
Acting so damn mysterious,
You got your shades on your eyes and your heels so high
That you can't even have a good time.

Pre-chorus 1

Everybody look to their left, everybody look to their right.
Can you feel that? Yeah

N.C.
We'll pay them with love tonight.

Chorus 1

F (etc.)
It's not about the money, money, money,
We don't need your money, money, money.
We just wanna make the world dance,
Forget about the price tag.
Ain't about the, oh, cha-ching, cha-ching,
Ain't about the, yeah, ba-bling, ba-bling.
Wanna make the world dance,
Forget about the price tag.

Verse 2

We need to take it back in time
When music made us all unite.
And it wasn't low blows and video hoes,
Am I the only one gettin' tired?
Why is everybody so obsessed?
Money can't buy us happiness.
Can we all slow down and enjoy right now?
Guarantee we'll be feelin' alright.

Pre-chorus 2 As Pre-chorus 1

Chorus 2 As Chorus 1

Rap Yeah, yeah, well, keep the price tag and take the cash back,
Just give me six strings and a half stack.
And you can keep the cars, leave me the garage,
And all I, yes, all I need are keys and guitars.
And guess what, in 30 seconds I'm leaving to Mars,
Yes, we leaving across these undefeatable odds.
It's like this man, you can't put a price on life,
We do this for the love, so we fight and sacrifice every night.
So we ain't gon' stumble and fall, never,
Waiting to see, a sign of defeat, uh uh.
So we gon' keep everyone moving their feet,
So bring back the beat and then everybody sing.

Chorus 3 As Chorus 1 (*Play x2*)

Outro (Ah, ah, ah, ah.)

Yeah, yeah, oh, forget about the price tag. (Ah.)

The rhythm here is a sixteenth-note groove. Pay careful attention to the up- and down-strums, but remember that your strumming hand will be moving continuously anyway—you just need to be aware of which notes you actually strum and which you miss out. I think it helps to think 'light' too—trying to play these patterns too heavy-handedly usually sounds harsh and far from funky!

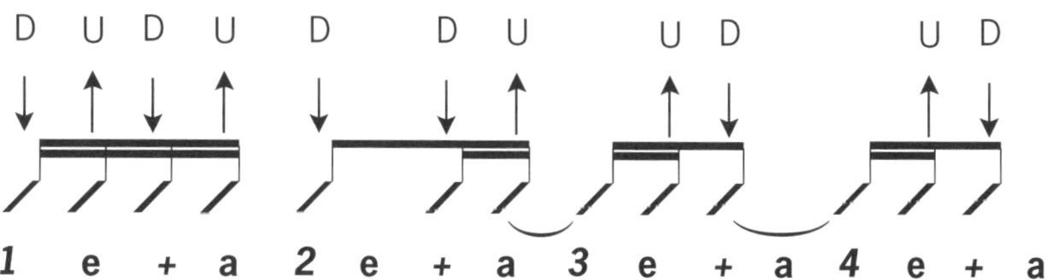

Rule The World

Words & Music by Mark Owen, Gary Barlow, Jason Orange & Howard Donald

Verse 1

```
     Bm      F♯m        Em        F♯m
You light the skies up a - bove me,
   Bm    F♯m       Em       F♯m
A star, so bright you blind me, yeah.
      Em        Bm                 F♯m                 A
Don't close your eyes, don't fade a - way, don't fade a - way, oh.
```

Chorus 1

```
D                           | Bm       F♯m
   Yeah, you and me we can ride on a star,
      | F♯m         G       | G      A   |
If you stay with me girl, we can rule the world.
D                           | Bm         F♯m |
   Yeah, you and me we can light up the sky,
      | F♯m        G       | G      A   |
If you stay by my side we can rule the world.
```

Verse 2

If walls break down, I will comfort you,
If angels cry, oh, I'll be there for you.
You've saved my soul, don't leave me now, don't leave me now, oh.

Chorus 2

As Chorus 1

Instrumental

```
| D        | Bm  F♯m | F♯m  G  | G  A   |
```

Bridge

```
        Em
All the stars are coming out tonight,
         G                          D          A
They're lighting up the sky tonight   for you,   for you.
        Em
All the stars are coming out tonight,
         G                          D          A          A
They're lighting up the sky tonight   for you,   for you.  Oh.
```

Chorus 3

As Chorus 1

Outro

```
          D
||: All the stars are coming out tonight,
         | Bm         F♯m   |
  They're lighting up the sky tonight
| F♯m  G  | G   A  :||  (Play x4)       D
   for you, for  you.
```

Introduction

This single, released in 2007, marked boy band Take That's return to form.

Both Grips In One Song?

One decision you have to make when playing a song using barre chords, is which type to play—your E-shape or A-shape? The chord Bm can be played easily in two places, so which one should you use? In this song I would use the higher position (R6 – Root on the sixth string) for the verses and R5 (Root on the 5th string) for the chorus.

The important thing here is the thinking behind your decision. In the verse we have the chords Bm, F♯m and Em, and if we played these chords down toward the nut we would probably have to play the Em as an open chord, which I would discourage, as it generally sounds better to play either all open chords or all barre chords, when possible.

In the latter part of the chorus we have an A chord. If we are playing higher up the neck (the Bm with R6) we will end up playing the A chord right up the neck which doesn't sound great and is harder to play, especially on acoustic guitar. Try what I suggest and try the opposite, and see what works for you! It's important that you learn from your own experience.

Rhythm

The best groove for this song is all 'pumping' eighth-note strumming, i.e. playing a down-strum on each strong beat and on each 'and'. Once you have mastered this, I would recommend putting a slight accent on beats 2 and 4 just to help the groove along. You might also like to throw in the occasional up-strum between the downs just to spice things up a bit, but don't overcomplicate the strumming—this is straight out pop music, and simple is usually best!

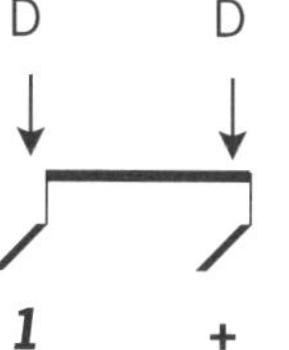

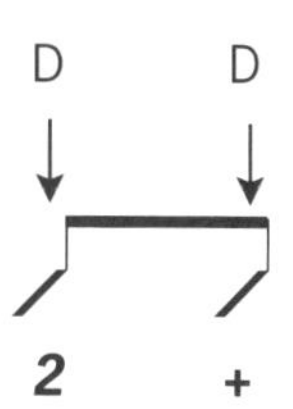

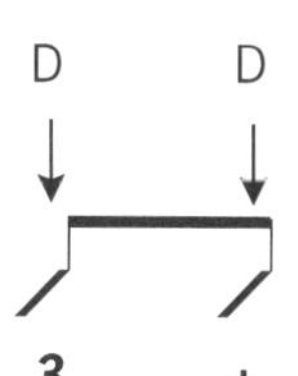

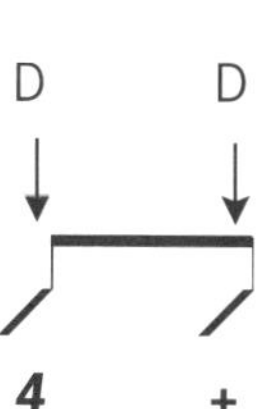

Run

Words & Music by Gary Lightbody, Jonathan Quinn, Mark McClelland, Nathan Connolly & Iain Archer

Beginner

Intermediate

Intermediate +

TAB

Intro |: Am F/A | Gsus4 | Am F/A | Gsus4 :|

Verse 1

| Am F/A | Gsus4
I'll sing it one last time for you
| Am F/A | Gsus4
Then we really have to go
| Am F/A | Gsus4
You've been the only thing that's right
| Am F/A | Gsus4
In all I've done.

Verse 2

And I can barely look at you, but every single time I do
I know we'll make it anywhere, away from here.

Chorus 1

C C G
Light up, light up, as if you have a choice
G Am Am F F
Even if you cannot hear my voice, I'll be right beside you dear
C C G
Louder, louder, and we'll run for our lives
Am
I can hardly speak I understand
Am F F
Why you can't raise your voice to say.

Link | Am F/A | Gsus4 | Am F/A | Gsus4 |

Verse 3

To think I might not see those eyes, it makes it so hard not to cry
And as we say our long goodbyes, I nearly do.

Chorus 2 As Chorus 1

Chorus 3

Slower, slower, we don't have time for that
All I want's to find an easier way, to get out of our little heads.
Have heart my dear, we're bound to be afraid
Even if it's just for a few days, making up for all this mess.

Solo

|: C | C | G | G |
| Am | Am | F | F :|

Chorus 4

C C G
Light up, light up, as if you have a choice
G Am | Am G | F F C
Even if you cannot hear my voice, I'll be right beside you dear.

Introduction

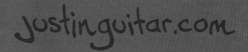

A favourite with *X Factor* contestants, this is Snow Patrol's original version of the song, released on their album, *Final Straw* (2003).

Main Riff

This is one of those songs that sounds best when you play it exactly like the recording. You can play the chords in a lot of different ways, but there is only one way that is right!

Play this riff with all down-strums and avoid the thinnest two strings. It's a bit of a stretch but shouldn't take too much practice.

```
    Am                      F/A                     Gsus4
 |------------------------------------------------|------------------------------------------------|
 |------------------------------------------------|------------------------------------------------|
 |-5-----5-----5-----5-----5-----5-----5-----5----|-5-----5-----5-----5-----5-----5-----5-----5----|
 |-2-----2-----2-----2-----2-----3-----3-----3----|-3-----0-----0-----0-----0-----0-----0-----0----|
 |-0-----0-----0-----0-----0-----0-----0-----0----|-0-----5-----5-----5-----5-----5-----5-----5----|
 |------------------------------------------------|-------3-----3-----3-----3-----3-----3-----3----|
   1  +  2  +  3  +  4  +                           1  +  2  +  3  +  4  +
```

Rhythm

The rhythm for this song is 'pumping 8ths', all down-strums, with a slight palm mute for the verses, and then lifting the mute for the chorus. For the chorus you can include slight accents, as shown below, to drive the song along.

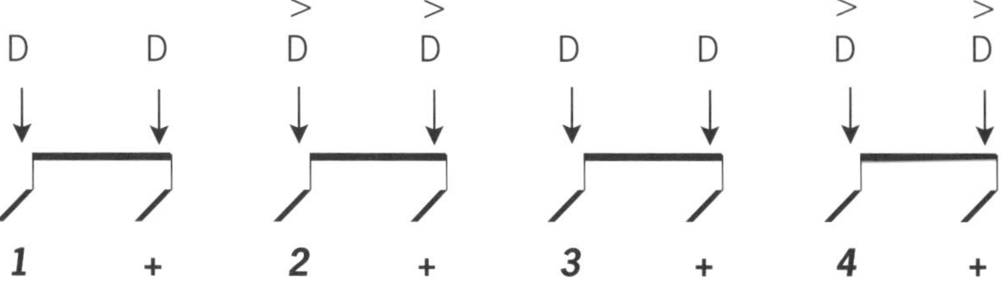

She's The One

Words & Music by Karl Wallinger

Beginner

Intermediate

Intermediate +

TAB

Intro

```
| A        | Dmaj7 | A        | Dmaj7 |
```

Verse 1

```
        A             Dmaj7           A             Dmaj7
I was  her, she was me,     we were one, we were free.
                         Bm                 E7             A    Dmaj7
And if there's some - body calling me on, she's the one.
                  Bm                 E7             A    Dmaj7
If there's some - body calling me on, she's the one.
```

Verse 2

```
           A                Dmaj7              A             Dmaj7
We were young, we were wrong, we were fine all a - long.
                  Bm                 E7             A    A7
If there's some - body calling me on, she's the one.
```

Bridge 1

```
D
   When you get to where you wanna go
          D                                         A        A7
And you know the things you wanna know, you're    smil - ing.
D
   When you said what you wanna say
          D
And you know the way you wanna play,
Bm                                 E7sus4  E7
   You'll be so high you'll be fly     -   ing.
```

Verse 3

```
              A             Dmaj7           A               Dmaj7
Though the sea will be strong, I know we'll carry on.
                          Bm                 E7             A    Dmaj7
'Cause if there's some - body calling me on, she's the one.
                  Bm                 E7             A    A7
If there's some - body calling me on, she's the one.
```

Bridge 2

As Bridge 1

Verse 4

```
      A            Dmaj7           A              Dmaj7
I was her, she was me,  we were one, we were free.
                         Bm                 E7             A    A7
And if there's some - body calling me on, she's the one.
                  Bm                 E7             A    A7
If there's some - body calling me on, she's the one.
```

Outro

```
                         Bm              E7              F♯m                    D
If there's some - body calling me on, she's the one, yeah, she's the one.
                         Bm              E7              F♯m                    G
If there's some - body calling me on, she's the one, yeah, she's the one
                         Bm              E7              F♯m                    D
If there's some - body calling me on, she's the one, yeah, she's the one
                         Bm              E7              A   Dmaj7  A  Dmaj7
If there's some - body calling me on, she's the one.
             A
She's the one.
```

Introduction

Written by Karl Wallinger for his band, World Party, this song was covered by Robbie Williams in 1998, and featured on his album *I've Been Expecting You*.

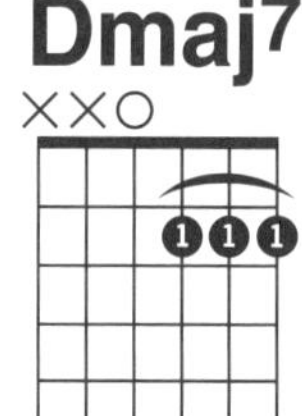

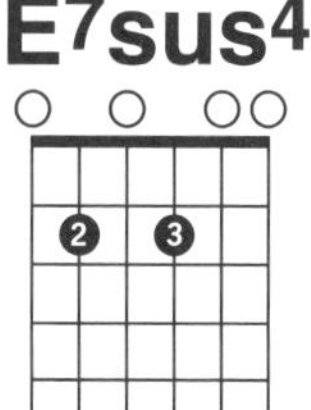

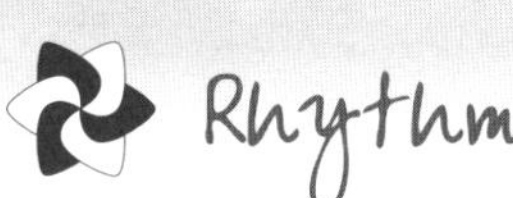

If you want to strum the guitar during this song, you should start with sixteenth-note strumming. Just play the down-strums initially, and then start to add in some up-strums to fill out the pattern for the Bridge sections.

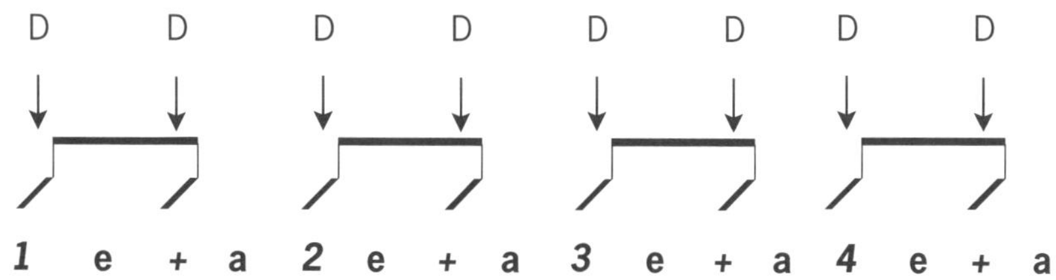

cont...

She's The One

Words & Music by Karl Wallinger

Play The Piano

This song is really lead by the piano part, which plays the melody lines in the Intro and generally drives the song along. When there is no set guitar part in a song, you have more freedom to experiment. Often you will find that you can play similar melody parts to the piano on the guitar, and without straying too far from the chords. Below is my arrangement of the piano part for the guitar. If you want to learn how to arrange melodies for the guitar, the best way is just to experiment, and the more you do it, the better you will become at it!

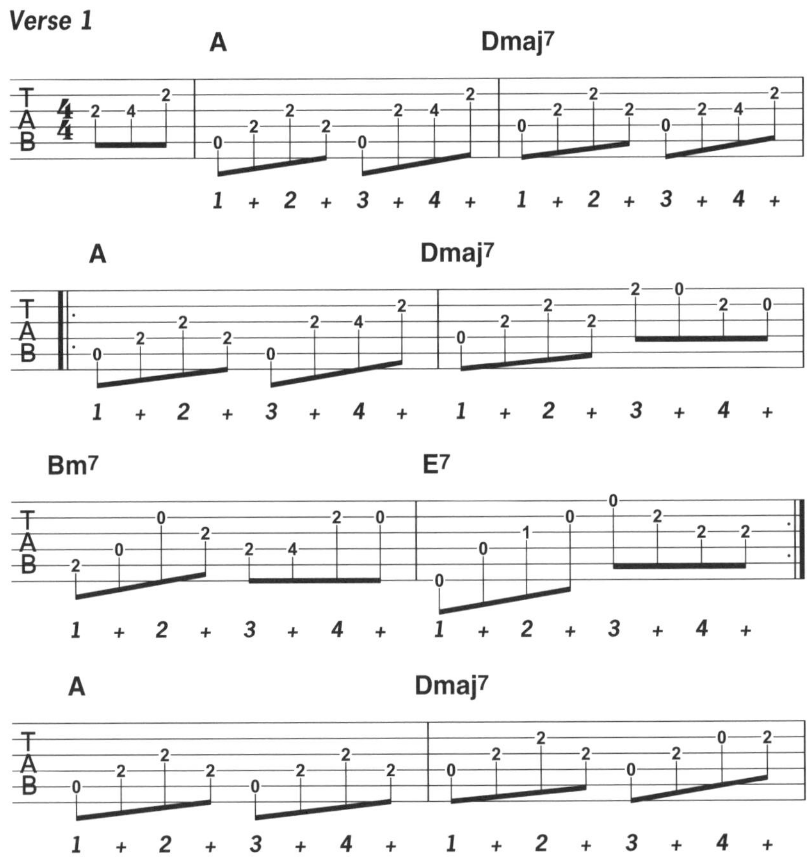

Somewhere Only We Know

Words & Music by Tim Rice-Oxley, Tom Chaplin & Richard Hughes

Introduction

This piano pop ballad launched Keane's career in 2004.

Arranging The Piano Part

This song poses some interesting questions for guitar players. Piano players can hit a lot more notes at once than us and it's very easy for them to keep the bass note the same in one hand, while fiddling with chords in the other, and this song is a prime example of that!

Rather than trying to write down every variation that pianist Tim Rice-Oxley plays, I have simplified the chords a little so that they work well on guitar. The original piano part includes a lot of 6th chords which often end up sounding awkward on the guitar, so I've edited a lot of them out.

Note that during the verses, in the bars containing both Dsus4 and D, (e.g. the last bar of the verses), you should play 3 strums on the Dsus4, 3 on the D and then 2 on the Dsus4 again. But during the chorus, in the bars containing G/B, Dsus4 and D, you will play 4 strums on the G/B, and then 2 on the sus4, followed by 2 on the D.

Watch out for the rogue D♭ chord in the outro—I'd leave it out if I were you, although you can play it as a barre chord. It's your call!

cont...

Somewhere Only We Know

Words & Music by Tim Rice-Oxley, Tom Chaplin & Richard Hughes

Beginner

Intermediate

Intermediate +

TAB

Intro ‖: G | G/F♯ | Am | Dsus4 D Dsus4 :‖

Verse 1

```
G                     G/F♯
  I walked across       an empty land
Am                                  |Dsus4        D      Dsus4 |
  I knew the pathway like the back of my hand
G                   G/F♯
  I felt the earth      beneath my feet
Am                             |Dsus4              D     Dsus4 |
  Sat by the river and it made me comp - lete.
```

Bridge 1

```
Em                    Bm
 Oh simple thing       where have you gone?
C                                    |C                Dsus4 D |
  I'm getting old and I need something to re - ly     on
Em                    Bm
  So tell me when       you're gonna let me in
C                                      |C                  Dsus4 D |
  I'm getting tired and I need somewhere to be - gin.
```

Verse 2

I came across a fallen tree,
I felt the branches of it looking at me
Is this the place we used to love,
Is this the place that I've been dreaming of?

Bridge 2 As Bridge 1

Chorus 1

```
Am                         |G/B                 Dsus4 D |
  And if you have a minute why don't we   go
Am                 |G/B               Dsus4 D |
  Talk about it somewhere only we   know
Am                         |G/B           Dsus4 D |
  This could be the end of every - thing
C                          |D                G       |
So why don't we go, somewhere only we know.
```

Link

```
 C  D                                 C  |Dsus4 D  |
      Somewhere only we know.
```

Bridge 3 As Bridge 1

Chorus 2

And if you have a minute why don't we go?
Talk about it somewhere only we know.
This could be the end of everything,

```
C                            |C              D   |
So why don't we go, so why don't we go.
```

Link

```
| Am      | G/B    Dsus4 D | Am      | G/B   Dsus4 D |
```

Outro

```
Am                          |G/B         Dsus4 D |
 This could be the end of every - thing
C                           | D                G      |
So why don't we go, somewhere only we know
C      | D                     (D♭)    | C
       Somewhere only we know
|D                     C        | G
Somewhere only we know.
```

Beginner
Intermediate
Intermediate +
TAB

Rhythm

This song uses all down-strums, (aka pumping 8ths), and this strumming pattern will really keep the song moving. Remember to bring the volume down (strum lighter, rather than adjusting the volume knob!) for the verses to create some dynamic contrast.

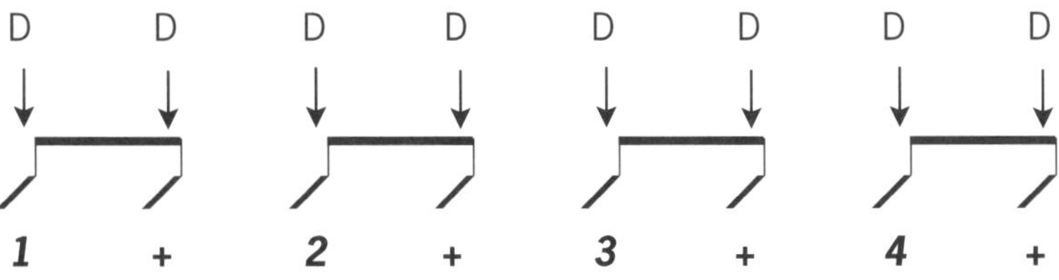

Torn

Words & Music by Anne Preven, Phil Thornalley & Scott Cutler

Beginner

Intermediate

Intermediate +

TAB

Intro

```
| F          | Fsus4      | F          | Fsus2      |
```

Verse 1

```
F          F                           Am
   I thought I saw a man brought to life,
            Am                                   B♭
He was warm, he came around like he was dignified,
   B♭
He showed me what it was to cry.
```

Verse 2

```
F                 F                     Am                      Am
   Well you couldn't be that man I adored,    you don't seem to know,
                                 B♭           B♭
Don't seem to care what your heart is for, but I don't know him anymore
```

Pre-chorus 1

```
            Dm                               C
There's nothing where he used to lie,    my conversation has run dry,
Am                          C
   That's what's going on,    nothing's fine, I'm torn.
```

Chorus 1

```
F                C                       Dm
  I'm all out of faith, this is how I feel,
                      B♭                            F
I'm cold and I am shamed, lying naked on the floor.
                  C                          Dm
Illusion never changed into something real,
                      B♭                         F
Wide awake and I can see the perfect sky is torn,
                 C                  Dm          B♭
You're a little late, I'm already torn.
```

Verse 3

So I guess the fortune teller's right,
I should have seen just what was there
And not some holy light,
But you crawled beneath my veins.

Pre-chorus 2

And now I don't care, I had no luck, I don't miss it all that much,
There's just so many things, that I can search, I'm torn.

Chorus 2

As Chorus 1

```
| Dm       | B♭  Dm  Dm  F     C
Torn,            Oo, oo, oo.
```

Pre-chorus 3

There's nothing where he used to lie, my inspiration has run dry,
That's what's going on, nothing's right, I'm torn.

Chorus 3

I'm all out of faith, this is how I feel,
I'm cold and I am shamed, lying naked on the floor.
Illusion never changed into something real,
Wide awake and I can see the perfect sky is torn.

Chorus 3

```
F                C                  Dm
I'm all out of faith, This is how I feel,
                  B♭                              F
I'm cold and I'm ashamed, Bound and broken on the floor.
                C                  Dm        B♭   Dm    C  C
You're a little late, I'm already torn...        Torn...
```

Guitar Solo

‖: F | C | Dm | B♭ :‖

Introduction

Natalie Imbruglia's million-selling hit from 1997 is a great workout for barre chords and sixteenth-note strumming.

Monster Barre Workout

This song is usually played as all barre chords, but on an acoustic guitar you will find it hard to hold these big barre grips down solidly for the whole song (unless it has a really low action). I remember playing this song in a duo with a singer, and by the end of the song I thought I was going to have to call a break! It really works out the muscle between your thumb and 1st finger.

Although it's great to practise this whole song all the way through with barres, if you feel your muscles getting tense, look for open chord alternatives. In this song you have an escape with the C and Dm, so even if it's just for a bar or two you might find that short respite from playing barre chords will relax your hand enough to keep going.

cont...

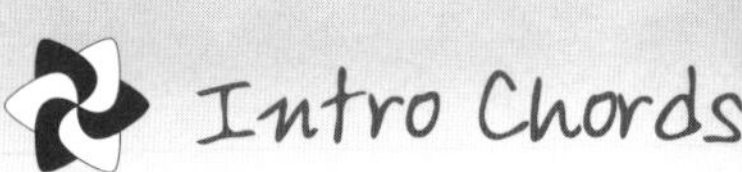

The intro has a nice chord movement.

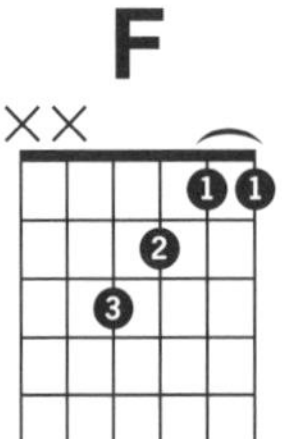

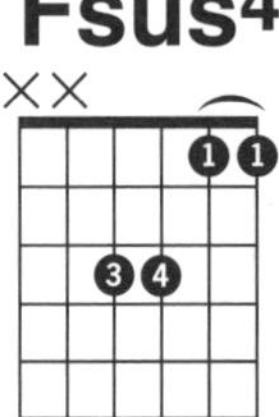

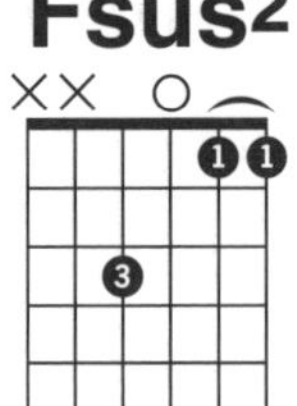

The rhythm in this song is quite specific, and I often teach it as an excellent example of a sixteenth-note strumming pattern. Spend a little time mastering this pattern and you will probably find yourself using it often! Make sure you keep your strumming hand moving too, to keep yourself in the groove.

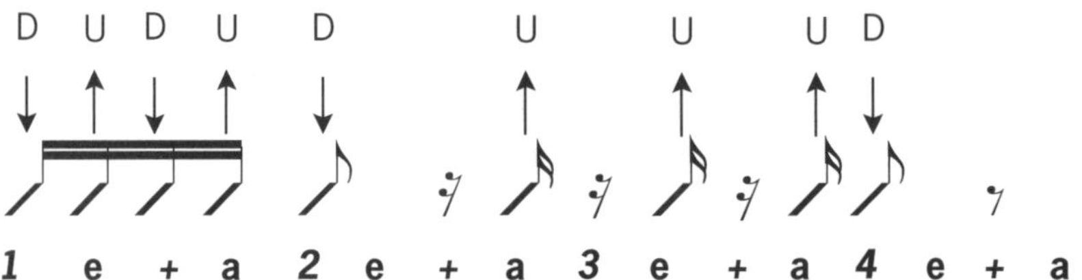

When You're Gone

Words & Music by Bryan Adams & Eliot Kennedy

Introduction

The unlikely pairing of Bryan Adams and Spice Girl Melanie C took this song to the UK Top 3 in 1998.

A-Shape Sus

This song uses a really cool (and quite common) chord movement, adding a sus4 to an A-shape barre grip. It's not very difficult, sounds great and is something you can use quite often to spice up a rhythm guitar part. Simply add your little finger to the second string one fret above the barre. It will take some practice, and you should make sure that the thinnest string is muted the whole time or it will alter the chord and spoil the effect!

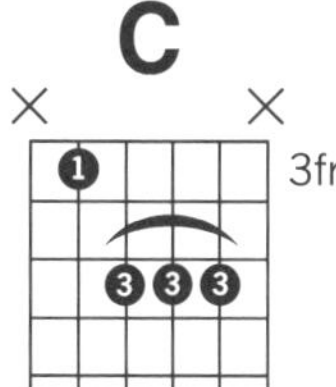

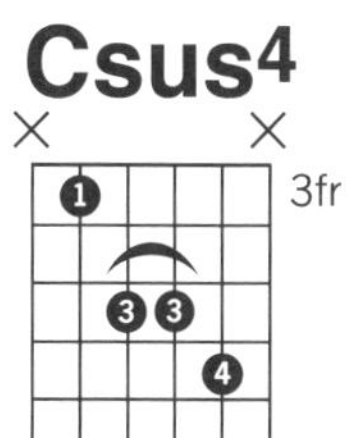

To Barre Or Not To Barre

There are two guitar parts on the recording: an acoustic part which strums open chords, and an electric part, which plays barre chords and has a few little riffs thrown in too. Both work really well—although for live performances, Bryan often plays the strumming part on an electric guitar which sounds great too.

When You're Gone

Words & Music by Bryan Adams & Eliot Kennedy

Intro | Dm | F | C | G |

Verse 1

Dm G
I've been wandering around the house all night
C | Csus4 C
Wondering what the hell to do.
| Dm G | Csus4 C | C
Yeah, I'm trying to concentrate but all I can think of is you.
Dm G
Well the phone don't ring 'cause my friends ain't home,
C | Csus4 C |
I'm tired of being all alone.
Dm B♭ G
Got the T.V. on 'cause the radio's playing songs
G
That remind me of you.

Chorus 1

Dm F
Baby when you're gone,
C G
I realise I'm in love.
Dm F
The days go on and on,
C G
And the nights just seem so___ long.
Dm F
Even food don't taste that good,
C G
Drink ain't doing what it should.
Dm B♭ G G
Things just feel so wrong, baby when you're gone.

Verse 2

I've been driving up and down these streets,
Trying to find somewhere to go.
Yeah, I'm looking for a familiar face but there's no one I know.
Ah, this is torture, this is pain,
It feels like I'm gonna go insane.
I hope you're coming back real soon,
'Cause I don't know what to do.

Chorus 2

As Chorus 1

Solo ‖: **Dm** | **G** | **C** | **C** :‖ *Play x 3*
| **Dm** | **B♭** | **G** | **G** |

Chorus 3 As Chorus 1

Dm **B♭** **F**
...Baby when you're gone, yeah, baby when you're gone.

Rhythm

There are a couple of approaches to strumming this song: if you are going for an acoustic vibe, you can use 'Old Faithful', which will sound pretty cool. However, for the proper pop rock effect you really want to use 'pumping 8ths', playing all down-strums and really rocking out. To get the right feel, you will want to accent some notes (especially during the Csus4 bit) and create little 'builds' in volume (crescendo) when going into the choruses. You will achieve this best by listening to and playing along with the recording.

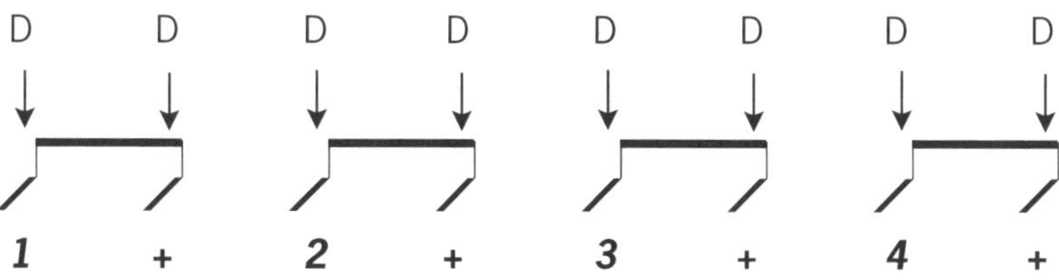

Wires

Words & Music by Joel Pott, Carey Willetts, Steve Roberts & Tim Wanstall

Intro | D♯m | D♯m | C♯ | C♯ |

Verse 1
D♯m D♯m C♯ C♯
You got wires going in, you got wires coming out of your skin.
D♯m D♯m C♯ C♯
You got tears making tracks, I got tears that are scared of the facts.

Chorus 1
G♯m G♯m
Running down corridors, through automatic doors,
D♯m C♯
Got to get to you, got to see this through.
G♯m G♯m
I see hope is here, in a plastic box
D♯m C♯ C♯
I've seen Christmas lights, reflect in your eyes.

Instrumental ||: D♯m | D♯m | C♯ | C♯ :||

Verse 2
You got wires going in, you got wires coming out of your skin.
There's dry blood on your wrist, your dry blood on my fingertip.

Chorus 2
Running down corridors, through automatic doors,
Got to get to you, got to see this through.
First night of your life, curled up on your own,
Looking at you now, you would never know.

Bridge
G♯m D♯m
I see it in your eyes, I see it in your eyes,
F♯ C♯
You'll be al - right.
G♯m D♯m
I see it in your eyes, I see it in your eyes,
F♯ C♯ E | D♯sus4 D♯ |
You'll be al - right. Al - right. (Running...)

Chorus 3
C♯m7 C♯m7
Running down corridors, through automatic doors,
G♯m F♯
Got to get to you, got to see this through.
C♯m7 C♯m7
I see hope is here, in a plastic box
G♯m F♯
I've seen Christmas lights, reflect in your eyes.

Chorus 4 As Chorus 3 *(Lyrics as Chorus 2)*

Introduction

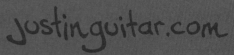

This song, written about the premature birth of singer Joel Pott's daughter, was released by Athlete in 2005.

Rhythm Variations

This song has quite a few rhythm variations that are worth closer inspection. The main rhythm in the verses is shown below. Notice the rests—at these points, you need to mute the strings with the outside of your strumming hand, which really helps the groove in this song.

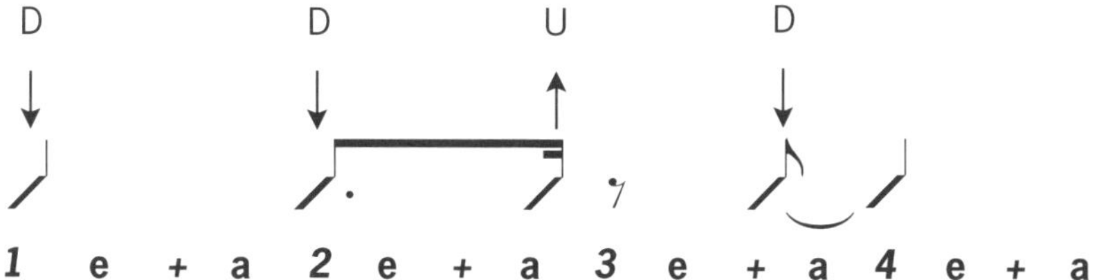

Later in the song there are several variations on this pattern, which become slightly busier towards the end. The pattern shown below seems to happen often, although sometimes the very last strum is left out!

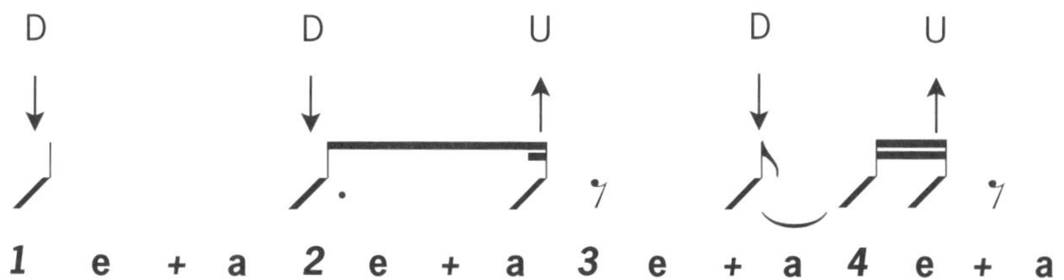

The chorus also has a very distinct strumming pattern, although it isn't very loud on the recording, and only comes into focus during the breakdown after the Bridge. It's a really interesting pattern.

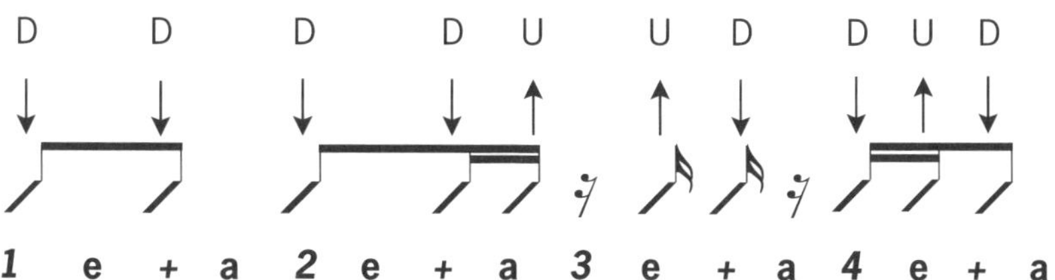

Introduction

Now we're going to make things a little more interesting!

It's good to keep learning new techniques and ideas, and fortunately there is a wealth of riffs and songs out there to keep you inspired. In this exciting selection, we look at songs that feature riffs, interesting chord grips, fingerstyle patterns and a whole lot more.

With any of the more complex songs, the key to learning them well is to practise them really slowly at first. When I teach private lessons I see—time and time again—students attempting to play songs too fast, too early on in their practice. See the 'Practice Tips' at the front of this book for a structured guide on practising more advanced material.

Intermediate + Stage: Your Notes

All These Things That I've Done

Words & Music by Brandon Flowers, Dave Keuning, Mark Stoermer & Ronnie Vannucci

Intro

G   G
   When there's nowhere else to run,
G   G   C   C
   Is there room for one more son?
            G   Bm/F♯
One more son.
         Em   Em
If you can hold on,
         C   C   (G)
If you can hold on,   hold on.

Link 1
(riff 1)

G	G	G	G
G	G	G	G
C	C	G	G

Verse 1

G   G
   I wanna stand up,   I wanna let go
G   G
   You know, you know,   no you don't, you don't.
C   C   G
   I wanna shine on   in the hearts of men
                                     G   (G)
I want a meaning from the back of my broken hand.

Verse 2

Another head aches, another heart breaks
I'm so much older than I can take.
And my affection, well it comes and goes
I need direction to perfection, no, no, no, no

Chorus 1

          G   G   G
Help me out, yeah, you know you got to help me out.
     G   C   C
Yeah, oh don't you put me on the backburner.
                                    G   G
You know you got to help me out, yeah.

Verse 3

And when there's nowhere else to run,
Is there room for one more son?
These changes ain't changing me,
The cold-hearted boy I used to be.

Chorus 2

G   G   G
   Yeah, you know you got to help me out
     G   C   C
Yeah, oh don't you put me on the backburner
                                    G   G
You know you got to help me out, yeah.
                                  Em
You're gonna bring yourself down

(cont.)

```
   Em                                C
Yeah, you're gonna bring yourself down
   C                                 (G)
Yeah, you're gonna bring yourself down.
```

Link 2

| G5 | G5 |

Bridge

```
|: G5                 G5                    G5                   G5
    I got soul, but I'm not a soldier.    I got soul, but I'm not a soldier.
   C5                 C5                    G5                   G5          :|
    I got soul, but I'm not a soldier.    I got soul, but I'm not a soldier.
   Em                 Em                    C5                   C5
    I got soul, but I'm not a soldier.    I got soul, but I'm not a soldier.
```

Link 2

| G | G | G | G |

Chorus 3
(chords as Chorus 1)

Yeah, you know you got to help me out
Yeah, oh don't you put me on the backburner
You know you got to help me out, yeah.
You're gonna bring yourself down

Chorus 4
(chords as Chorus 1)

Yeah, you're gonna bring yourself down
Yeah, oh don't you put me on the backburner
You're gonna bring yourself down.
Yeah, you're gonna bring yourself down.

Outro

```
Em                 Am      Am       C
   O - ver and in, last call for sin.
                       C                D
While everyone's lost, the battle is won
                 D                 G      G    G
With all these things that I've done.
             G                 Em     Em     Em     Em
All these things that I've done.
       C           C
If you can hold on,
       D           D
If you can hold on.
```

| G | G | G | G |

Introduction

This is The Killers' hit single from 2005. To play this song along with the recording, you are going to need to tune your guitar down by one semitone. There isn't any way around this because the main riff uses open strings.

Beginner
Intermediate
Intermediate +
TAB

Beginner
Intermediate
Intermediate +
TAB

There is just one main melodic theme played on the guitar, shown in TAB below. Make sure that you listen to the rhythm, which is pretty easy if you are familiar with the song.

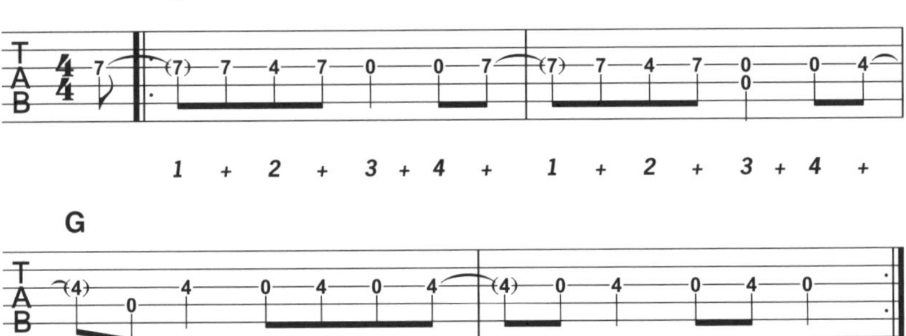

Other Features

The Intro is played on the organ, so for this section, you probably just want to strum each chord once and let it ring out. There is one interesting chord use, Bm/F♯ which is shown below:

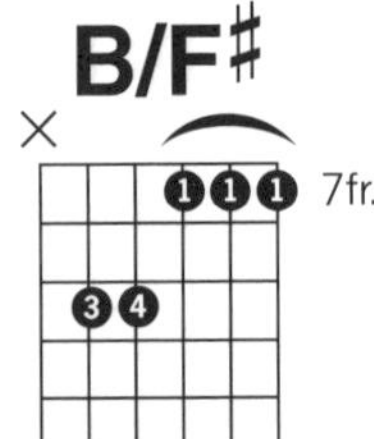

Otherwise this song mostly uses pumping 8ths (all down-strums) with a little palm muting. There is a cool 2nd guitar part in the Bridge, which plays the same chords with a slightly different rhythm, so you might like to work out that rhythm yourself if you're jamming with another guitarist or if you fancy a challenge.

Coffee & TV

Words & Music by Graham Coxon, Damon Albarn, Alex James & David Rowntree

Introduction

One of a handful of Blur singles to feature guitarist Graham Coxon on lead vocals, this song was the poppiest track on their album *13* (1999).

Graham's Creative Chords

The original electric guitar part, played by guitar genius Graham Coxon is full of inventive ways of playing a chord sequence. Shown on the next page is the chord sequence using regular barre chords (as would be played on a second guitar at a live Blur gig), while directly below is a TAB of the electric guitar part played during the verses, just for fun! Check out the way he uses octave shapes to outline the chords without having to play the full chord each time. Very cool.

Over the page we have the chorus sequence, which similarly mixes barre chords and octave shapes. Notice that on the C♯m7 chord, the notes in the TAB are quite approximate, and are basically the notes that you'll hit if you strum correctly, following the strumming pattern over the page.

Verse / Intro

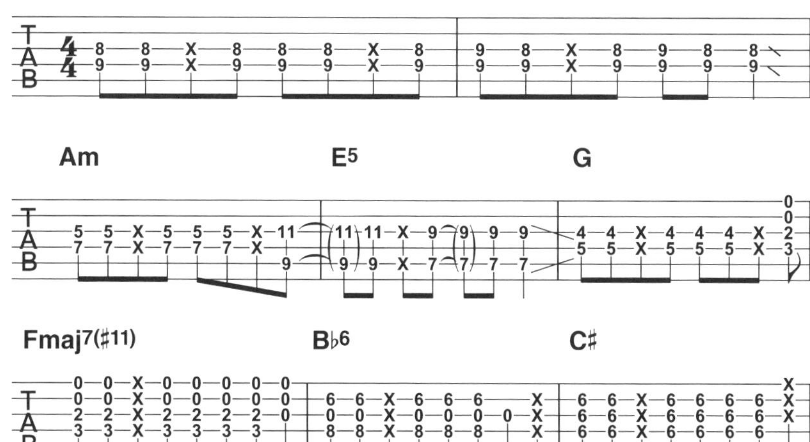

Coffee & TV

Words & Music by Graham Coxon, Damon Albarn, Alex James & David Rowntree

Intro

```
| B     | B     | Am    | E     |
| G     | F     | B♭    | C♯    |
```

Verse 1

```
B                       B             Am          E5
   Do you feel like a chain-store, practically floored,
G                 F        B♭                 C♯
   One of many zeros,        kicked around bored?
B                                  B        Am                 E5
   Your ears are full, but you're empty,  holding out your heart
G                            F        B♭6              A      A
   To people who never really,      care how you are.
```

Chorus 1

```
               C♯m              C♯m    B     A
So give me coffee and T - V,        easi - ly,
     C♯m                    E                        A                      B
I've seen so much, I'm going blind and I'm brain-dead, virtua - lly.
C♯m       C♯m      B                    A
Sociabili - ty     is hard enough for me,
C♯m                          E                         A                D
Take me away from this big bad world and a - gree to marry me
D                       A             A
  So we can start over again.
```

Verse 2

Do you go to the country? It isn't very far.
There's people there who'll hurt you, 'cause of who you are.
Your ears are full of their language, there's wisdom there, you're sur
Till the words start slurring, and you can't find the door.

Chorus 2

As Chorus 1

Solo

```
| B     | B     | Am    | E     |
| G     | F     | B♭6   | C♯    |
| B     | B     | Am    | E5    |
| G     | F     | B♭    | A     | A     |
```

Chorus 3

```
As Chorus 1...
D                       A          | A      B♭ |
...So we can start over again.
```

Outro

```
|: B   | B   | D        | D          | A        | A      B♭ :|
                 Oh,        we can start over again.
```

Chorus Sequence

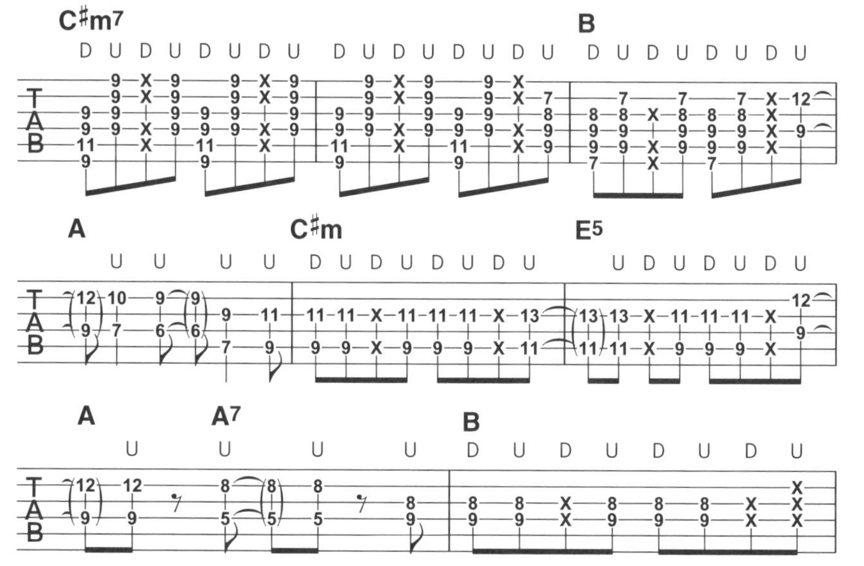

Rhythm

The main rhythm used in this song is shown below. On the rest you should relax the chord grip, but you can choose to keep strumming the chord (which will give you a muted hit) or miss it out altogether so that you have a complete break. Either way, it's a very common and great sounding rhythm pattern, so study it well!

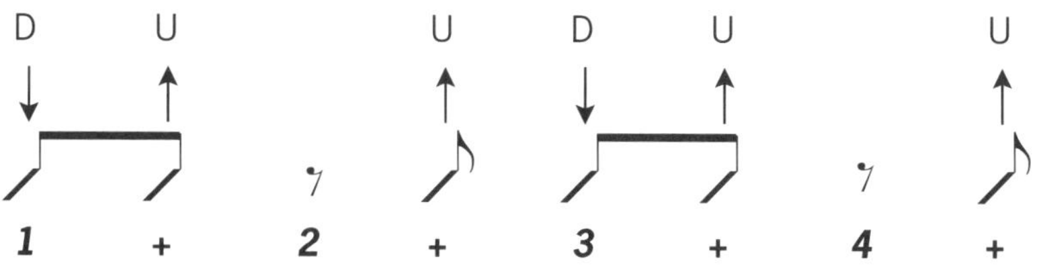

Candle In The Wind

Words & Music by Elton John & Bernie Taupin

Intro | B | A E/G♯ F♯m | E | B |

Verse 1

E   E   A   A
Goodbye Norma Jean, though I never knew you at all
E/G♯   E/G♯   A   A
You had the grace to hold yourself, while those around you crawled.
E   E   A   A
They crawled out of the woodwork, and they whispered into your brain
E/G♯   E/G♯   A   A
They set you on the treadmill, and they made you change your name.

Chorus 1

B   B   E   A
And it seems to me you lived your life, like a candle in the wind,
E   A/E   B   B
Never knowing who to cling to, when the rain set in.
A   A
And I would have liked to have known you,
C♯m   C♯m   B
But I was just a kid, your candle burned out long before
A | A E/G♯ F♯m | E
Your legend ever did.

Link 1 | E Esus4 E | B | A E/G♯ F♯m | E | B |

Verse 2

Loneliness was tough, the toughest role you ever played.
Hollywood created a superstar, and pain was the price you paid.
Even when you died, oh the press still hounded you,
All the papers had to say, was that Marilyn was found in the nude.

Chorus 2 As Chorus 1
Link 2 As Link 1

Verse 3

Goodbye Norma Jean, though I never knew you at all
You had the grace to hold yourself, while those around you crawled.
Goodbye Norma Jean, from the young man in the 22nd row
Who sees you as something more than sexual,
More than just our Marilyn Monroe.

Chorus 3 As Chorus 1

Outro

E   B
Your candle burned out long before
A | A E/G♯ F♯m | E |
Your legend ever did.

Introduction

This song is Elton John's tribute to Marilyn Monroe, later to be reworked as a tribute to Princess Diana.

E/G♯

This is quite a common chord, but it's also reasonably awkward and there are a few options for playing it. Those with long little fingers (not me!) seem to prefer playing a regular E grip and stretching out the little finger (see the first chord box below) to reach the low G♯ note. I find that too much of a stretch, so I usually play a variant on a D-shape barre chord (although I don't play this chord with a barre), as shown in the second chord box below. Below are three options—you will have to chose which sounds best to you for the situation!

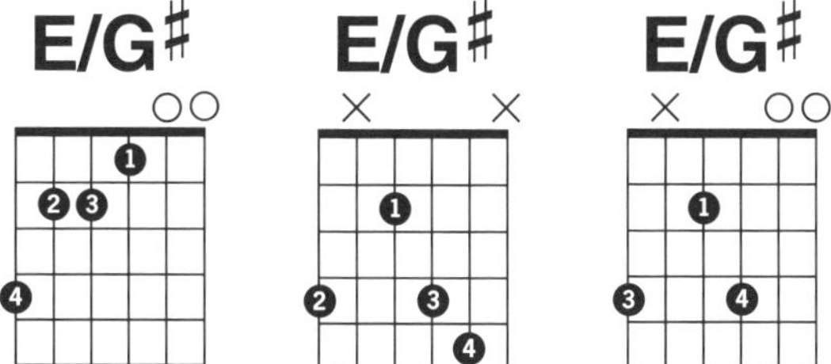

Rhythm

The verses are best kept quite sparse, and so a good approach would be to limit yourself to just one strum per bar. To get more of groove going, you should still keep your playing simple—along the lines of the pattern below, but with a bit of experimentation, as you see fit.

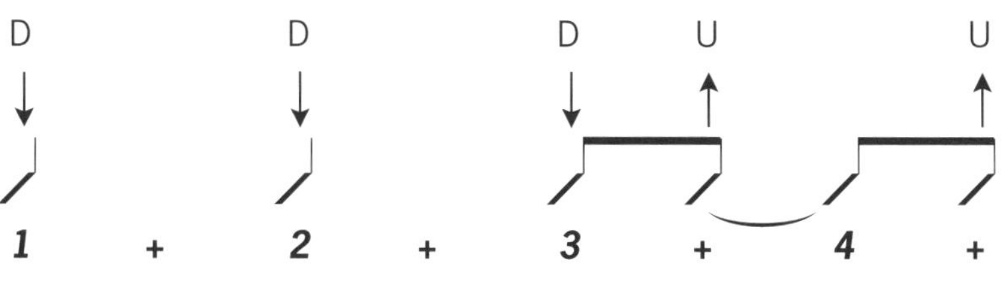

cont...

Rhythm Fill

As well as using some interesting chords, this song also features a rhythm fill, where a short chord sequence becomes a 'hook', first heard in the intro and repeated through the song. This chord 'hook' is played on piano but works fine on guitar too. As usual you should start off slowly, counting the rhythm and listening to the track so you can pick up the feel. You can of course add in more notes and copy the piano part more precisely if you chose to, but it's better to start off simply, with a solid rhythm before embellishing the part.

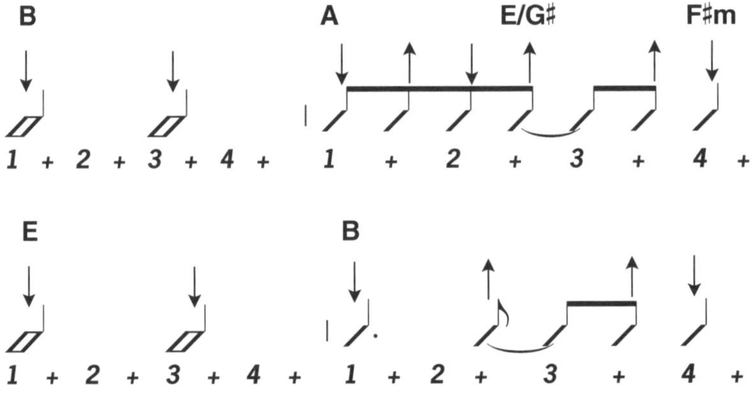

Crazy

Words & Music by Guy Sigsworth & Seal Henry Olusegun Olumide Adeola Samue

Introduction

The only Seal that likes clubbing had a massive smash hit with this single in 1990.

The Power Of E

A really interesting feature of this song is the repeated E note in the bass, which continues throughout the verse, even while the chords (on piano and guitar) change above it. This repeated E note continues into the chorus to a certain extent, but I think it works best to keep the E bass note for the verses and then bring out the regular chords (without the extra E bass note) for the chorus, which will add an extra lift to the song.

I should point out that I sometimes swap my 1st and 2nd fingers round on the chord grips fpr the A/E and Asus4/E, shown below. I thought I'd point out that option as well, in case you find it easier.

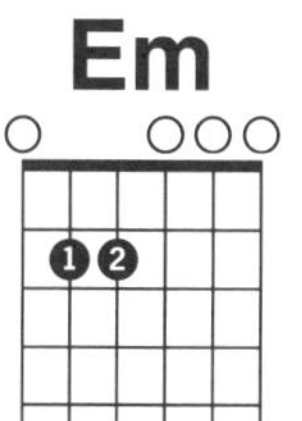

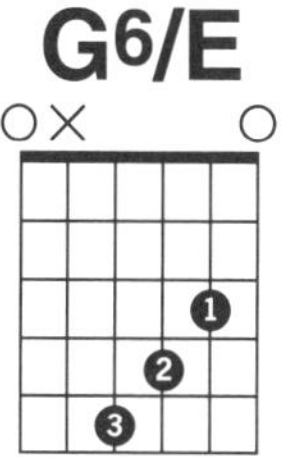

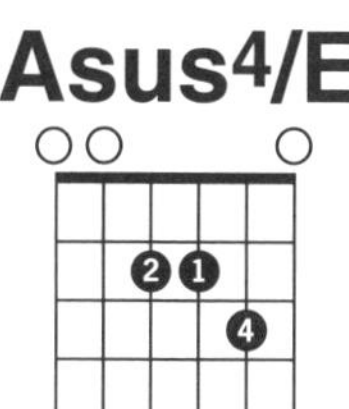

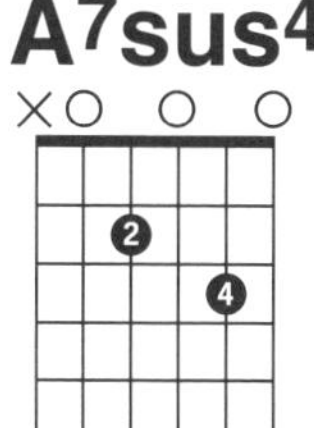

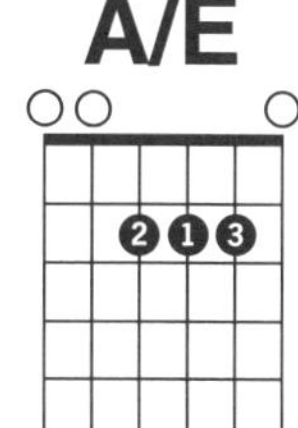

Crazy

Words & Music by Guy Sigsworth & Seal Henry Olusegun Olumide Adeola Samue

Beginner
Intermediate
Intermediate +
TAB

Intro

```
Em
Take the chance, price of faith
Em                                  Asus4/E   A/E
Talk about the people going under.

|: Em         | G6/E    | Asus4/E   | A/E      :|
Only child knows. (2nd time only)
```

Verse 1

```
Em                                G6/E
   A man decides after se - venty years
                Asus4/E                    A/E
That what he goes there for, is to un - lock the door,
Em                                      G6/E             Asus4/E   A/E
   While those around him criti - cize and sleep.
Em                                  G6/E
   And through a fractal on a breaking wall,
     Asus4/E                                A/E
I see you my friend and touch your face again,
Em                           G6/E           Asus4/E   A/E
   Miracles will happen as we dream.
```

Chorus 1

```
C                                    G         D                      A
   But we're never gonna sur - vive, un - less we get a little  crazy.
C                                    G         D                      A   N.C.
   No, we're never gonna sur - vive, un - less we are a little        (crazy)
```

Verse 2

Crazy yellow people walking through my head,
One of them's got a gun to shoot the other one.
And yet together they were friends at school.
Oh, get it, get it, get it, get it, no, no.
If I were there when we first took the pill,
Then maybe, then maybe, then maybe, then maybe
Miracles will happen as we speak.

Chorus 2

But we're never gonna survive, unless we get a little crazy.
No, we're never gonna survive, unless we are a little crazy.
No no, never survive, unless we get a little bit.

Interlude 1

```
| N.C.    | N.C.    | N.C.    | N.C.    |
| Em      | Em      | Em      | Em      |
```

Bridge

```
     Am                          Bm                              Cmaj7     D
In a sky full of people, only some want to fly, isn't that crazy?
     Am                              Bm                              Cmaj7  D
In a world full of people, only some want to fly, isn't that crazy,   crazy?
```

(cont.)

```
     Em                              Em                          A7sus4
In a heaven of people there's only some want to fly, ain't that crazy?
    A7sus4
Oh babe, oh darling.
     Em                                Em
In a world full of people there's only some want to fly,
          A7sus4                                 A7sus4           A7sus4
Isn't that crazy, isn't that crazy, isn't that crazy, isn't that crazy?
```

Chorus 3

Oh, but we're never gonna survive
Unless we get a little crazy.
No, we're never gonna to survive unless we are a little.
But we're never gonna survive unless, we get a little crazy.
No, we're never gonna to survive unless, we are a little crazy.
No, no, never survive unless we get a little bit.

The guitar parts in this song are mostly wah-wah pedal fills and muted grooves, chorus-effected spread chords and other fill lines. So if you are going to play the song solo, you should try to get the feeling of the keyboard part, which forms the main instrumental 'hook' of the song.

Below I have written a suitable accent pattern—you could play continuous sixteenth-note strumming and add these accents, or just play the accented strums (remembering to keep your hand moving the whole time, as if you were playing all sixteenth-notes). You will need to vary the dynamics—try playing along with the song, playing quietly when the track dips and louder as it builds. Listen and learn to use dynamics, as they will add life and interest to your performances!

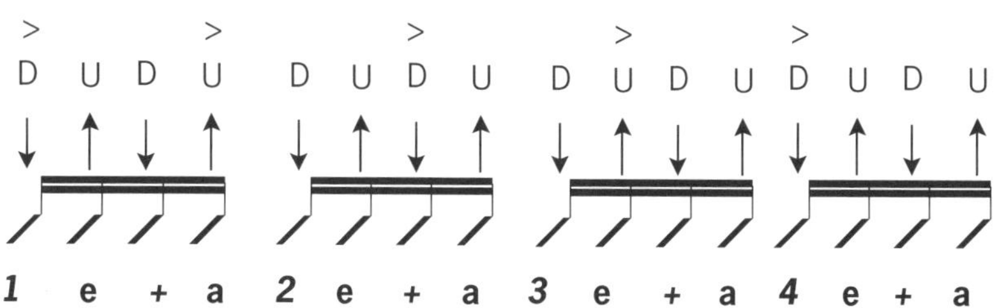

Leave Right Now

Words & Music by Francis Eg White

Intro (riff 1)

| G Gsus4 | G | Am7 Em/G | D/F♯ |

Verse 1

| G Gsus4 | G
I'm here, just like I said,

| Am7 Em/G | D/F♯
Though it's breaking every rule I've ever made.

| G Gsus4 | G
My racing heart is just the same,

| Am7 Em/G | D/F♯
Why make it strong to break it once a - gain?

(riff 2)

C Bm7 C
And I'd love to say I do, give everything to you,

| Am7 D7 |
But I can never now be true. So I say

Chorus 1 (riff 3)

| C D/F♯ | Bm7 G |
I think I better leave right now before I fall any deeper

| C D/F♯ | Bm7 G |
I think I better leave right now, I'm feeling weaker and weaker.

| C D/F♯ | Bm7 G |
Somebody better show me how before I fall any deeper,

| C D7 | G
I think I better leave right now.

Verse 2

I'm here, so please explain
Why you're opening up a healing wound again?
I'm a little more careful, perhaps it shows?
But if I lose the highs at least I'll spare the lows
And I would tremble, what would be the harm
To feel my spirit come? So I say,

Chorus 2

As Chorus 1

C D7 (Em)
...I think I better leave right now.

Bridge

Em Bm7
I wouldn't know how to say how good it feels seeing you today

Am7 | Bm7 B7 |
I see you've got your smile back, like you say you're right on track but,

Em Bm7
You may never know why once bitten, twice is shy.

Am7
If I'm proud perhaps I should explain,

| D7 B7/D♯ |
I couldn't bear to lose you again.

Instrumental

||: C D/F♯ | Bm7 G :||

Chorus 3

I think I better leave right now before I fall any deeper
I think I better leave right now, I'm feeling weaker and weaker.
Somebody better show me how before I fall any deeper

|C D7 |C D/F♯ |Bm7 G |
I think I better leave right now.

|C D/F♯ |Bm7
Yes I will, I think I better leave right now,

G |
I'm feeling weaker and weaker.

|C D/F♯ |Bm7 G |
Somebody better show me how before I fall any deeper,

|C D7 |G
I think I better leave right now.

Introduction

This song is Will Young's UK No. 1 single from 2003.

Double Tracked Guitar

There are some lovely acoustic guitar parts in this song. The guitar parts have been 'double tracked'—a common pop technique whereby the same instrument is recorded twice, playing similar (but not identical) parts. Both parts are then played back simultaneously, often panned so that they come out of different speakers. I've written out a TAB of the left-hand speaker part but filled it out a little so that it works as one guitar part.

Riff 1 (Intro + Verse)

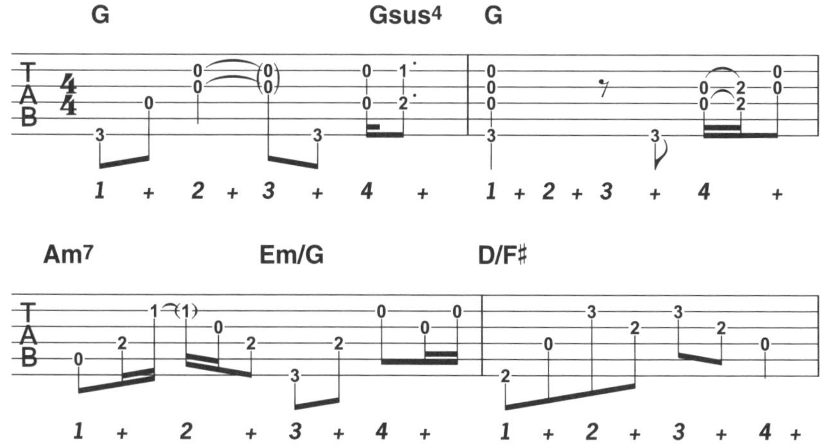

Beginner

Intermediate

Intermediate +

TAB

Riff 2 (Last 4 bars of Verse)

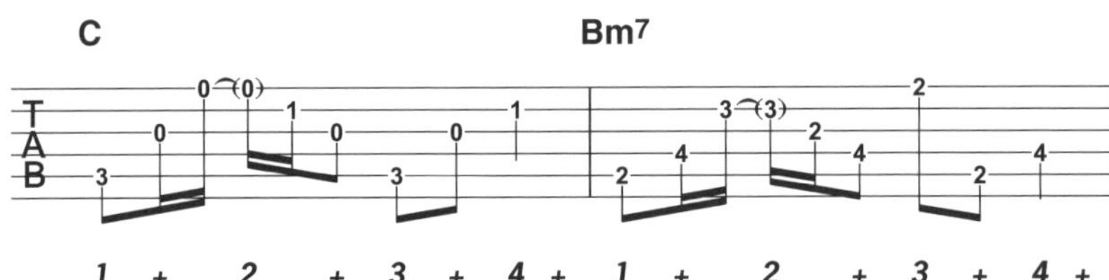

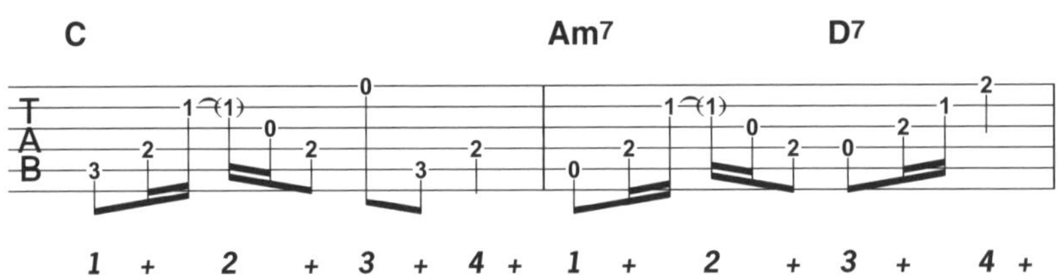

Riff 3 (Chorus)

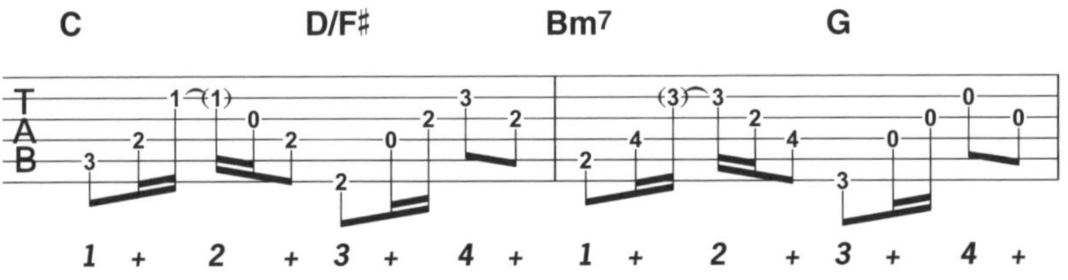

Later On...

Later in the song, the guitar part fills out more. You might like to start with the parts I've given you and just add in a few more picks.

For the Bridge section you will most likely want to strum the chords—you can just about hear a guitar playing here but it's overwhelmed with string pads and keyboards at this point! So you can play the chords any way you want.

Fix You

Words & Music by Guy Berryman, Chris Martin, Jon Buckland & Will Champion

Introduction

This song was a worldwide hit for Coldplay in 2005.

To Capo Or Not?

It's a lot easier to play this song with a capo at the 3rd fret. This means that the verse sequence uses some quite basic open chords. I'd recommend that you a slightly different voicing for the G chord, however, as this will allow you to change easily between the Gsus4 chord, and the standard G chord. See below for details, and bear in mind that your 3rd finger should lie across and mute the fifth string.

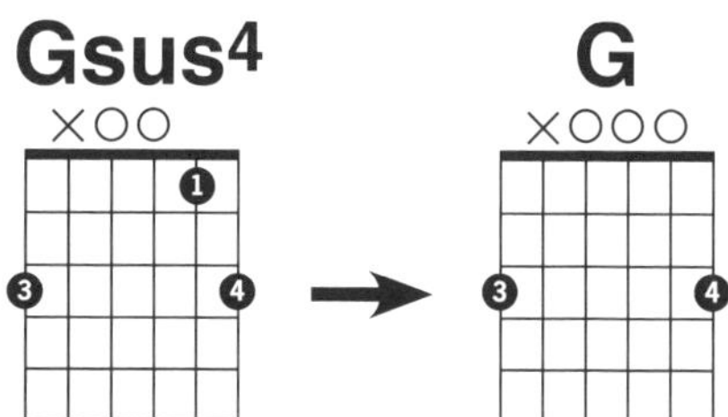

Instrumental 2

Although it's impossible to represent the whole musical arrangement on just a solo guitar, you can incorporate some of the lead guitar lines into your strumming, especially during the 2nd Instrumental section. Here the lead guitar plays a high G note, on the 4th beat of each bar. You can add in this note, by playing it with your little finger on the 3rd fret of the thinnest string. See the three chords below for examples of how to include this high G note.

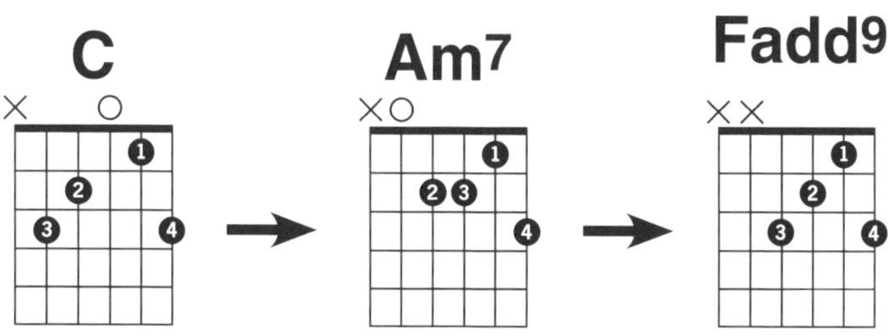

Beginner Intermediate Intermediate + TAB

Fix You

Words & Music by Guy Berryman, Chris Martin,
Jon Buckland & Will Champion

Beginner

Intermediate

Intermediate +

TAB

Intro | C Em | Am G | C Em | Am G |

Verse 1

```
          |C                   Em        |Am  G
When you try your best but you don't  succeed.
          |C                       Em           |Am  G
When you get what you want but not what you need.
          |C              Em           |Am  G
When you feel so tired but you can't sleep.
            |C     Em |Am  G
Stuck in re - verse.
```

Verse 2

And the tears come streaming down your face.
When you lose something you can't replace.
When you love someone but it goes to waste.
Could it be worse?

Chorus 1

```
|F       C/E  |Gsus4  G   |F
   Lights will   guide      you home,
    C/E |Gsus4 G     |F
And ig  - nite        your bones.
      C/E |Gsus4  G          |
And I will   try        to fix you.
```

Instr. 1 | C Em | Am G | C Em | Am G |

Verse 3

```
|C                  Em          |Am  Gsus4
High up above or down below.
             |C            Em      |Am  Gsus4
When you're too in love to let it go.
          |C             Em        |Am  Gsus4
But if you never try you'll never know
                |C     Em    |Am  Gsus4 |
Just what you're worth.
```

Chorus 2 As Chorus 1

Instr. 2

||: C | Fmaj7 Fadd9 | C | Gsus4 |

| Am Am7 | Fmaj7 Fadd9 | C | Gsus4 G :||

Bridge

```
C                  Fadd9
  Tears stream     down your face,
C                                  Gsus4
  When you lose something you cannot replace.
Am                 Fadd9                 C  | Gsus4  G |
  Tears stream     down your face and I.
C                  Fadd9
  Tears stream     down your face,
C                         Em
  I promise you I will learn from my mistakes.
Am                 Fadd9                 C  | Gsus4  G |
  Tears stream     down your face and I.
```

Outro

```
|F        C/E  | Gsus4  G    | F
  Lights will   guide        you home
    C/E | Gsus4  G    | F
And ig  -  nite        your bones,
        C/E  | Gsus4  G        | C
And I   will   try              to fix you.
```

Rhythm

As this is a piano-based song, you have a bit more freedom on the guitar, and can really explore the rhythm. A simple pattern will work well for the most of the song, and I have written out a sixteenth-note pattern for you, although you could just as effectively use a simple eighth-note pattern. When the track starts to build up you might want to switch to 'pumping 8th' strumming—a common trick, especially in Coldplay songs—to build up the dynamics.

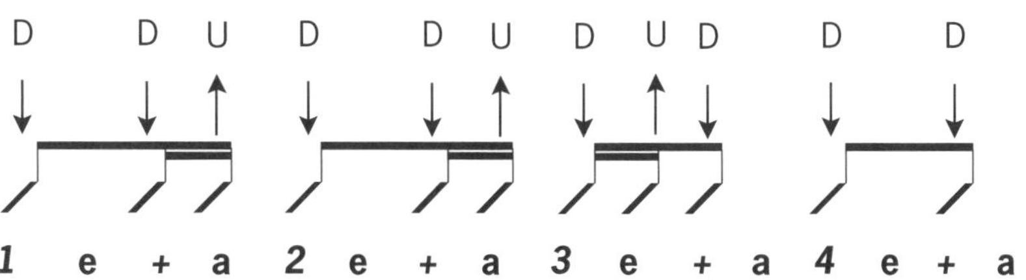

I'm Yours

Words & Music by Jason Mraz

Chord sequence for Verses & Choruses

B	B	F♯	F♯
G♯m	G♯m	E	E

Verse 1

Well you done done me in, you bet I felt it,
I tried to be chilled, but you're so hot that I melted.
I fell right through the cracks, now I'm trying to get back.
Before the cool done run out, I'll be giving it my bestest,
And nothing's going to stop me but divine intervention,
I reckon it's again my turn to win some or learn some.

Chorus 1

But I won't hesitate no more, no more,
It cannot wait, I'm yours, mmm. Hey, hey.

Verse 2

Well open up your mind and see like me,
Open up your plans and damn you're free.
Look into your heart and you'll find love, love, love, love.

```
B                          B                           F♯
Listen to the music of the moment people dance and sing,
           F♯             G♯m
We're just one big fami - ly.
            G♯m
And it's our God-forsaken right to be
E            E            C♯7/E♯   C♯7/E♯
Loved, love, love, loved, loved.
```

Chorus 2

So I won't hesitate no more, no more,
It cannot wait I'm sure.
There's no need to complicate, our time is short,
This is our fate, I'm yours.

Bridge

```
       B               F♯/A♯                     G♯m
Do ya, do, do, do you,       but do ya, do ya do, do,
                                F♯                E          E
But do you want to come and  scooch on over closer dear,
                         C♯7/E♯   C♯7/E♯
And I will nibble your ear.
```

Bridge 2

As Bridge 1 (*Vocals ad lib.*)

Verse 3

I've been spending way too long checking my tongue in the mirror,
And bending over backwards just to try to see it clearer,
But my breath fogged up the glass,
And so I drew a new face and I laughed.
I guess what I be saying is there ain't no better reason,
To rid yourself of vanities and just go with the seasons,
It's what we aim to do, our name is our virtue.

Chorus 3

But I won't hesitate no more, no more,
It cannot wait I'm yours.

Verse 4

Well open up your mind and see like me,
Open up your plans and damn you're free,
Look into your heart and you'll find that the sky is yours.

```
   B                            B
So please don't, please don't, please don't,
             F#              F#               G#m
There's no need to complicate, 'cause our time is short,
G#m                            E          E      C#7/E#   N.C.
This, oh this, oh this is our fate, I'm yours.______
```

Outro

```
|: B  | B   | F#  | F#  |
 | G#m | G#m | E   | E   :|
```

Introduction

Jason Mraz's huge hit has a great reggae-style feel and is catchy as a cold.

Barres 'n' Capos

I checked online to see how Jason Mraz plays this song live, and which chord grips he uses. I was a little surprised to see him using a capo, even though mainly plays barre chords. Why do that? Well, sometimes you need a break from lots of barre chords, and with the capo on the 2nd fret, you will be able to play the F♯ chord with a nice open E grip, and play the E chord with an open D grip.

But then I checked his grips a little closer and saw an even cooler thing going on. When playing the verses he frequently plays quite high up the neck, and uses an F♯ 1st inversion grip (putting the note A♯ in the bass, as shown below) and by having the capo on he can use the 'open' bass note on the 6th string.

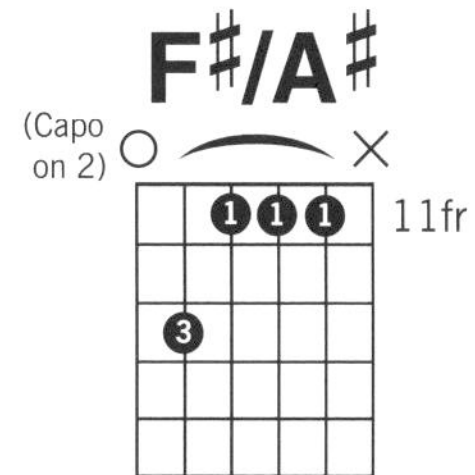

cont...

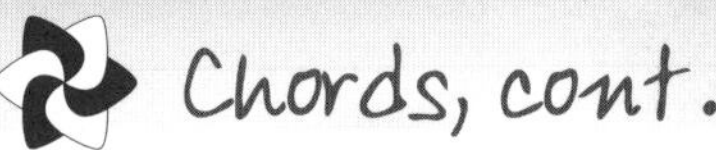

Chords, cont.

Mraz uses a few other tasty chords in this song, including a C♯7/E♯ which he plays using a pretty unusual grip.

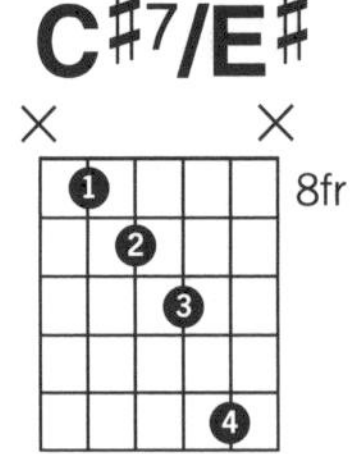

It is also worth noting that Mraz often uses a C-shape barre chord for the F♯/A♯ in the Bridge (shown below), although if you struggle with it, you can use the grip above or just a regular F♯ chord.

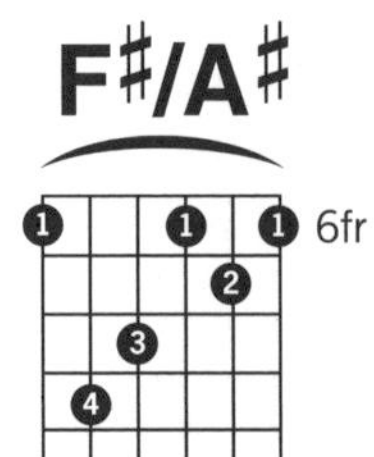

Rhythm

There is a fantastic groove in this tune, played right 'in the pocket' and it really gets your foot tapping. Writing down precisely how to play a groove is very difficult—I'll try, but you will still have to listen to the recording a bunch of times to get it in your head.

The first thing to notice is the palm muting, which is pretty heavy. You will need to experiment with your hand position to get the right sound. Rest the outside part of your right hand on the string. Then strum up and down, moving your hand closer and further from the bridge until you find a spot that sounds roughly like the muted sound on the recording. This will provide a starting point for you.

Notice that it's mostly the thicker strings that are being strummed—mainly just the thickest 3 strings, but sometimes a few other strings sneak in, and sometimes only one or two strings are strummed.

Make sure that you observe the accents, as some strums are louder than others. The down-strums on beats 2 and 4 are the loudest, although there is sometimes a slightly softer accent on the 'and' after 2. Beats 1 and 3 are the softest, when often just the lowest note of the chord is played.

As the song develops, the strumming gets fuller, less muted, and more strings are strummed. The groove stays pretty much the same, keeping the accents on 2 and 4 but with some variations. The Bridge section just uses down-strums.

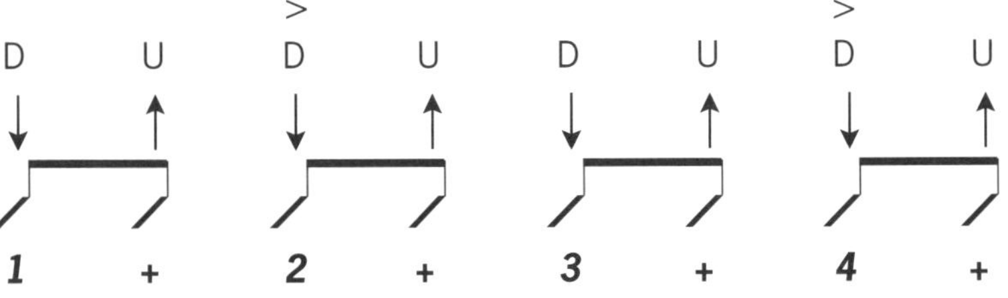

I Kissed A Girl

Words & Music by Katy Perry, Lukasz Gottwald, Max Martin & Cathy Dennis

Beginner
Intermediate
Intermediate +
TAB

Verse 1

```
A5              | G7/B  C  | Dm7         | F5      Am/E |
   This was nev - er the way I planned, not my in - tention.
A5         | G7/B  C      | Dm7      | F5    Am/E |
   I got so brave, drink in hand, lost my dis - cretion.
A5           | G7/B   C    | Dm7  | F5     Am/E | A5
   It's not what   I'm used to,   just wanna try you on.
        | G7/B  C    | Dm7     | F5     Am/E |
I'm curi - ous for you    caught my at - tention.
```

Chorus 1

```
A5          C5            | D5              E5 | F5    E5      |
   I kissed a girl and I liked it,   the taste of her cherry Chapstick.
A5          C5           | D5            E5  | F5          E5     |
   I kissed a girl just to try it,   I hope my boy - friend don't mind it.
A5          C5           | D5               E5 | F5    E5     |
   It felt so wrong, it felt so right, don't mean I'm in love tonight.
A5          C5            | D5  E5 | F5  E5 | A5
   I kissed a girl and I liked it,          I liked it.
```

Verse 2

No, I don't even know your name, It doesn't even matter
You're my experimental game, just human nature
It's not what good girls do, not how they should behave.
My head gets so confused, hard to obey.

Chorus 2

As Chorus 1

Bridge

```
F             Em            Am              Em            F
   Us girls we are so magi - cal, soft skin, red lips, so kissa - ble.
              Em              Am              G
Hard to re - sist, so toucha - ble, too good to   deny it.
Dm              Dm              Dm       Dm
   It ain't no big deal, it's inno - cent.
```

Chorus 3

As Chorus 1

Introduction

This song is Katy Perry's breakthrough single from 2008.

Verse Guitars

There are some interesting guitar parts in this poptastic tune, which is a trademark of producer Dr. Luke, who often features cool layers of guitar in his productions. He is an excellent guitar player as well as being a Grammy Award-winning producer!

In the verses there are three quite distinct parts; the first two are single-note lines (one in each speaker so you can hear them clearly) that work together to create the harmony.

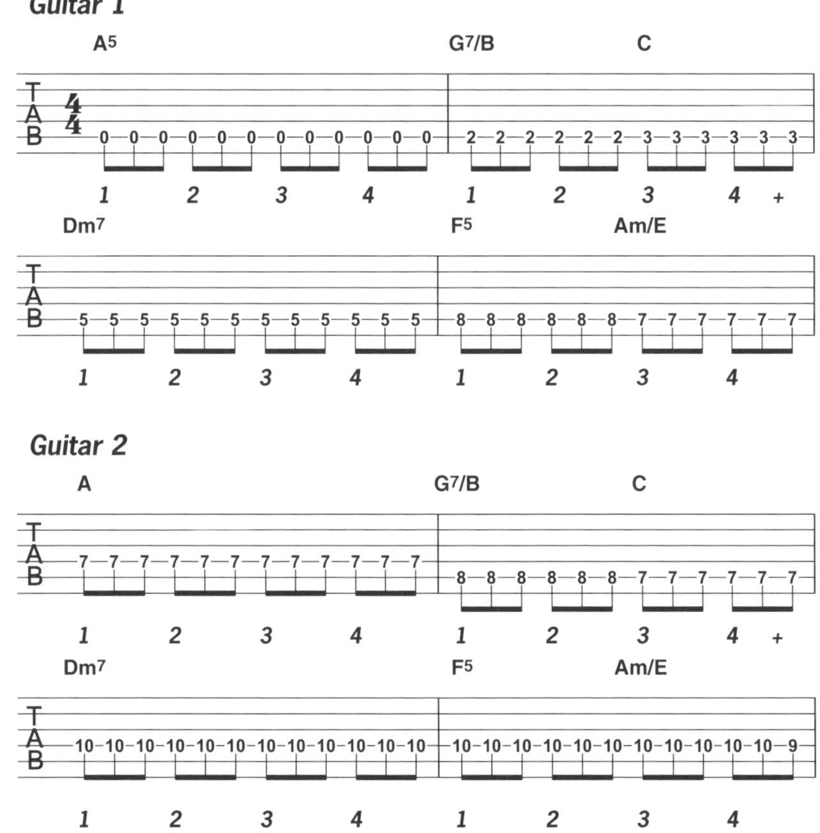

The 3rd guitar part only pops in a little later and is simply playing a little diad (a two-note chord) on beats 2 and 4.

Guitar 3

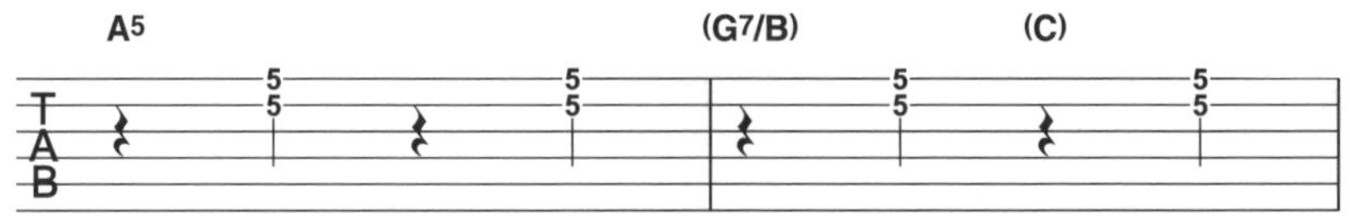

Chorus Guitar

The chorus employs a simpler guitar part, rocking out with power chords. The trick to playing this well is to listen to the track and hear the way that some of the chords have a slide off. To copy this, play the chord and then slide it down toward the nut—it's a very common rock technique. Also, because we're dealing with 'electro' music here, it's very important to make sure you have the rhythm really tight. For this genre, it's essential that you play perfectly in time, otherwise your guitar playing will jar with the rest of the song, and sound pretty weak.

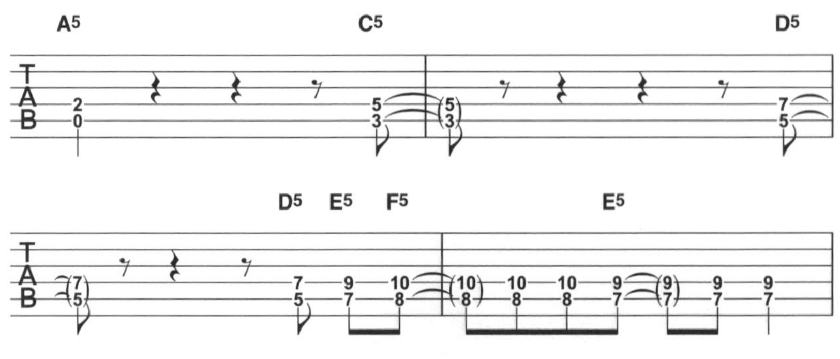

Fireflies

Words & Music by Adam Young

Introduction

Internet sensation Owl City scored a hit with this infectious, synth-heavy pop song in 2009.

Arranging Tips

With a 'pure pop' song like this, where the instrumentation is pretty synth heavy, you have a lot more freedom and can really have fun with the song. You could play this song with a basic strumming pattern on an electric guitar, which will sound cool, or you could try playing it on acoustic guitar to achieve a mellow, 'campfire' vibe. You could even play as a ballad, slowing the song down until it sounds very different to the recording.

Personally I like to cover a song in a way that is influenced by the original but is clearly a different version of the song. As with this little arrangement I've made of the beginning riff—it's not the same as the original, but has a similar vibe once you get it up to speed. Remember to start slowly because this riff is pretty quick at full speed!

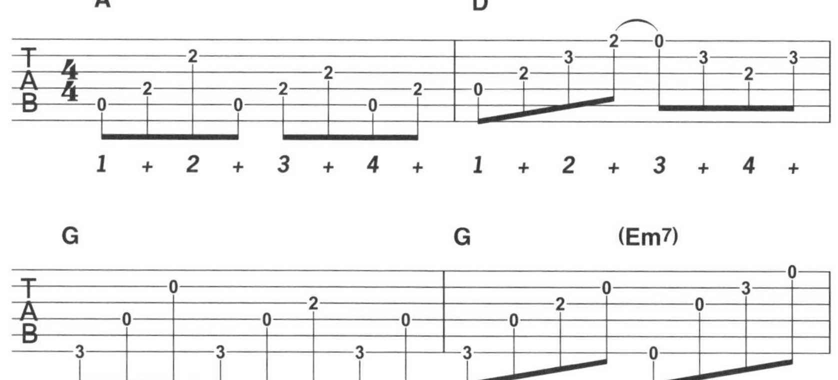

Beginner

Intermediate

Intermediate +

TAB

Fireflies

Words & Music by Adam Young

Intro

|: A | D | G | G :| *(Play x4)*

Verse 1

```
A                        D                G                     G
   You would not be - lieve your eyes   if ten million fire - flies
A               D                  G       G
   Lit up the world as I fell a - sleep,
A                          D       G                         G
'Cause they'd fill the open air   and leave teardrops everywhere.
       A                      D                        G         G
You'd think me rude, but I would just stand and    stare.
```

Chorus 1

```
|G           Bm                  |Asus4               |G     D     |F#m   G
   I'd like to make myself be - lieve that planet Earth turns slow - ly.
  |G                        D            |G          Asus4    Bm    |
It's hard to say that I'd rather stay a - wake when I'm a - sleep,
        G                 D            |E  /  /  D/F#  |
'Cause everything is never as it seems.
```

Verse 2

'Cause I'd get a thousand hugs, from ten thousand lightning bugs
As they tried to teach me how to dance
A foxtrot above my head, a sock hop beneath my bed,
A disco ball is just hanging by a thread.

Chorus 2

```
I'd like to make myself believe that planet Earth turns slow - ly
It's hard to say that I'd rather stay a - wake when I'm asleep,
        |G                D            |Asus4         Bm    |G
'Cause everything is never as it seems when I fall a - sleep.
```

Verse 3

Leave my door open just a crack, (*Please take me away from here*)
'Cause I feel like such an insomniac. (*Please take me away from here*)
Why do I tire of counting sheep, (*Please take me away from here*)
When I'm far too tired to fall asleep?

Verse 4

To ten million fireflies, I'm weird 'cause I hate goodbyes,
I got misty eyes as they said farewell.
But I'll know where several are, if my dreams get real bizarre,
'Cause I saved a few and I keep them in a jar.

Chorus 3 As Chorus 1
Chorus 4 As Chorus 2

Outro chorus I'd like to make myself believe that planet Earth turns slowly.
It's hard to say that I'd rather stay awake when I'm asleep,

| **G**   **D** | **Asus4**   **A** |
Be - cause my dreams are bursting at the seams.

As I mentioned earlier, I'd recommend exploring different styles and ways of playing this song, and seeing what you come up with. But if you want to just keep it simple, then you could start by just playing 4 down-strokes per bar, gradually bringing in more up-strokes as you start to feel the groove of the song.

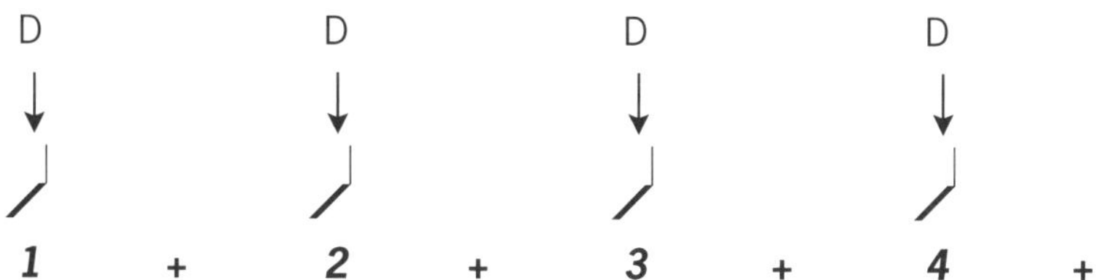

You might end up with a pattern like the one shown below which has some interesting sixteenth-note syncopations, although keeping it simple will work too, especially if you are going to be singing as well!

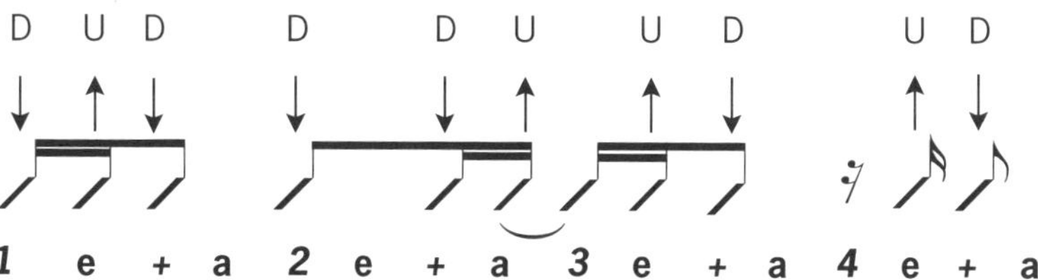

Mmm Mmm Mmm Mmm

Words & Music by Brad Roberts

Intro

| Em Bm | Em Bm | Fsus2 Gsus4 | Fsus2 Gsus4 |

Verse 1

|Am G |C C/E |
Once there was this kid who
|F C |G C
Got into an accident and couldn't come to school.
|F |G C |
But when he finally came back
|G C |F C |G |G
His hair, had turned from black into bright white.
A♭ |C A♭ |G/F F
He said that it was from when the cars had smashed so hard.

Chorus 1

| Em Bm | Em Bm |
Mmm Mmm Mmm Mmm, Mmm Mmm Mmm Mmm.

| Fsus2 Gsus4 | Fsus2 Gsus4 |

Verse 2

Once there was this girl who
Wouldn't go and change with the girls in the change room.
And when they finally made her,
They saw birthmarks all over her body.
She couldn't quite explain it, they'd always just been there.

Chorus 2

As Chorus 1 *(Play x2)*

Middle

Dm |C G |
But both girl and boy were glad
Dm |C G | Fsus2 $\frac{2}{4}$| Fsus2 |
'Cause one kid had it worse than that.

Verse 3

'Cause then there was this boy whose
Parents made him come directly home right after school.
Well, and when they went to their church
They shook and lurched all over the church floor.
He couldn't quite explain it, they'd always just gone there.

Chorus 3

As Chorus 2

Outro

||: Dm | C G | Dm | C G | Fsus2 | C/E :||
Aah, aah, aah, aah. Aah, aah, aah, aah.

(Repeat to fade)

Introduction

This songs is Crash Test Dummies' alt-rock gem from 1993, and is a fantastic showcase for any singers in possession of a deep bass voice!

Grab Your Acoustic!

This is a classic pop song with a lovely acoustic guitar part—it's so good in fact that I have transcribed the intro, verse and chorus for you to play. There are some small variations but this transcription is a good starting point. For the bridge and outro section you should strum the chords with even eighth-note down-strums.

The TAB below mainly uses a four-note pattern. Your thumb will always play the bass note; your index will play the next note and your middle and ring fingers will then pick the notes together, and then the last note in the sequence of four will be played by your index finger again. There are a couple of spots where the pattern changes but the fingering should be quite obvious. I have simplified the TAB just a tiny bit to keep the pattern consistent, since the slight variations you'll hear in the recorded version make it considerably more difficult to play, for little gain. Note the clever use of the open D string which gives you time to make the chord changes, especially during the C to A♭ change which happens pretty quickly.

To play Fsus2 with a bass note you will need to use your thumb—if you find this hard you'll just have to leave off the bass note until you develop enough dexterity.

Intro / Chorus

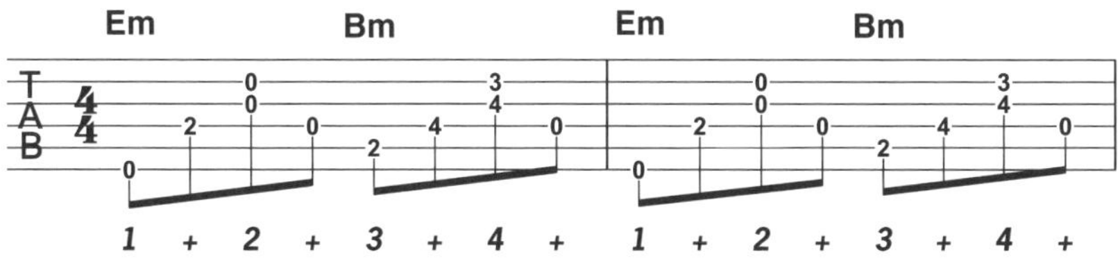

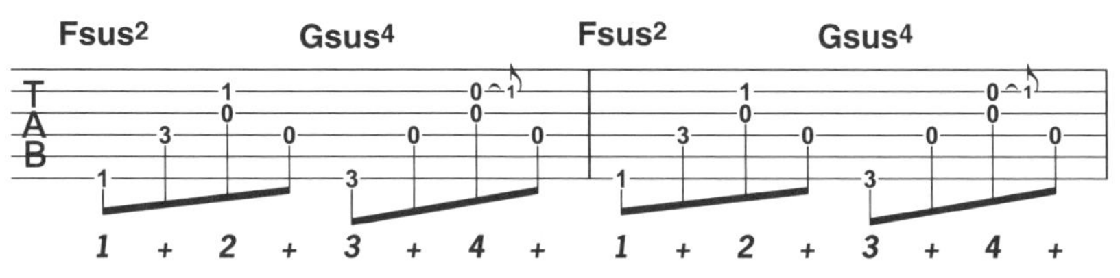

Verse

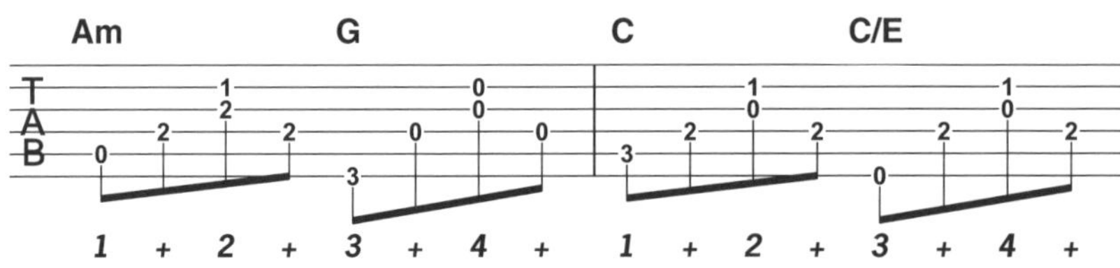
Am G C C/E
1 + 2 + 3 + 4 + 1 + 2 + 3 + 4 +

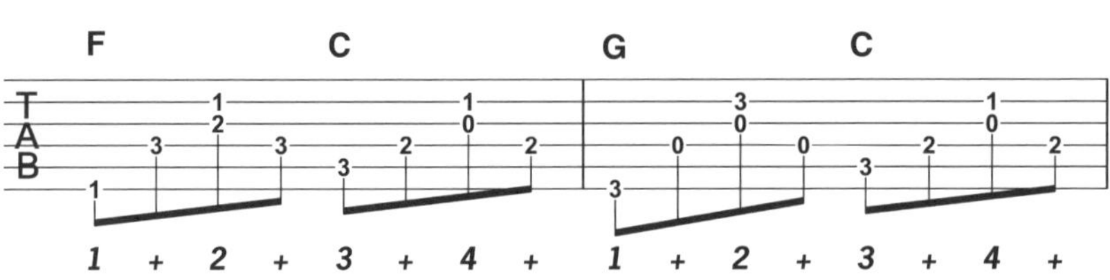
F C G C
1 + 2 + 3 + 4 + 1 + 2 + 3 + 4 +

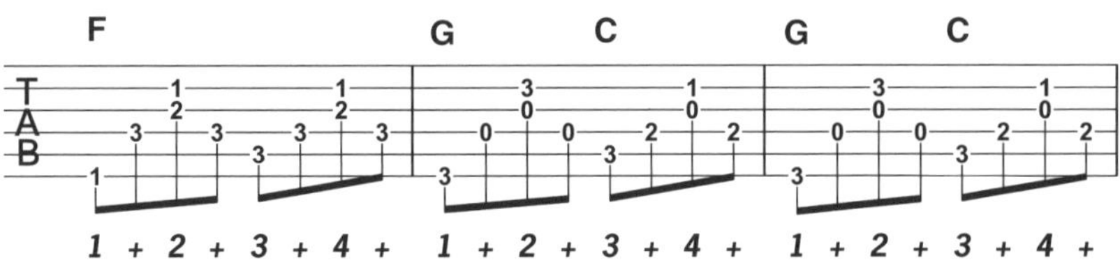
F G C G C
1 + 2 + 3 + 4 + 1 + 2 + 3 + 4 + 1 + 2 + 3 + 4 +

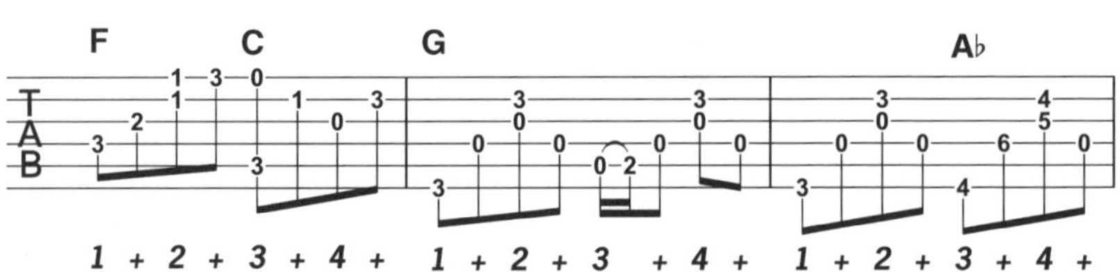
F C G A♭
1 + 2 + 3 + 4 + 1 + 2 + 3 + 4 + 1 + 2 + 3 + 4 +

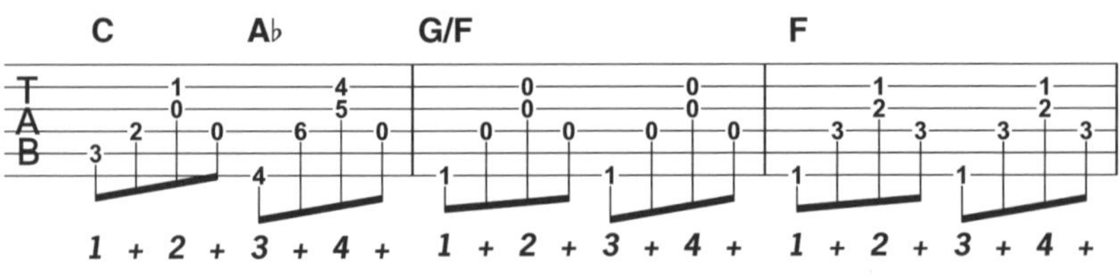
C A♭ G/F F
1 + 2 + 3 + 4 + 1 + 2 + 3 + 4 + 1 + 2 + 3 + 4 +

Road Rage

Words & Music by Cerys Matthews, Mark Roberts, Aled Richards, Paul Jones & Owen Powell

Introduction

This quirky pop tune was a big hit for Cerys Matthews and her band, Catatonia, in 1998.

Barre Crazy

So you think you've mastered your barre chords? Now's the time to prove it! This song is full of key changes, and will really keep you on your toes.

It's not uncommon for songs to have a few key changes, and it's well worth learning to remember the sequence of root notes in a song, not just the individual chord shapes, so that you can figure out which key you are playing in. Look for visual patterns—e.g. we start on chord X, and the next chord is a minor up Y frets, then over to the 6th string root… that kind of thing. It also helps knowing the function of each chord, but that goes beyond the scope possible in this book, although it is covered in my book, *Practical Music Theory*.

After watching a few clips of the band performing live, it seems that all guitars are detuned a semitone, so that all chords are played a semitone higher than what we have written out here! But that would spoil your barre chord fun, and won't sound very different. But for you Catatonia purists—just tune down one semitone and transpose the chords up one semitone.

Rhythm

There is no set rhythm pattern for this song, and in a band setting you should be playing a few notes from each chord, with your guitar processed through a lot of effects! But if you want a pattern to practice which will suit a kind of 'campfire' performance of the song then the pattern below is be a good starting point.

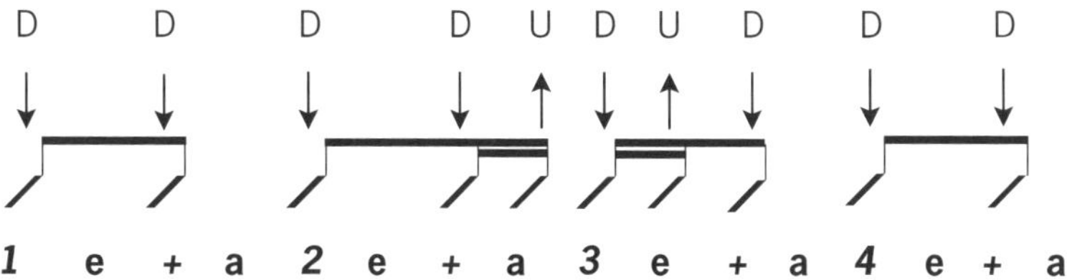

Beginner

Intermediate

Intermediate +

TAB

Road Rage

Words & Music by Cerys Matthews, Mark Roberts, Aled Richards, Paul Jones & Owen Powell


```
Verse 1
          A                   A              C♯m                 C♯m
If all you've got to do today is find peace of mind,
          D                 B                E      E
Come 'round, you can take a piece of mine.
              A                  A               C♯m       C♯m
And if all you've got to do today is hesitate,
          D               B                 E
Come here, you can leave it late with me.

Pre-chorus 1
C♯7                              F♯m
   You could be taking it ea - sy on yourself,
C♯7                              F♯m               C♯7
   You should be making it ea - sy on your - self,

Chorus
                             F♯               C♯7
'Cause you and I know it's all over the front page,
                D♯m                          G♯m
You give me road rage, racing through the best days.
            F♯                          C♯7
It's up to you boy, you're driving me crazy
                  D♯m                 G♯m
Thinking you may be losing your mind.

Verse 2
          B                 B                D♯m               D♯m
If all you've got to prove today is your innocence,
          E               C♯             F♯
Calm down, you're as guilty as can be.

Pre-chorus 2
E♭7                             A♭m
   You could be taking it easy on yourself,
E♭7                                A♭m            E♭7
   You should be making it ea - sy on yourself,

Chorus 2
                             A♭               E♭7
'Cause you and I know it's all over the front page,
                Fm                           B♭m
You give me road  rage, racing through the best days.
            A♭                          E♭7
It's up to you  boy, you're driving me crazy
                  Fm                 B♭m                        E♭
Thinking you may  be losing your mind, you're losing your mind.
```

```
            A♭  A♭                                   B♭m      E♭
Bridge      You,    you've been racing through the best days,
            A♭                     A♭
            Space age, road rage, fast lane.

                 D♭            D♭         Fm                 Fm
Verse 2     And if all you've got to do today is find peace of mind,
                 G♭        E♭           A♭
            Come here, you can take a peace of mine.
            F7                    B♭m
Pre-chorus 3  You could be taking it easy on yourself,
            F7                       B♭m        F7
              You should be making it easy on your - self,
                                  B♭          F
Chorus 3    'Cause you and I know it's all over the front page,
                        Gm                        Cm
            You give me road rage, racing through the best days.
                    B♭                    F7
            It's up to you boy, you're driving me crazy
                        Gm              Cm7
            Thinking you may be losing your mind.
                                B♭          F7
            But you and I know we all live in the space  age,
                              Gm                          Cm
            Coming down with road rage, racing through the best days.
                    B♭                   F7
            It's up to you boy, you're driving me crazy
                        Gm             Cm
            Thinking you may be losing your mind.

             B♭           F7
Outro       ||: It's not over,  it's not over,
            Gm           Cm
              It's not over.       :||    Repeat to fade (vocal ad lib.)
```

Rolling In The Deep

Words & Music by Adele Adkins & Paul Epworth

Intro | C5 | C5 |

Verse 1

C5 | C5 G5 |
There's a fire start - ing in my heart,
| G5 B♭5 | B♭5 G5 B♭5 |
Reach - ing a fever pitch and it's bring - ing me out the dark.
| C5 | C5 G5 |
Finally, I can see you crystal clear,
| G5 B♭5 | B♭5 G5 B♭5 |
Go a - head and sell me out and-a I'll lay your ship bare.

Verse 2

See how I'll leave with every piece of you,
Don't underestimate the things that I will do.
There's a fire starting in my heart,
Reaching a fever pitch and it's bringing me out the dark.

Pre-chorus 1

A♭ B♭ Gm
The scars of your love remind me of us,
A♭ A♭
They keep me thinking that we almost had it all.
B♭ Gm
The scars of your love, they leave me breathless,
G7
I can't help feeling…

Chorus 1

(G7) Cm B♭ A♭
We could have had it all,___ rolling in the deep.
| A♭ B♭ | Cm B♭
You had my heart in - side your hand
A♭ | A♭ B♭ |
And you played it to the beat.

Verse 3

Baby, I have no story to be told,
But I've heard one on you and I'm gonna make your head burn.
Think of me in the depths of your despair,
Make a home down there as mine sure won't be shared.

Pre-chorus 2 As Pre-chorus 1

Chorus 2 As Chorus 1

Verse 4

N.C.(Cm) **N.C.**
Throw your soul through every open door,
N.C. **N.C.**
Count your blessings to find what you look for.
Cm **Cm**
Turn my sorrow into treasured gold,
Cm **Cm**
You'll pay me back in kind and reap just what you've sown.

Chorus 3

Cm **B♭**
(*You're gonna wish you never had met me*),
A♭
We could have had it all,
| **A♭** **B♭** | **Cm** **B♭**
We could have had it all,___
A♭ | **A♭** **B♭** |
It all, it all, it all. We could have had it

Chorus 4

Cm **B♭** **A♭**
All,___ rolling in the deep.
| **A♭** **B♭** | **Cm** **B♭**
You had my heart in - side your hand
A♭ | **A♭** **B♭** |
And you played it to the beat, could have had it
Cm **B♭** **A♭**
All,___ rolling in the deep.
| **A♭** **B♭** | **Cm** **B♭**
You had my heart in - side your hand,
A♭ | **A♭**
But you played it, you played it, you played it,
B♭ | **Cm**
You played it to the beat.

Introduction

This moody track is a real showcase for Adele's powerful, bluesy voice. It was released as a single and on her album, *21*.

Rolling In The Deep

Words & Music by Adele Adkins & Paul Epworth

Strange Changes

One of the most interesting aspects of this song is the delayed chord changes during the verses, which are very unusual and sound cool. The easiest way to learn the chord sequence will be to play it slowly, following the chart below, and counting along with the eighth-notes. It's not a hard sequence, but it is a little counter-intuitive and will take practice before it starts to flow naturally. All the chords are muted power chords, played fairly evenly and without accents.

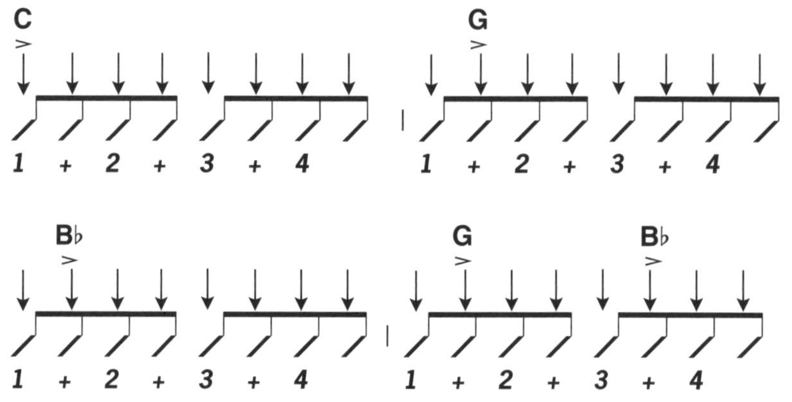

Pre-Chorus

When you get to the pre-chorus you should switch from power chords to full chords, but keep playing muted down-picks, so that the sound opens up a bit but not a lot. When you reach the chorus, you should be pumping the eighth-notes with down-strums, playing with a palm mute and picking most of the strings. This will bring the guitar part up in volume and energy.

Sex On Fire

Words & Music by Caleb Followill, Nathan Followill, Jared Followill & Matthew Followill

Introduction

This song, released in 2008 by Oklahoma's Kings of Leon is the band's most successful single to date.

Riff 1

The harmony in this song is really interesting and quite ambiguous. Often the harmony changes even though the guitar part stays the same—the movement in the bass guitar underneath suggests the new harmony. Therefore, what you see in the chord chart is often more representative of the overall harmony than what the guitar itself is playing. So let's break the guitar part down into riffs.

Below is the main riff, played by singer Caleb Followill. It isn't difficult but you must keep the rhythm really steady if you plan to sing while playing it, which will add an extra challenge. The part is played using the 3rd finger for all notes on string 5.

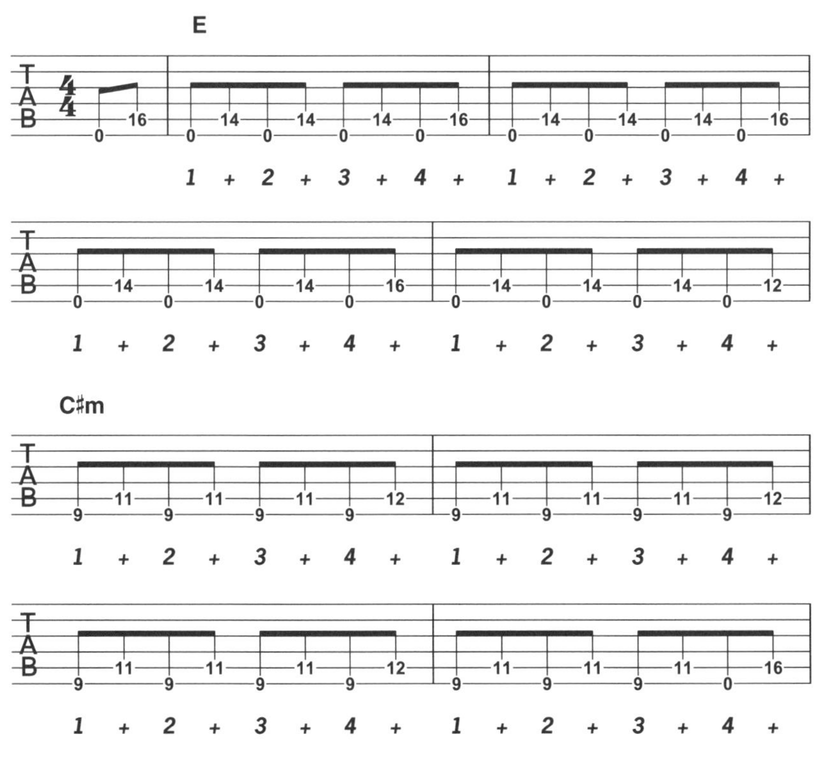

Sex On Fire

Words & Music by Caleb Followill, Nathan Followill,
Jared Followill & Matthew Followill

Intro
(riffs 1 + 2)

|: E | E | E | E |
| C♯m | C♯m | C♯m | C♯m :|

Verse 1
(riff 1 cont.)
(add riff 3)
(add riff 2)

(C♯m)   E   E   E   E
Lay where you're laying, don't make a sound,
                    C♯m   C♯m   C♯m   C♯m
I know they're watching, they're watching.
                 E   E   E   E
All the co - mmotion, the kiddie like play,
                 C♯m C♯m C♯m C♯m
Has people talking, talking.

Chorus 1
(riffs 4 + 5)

E E E   E   C♯m C♯m A   A
You,   your sex is on fire.

Verse 2

(A)   E   E   E   E
The dark of the alley, the breaking of day,
                              C♯m C♯m   C♯m   C♯m
The head while I'm driving, I'm driving.
                   E   E   E   E
Soft lips are open, the knuckles are pale,
                        C♯m   C♯m   A   A
Feels like you're dying, you're dying.

Chorus 2

You, your sex is on fire,
Consumed with what's to transpire.

Verse 3
(Chords as verse 2)

Hot as a fever, rattling bones, I can just taste it, taste it.
If it's not forever, if it's just tonight,
Oh, it's still the greatest, the greatest, the greatest.

Chorus 3

E E E   E   C♯m C♯m A   A
You,   your sex is on fire.
   E5   E5 E5   E5   G♯5 C♯m C♯m C♯m C♯m
And you,   your sex is on   fire,
    E5   E5 E5   E5   G♯5 C♯m C♯m A   A
Con - sumed   with what's to tran - spire.

Chorus 4

And you, your sex is on fire,
Consumed with what's to transpire.

Riff 2

This is played by the lead guitarist, and is played during the verses after a short break. It consists of simple stabs on the off-beat, but make sure you keep the rhythm tight, and relax your grip after playing the stabs to stop the notes ringing out.

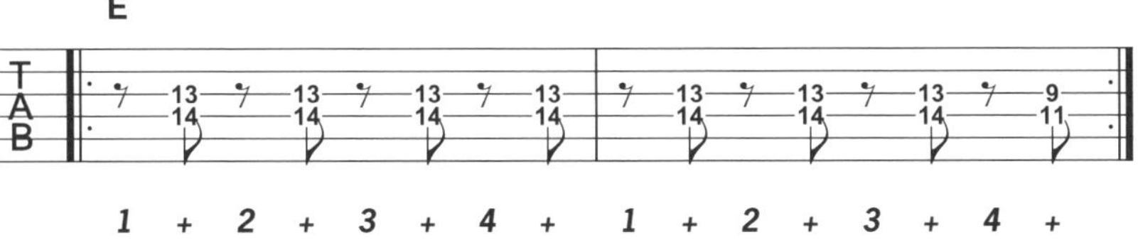

Riff 3

After a few repetitions of Riff 2, the lead guitarist switches to this arpeggiated chord riff, which stays the same over both the E and C♯m chords. The riff fits perfectly with the changing harmony. This is a great example of pop guitar playing—simple and very effective.

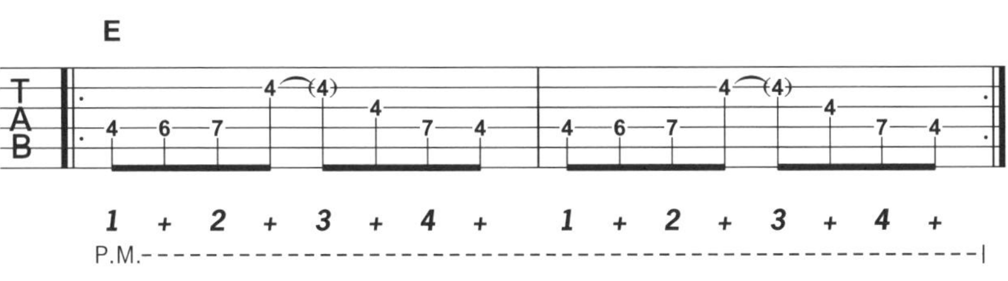

This is the chorus guitar part, played by singer Caleb Followill. Interestingly, he doesn't follow the movement of the bassline, even when the bass moves to the notes C♯ and A. He just keeps it rocking away, which creates some interesting harmonies.

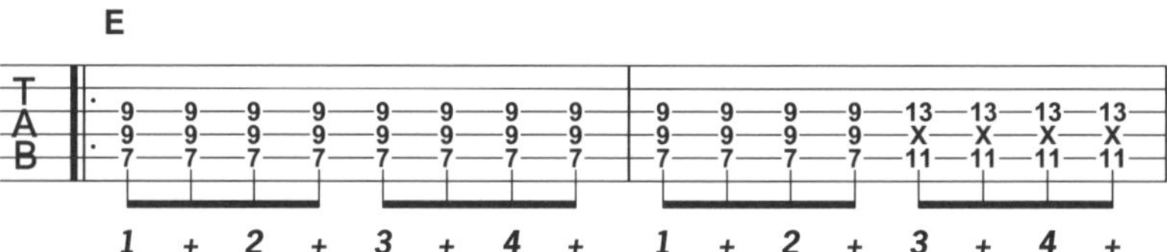

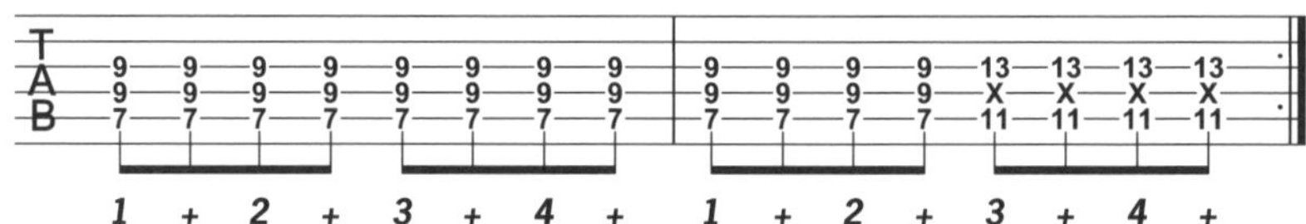

Riff 5

The lead guitar riff for the chorus is this amazingly catchy riff, which uses bends and two-note riffs. Make sure that you keep the string bends in tune and avoid hitting any unnecessary strings, while giving it lots of energy. In this kind of tune you have to put energy into it. Don't think too much about technique—you just have to give it lots and it'll come out rockin'!

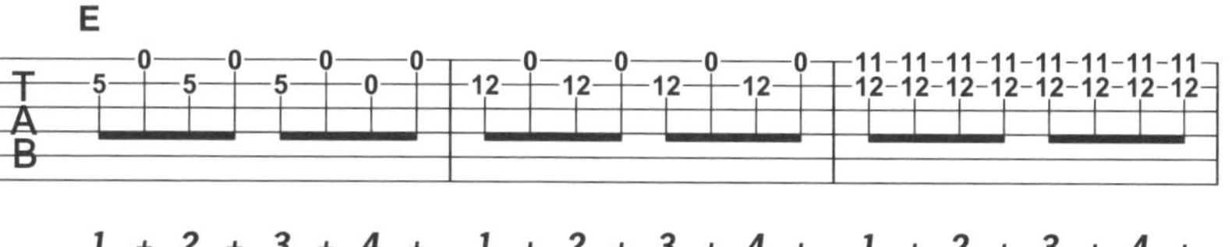

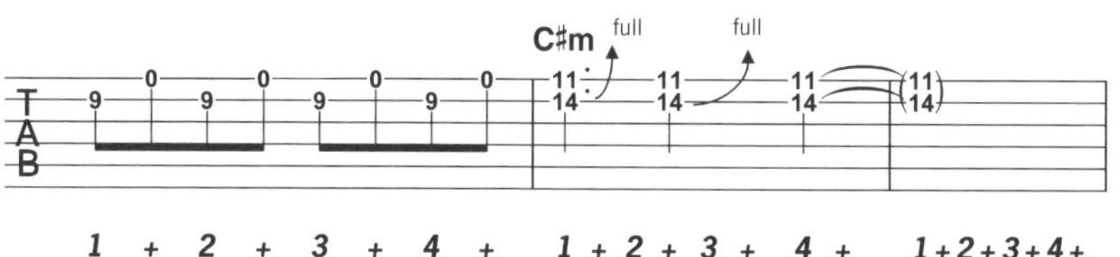

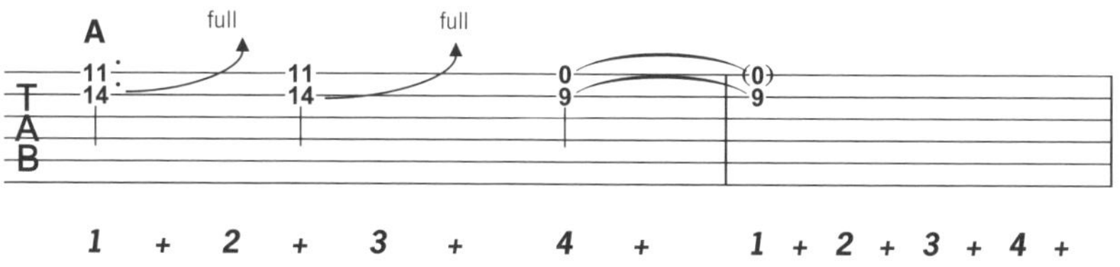

She Will Be Loved

Words & Music by Adam Levine, James Valentine, Jesse Carmichael, Mickey Madden & Ryan Dusick

Beginner

Intermediate

Intermediate +

TAB

Intro

```
| Bm7   | A7    | Bm7   | A7    |
```

Verse 1

```
Bm7                A7                Bm7                       A7
   Beauty queen of only eighteen, She    had some trouble with herself.
Bm7              A7
   He was always there to help her,
    Bm7               A7
She      always belonged to someone else.
Bm7          A7                   Bm7               A7
   I drove for miles and miles, and wound up at your door.
Bm7             A7                 Bm7               A7
   I've had you so many times, but somehow I want more.
```

Pre-chorus 1

```
D                          Asus4
   I don't mind spending every day
Bm7                           Asus4
   Out on your corner in the pouring rain.
D                             Asus4
   Look for the girl with the broken smile,
Bm7                         Gadd9
   Ask her if she wants to stay awhile.
```

Chorus 1

```
         D       Asus4           Bm7   Gadd9   Gadd9
And she will be loved, and she will be loved.
```

Verse 2

Tap on my window knock on my door,
I want to make you feel beautiful.
I know I tend to get so insecure, It doesn't matter anymore.
It's not always rainbows and butterflies,
It's compromise that moves us along, yeah.
My heart is full and my door's always open,
You come anytime you want, yeah.

Pre-chorus 2 As Pre-chorus 1

Chorus 2

```
         D       Asus4           Bm7   Gadd9
And she will be loved, and she will be loved.
         D       Asus4           Bm7   Gadd9
And she will be loved, and she will be loved.
```

Bridge

```
Bm7                    A                   Bm7
   I know where you hide alone in your car,
                  A
Know all of the things that make you who you are.
Bm7                    A                        Bm7
   I know that good - bye means nothing at all,
                               A                       G         G
Comes back and begs me to catch her every time she   falls, yeah.
```

Verse 3 Tap on my window knock on my door,
I want to make you feel beautiful.

Pre-chorus 3 As Pre-chorus 1

Chorus 3
```
                 D         Asus4              Bm7      Asus4
And she will be loved, and she will be loved.
                 D         Asus4              Bm7      Gadd9
And she will be loved, and she will be loved.
```

(Repeat, vocals ad lib.)

(A Capella) Please don't try so hard to say goodbye.

Introduction

This lovely ballad from Maroon 5 has a great jazz-tinged guitar riff, which you can play in a variety of ways. It's worth noting that the studio recording should be played with a capo, but the live versions of the song are not.

Main Riff

It's possible to play this song using regular strumming, but the main riff is played fingerstyle on the recording. Your thumb will play the bass note on the fifth string (or sixth string in the last example), while your fingers will play the next strings down sequentially.

On the original recording of the song, the riff is pretty much the same all of the way through. The most important thing is to get the timing and groove right. As soon as you have the notes firmly under your fingers, you should start thinking about the rhythm and the groove.

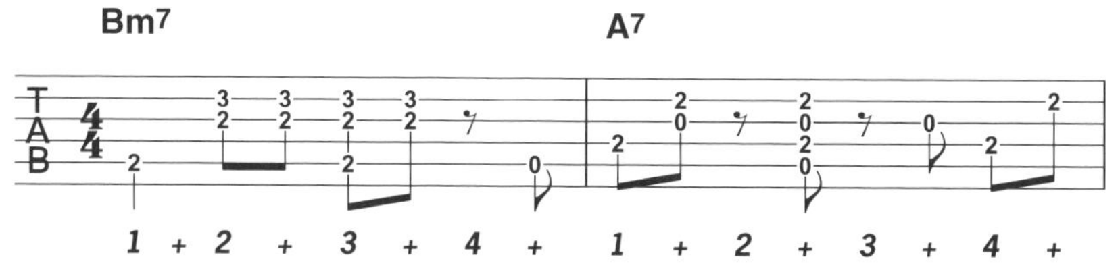

'Live' Variation

When performing live, guitarist James Valentine plays the riff with a few more notes and bit more bass action—this suits an stripped-down vibe, so if you are playing solo, you might prefer this option.

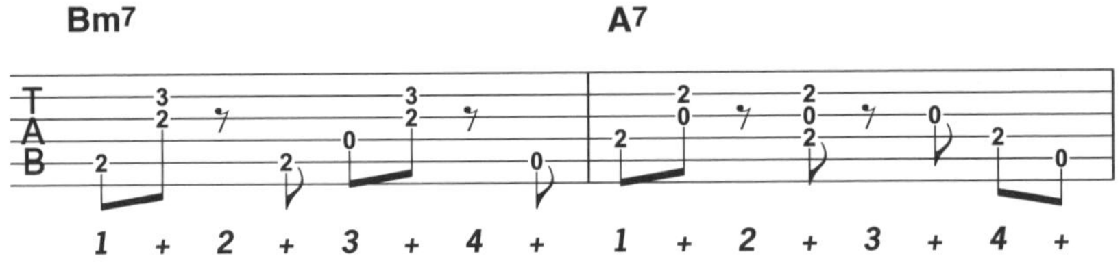

Acoustic Variation

I found a tasty variation of the riff on an acoustic session, so I thought I'd write that out for you too. It works really nicely—perhaps you might enjoy working out your own variations?

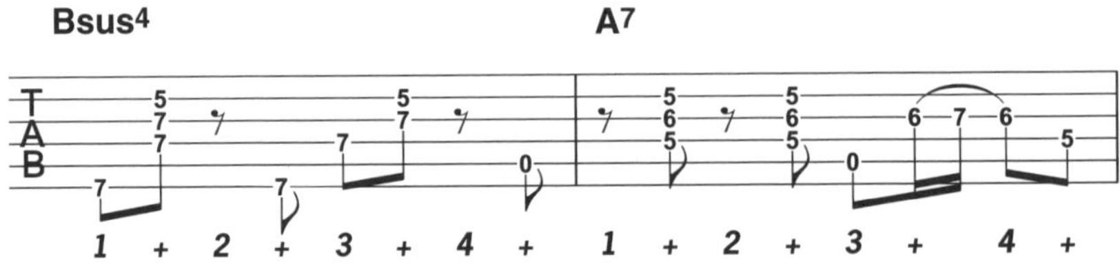

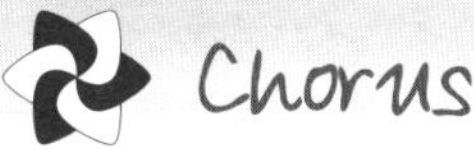

Chorus

In the chorus there is a lovely pedal note used—you can strum it or continue the verse 'feel' by playing it fingerstyle. For a solo acoustic version you might like to try the pattern used in the 'acoustic variation' (*left*), but apply it to the chorus chord sequence, and maybe, if you are up for it, add in a percussive hit on beats 2 and 4, written out below once through so you get the idea!

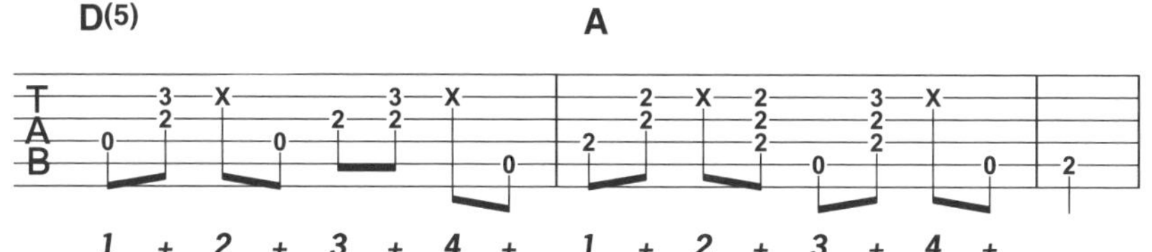

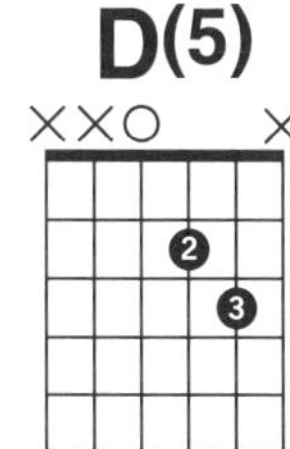

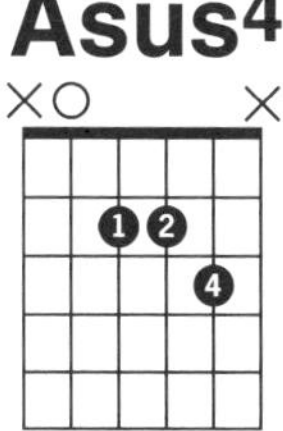

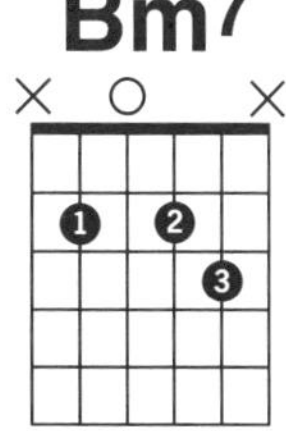

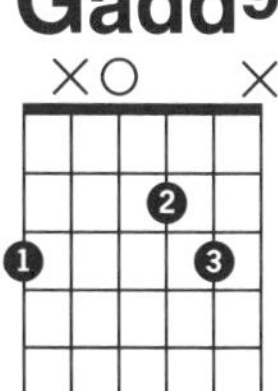

True Colors

Words & Music by Billy Steinberg & Tom Kelly

Intro
|: Am7 | C/B | C | F :|

Verse 1
Am G/B C C/E
You with the sad heart, Don't be dis - couraged
Fadd9 F Am G
Though I realise, It's hard to take courage.
C Dm C/E F
In a world full of people, you can lose sight of it all
Am G F C
And the darkness inside you, can make you feel so small.

Chorus 1
F C Gsus4 G
But I see your true colours shining through,
F C/E F | Gsus4 G |
I see your true colours, and that's why I love you.
F C Dm Am F/C C
So don't be a - fraid to let them show, your true colours,
F/C C Gsus4 Gsus4
True colours are beautiful, like a (rainbow).

Link 1
|: Am7 | C/B | C | F :|
...rainbow.

Verse 2
Show me a smile then, don't be unhappy,
Can't remember when I last saw you laughing.
If this world makes you crazy, and you've taken all you can bear
You call me up, because you know I'll be there.

Chorus 2
As Chorus 1

|: Am7 | C/B | C | F :|

Verse 3
Ooh____
(whispered) Can't remember when I last saw you laughing
(sung) If this word makes you crazy, you've taken all you can bear
You call me up, becuase you know I'll be there

Chorus 3
| F C | Gsus4 G
But I see your true colours shining through,
| F C/E | F Gsus4 G
I see your true colours, and that's why I love you.

(cont.)

| F C | Dm Am | F/C C | F/C C
So don't be a - fraid to let them show, your true colours, true colours,
| F/C C | Gsus4 G
True colours are shining through
| F C/E | F Gsus4 G
I see your true colours, and that's why I love you
| F C | E7 Am
So don't be afraid, to let them show
| F/C C | F/C C | Gsus4
Your true colours, true colours are beautiful,
N.C.
Like a rainbow.

Outro | Am7 C/B | C F |

Introduction

A true classic of a pop song, Cyndi Lauper's hit has been covered by numerous artists. Here is the original version of the song, released in 1986.

Main Riff

This is one of those songs that sounds a lot better if you play it exactly as it sounds on the record. You can strum the chords if you like but the intro riff sounds awesome on the guitar! It was originally played on a synth but happens to work really well on the guitar, played fingerstyle. Keep your little finger firmly down until the F chord, at which point your first finger will play the note on the second string. You will most likely have to get your thumb over to play the F bass note (on string 6), but if you struggle, you can use your 1st finger instead, and then put it down as a barre to get the note on the second string.

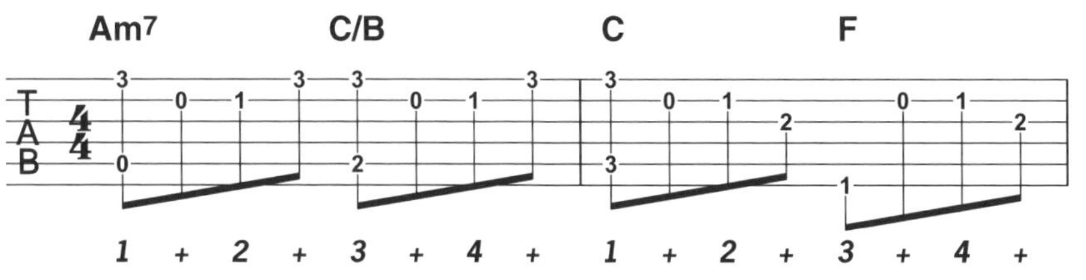

Beginner
Intermediate
Intermediate +
TAB

Bass Movements

There are two ways of playing an open C/E—either by simply adding the thickest (E) string to the chord, or by playing just the thinnest 4 strings of a regular C chord. Either will work fine—it mainly depends on which F chord voicing you then move to. I prefer using the C/E on the thinnest 4 strings for this song, as it creates a nice movement, especially for the C, Dm, C/E, F section.

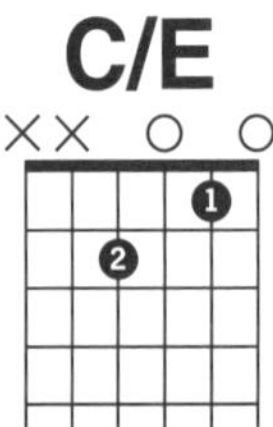

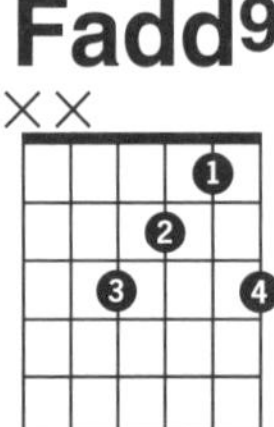

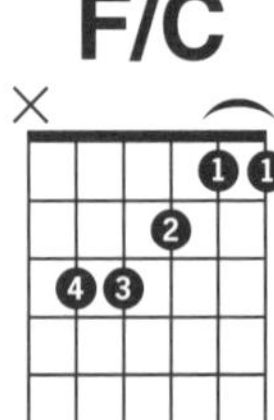

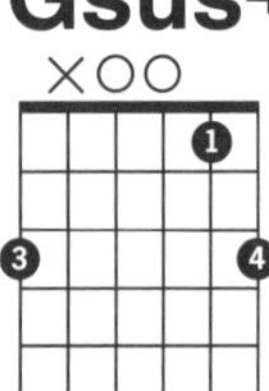

Pushes

There are many chords in this song that are 'pushed', meaning that they are played an eighth-note early, on the 'and' after beat 4 of the previous bar. Writing them all in would make the chart horrendously complex and hard to read—plus, you're not obliged to play every single one—so it's better if you listen to the recording and choose with 'pushes' to include.

Spread 'Em

In the verses it sounds great if you play each chord just once, as a spread chord, which is a slow strum with the last note falling right on the beat, as covered in the Intermediate Course (IM-155). You can add in some single, picked notes if you like, but a minimal style of guitar playing will suit the verses best.

TAB STAGE

Introduction

In this last section of the book, all of the songs are presented as full TAB, so you can really work on the finer details of some great songs. I've picked five awesome songs for you, spanning the decades from the present day back to the 1960s. We have the Killers' classic, 'Mr. Brightside', which features a real humdinger of a riff, alongside Adele's beautiful ballad, 'Someone Like You', where the piano part has been arranged for guitar. From the 'vaults', we have The Police's 'Every Breath You Take', although you may well know the guitar part from the numerous songs that it's been sampled in, and from further back we have the Beatles' bluesy 'Day Tripper', which features a fantastic guitar hook that every guitarist needs to learn at some point! Lastly we have a transcription of the awesome guitar playing on Michael Jackson's 'Beat It', including the famous guitar riff and a trademark Van Halen face-melting, finger tapping solo!

With all of these songs, you should practise slowly and carefully, making sure you are playing correctly before speeding them up. Practising slowly is the key to playing quickly!

I hope you enjoy these classic songs as much as I do.

TAB Notation Guide

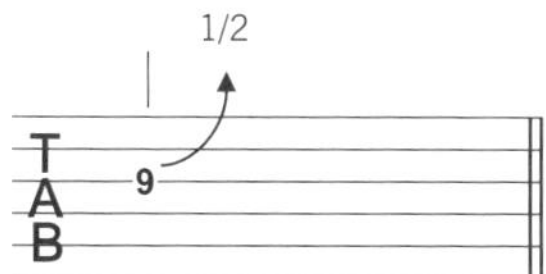

SEMI-TONE BEND: Strike the note and bend up a semi-tone (½ step).

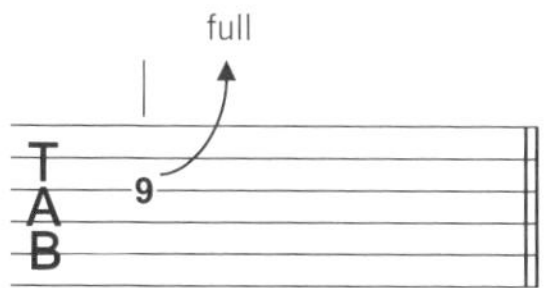

WHOLE-TONE BEND: Strike the note and bend up a whole-tone (full step).

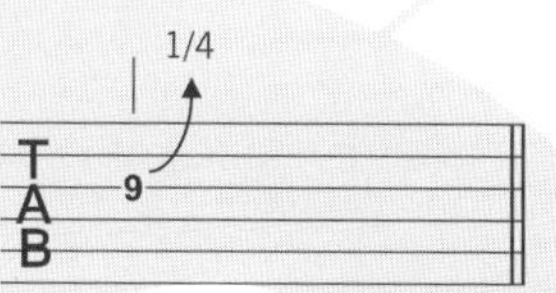

QUARTER-TONE BEND: Strike the note and bend up a ¼ step

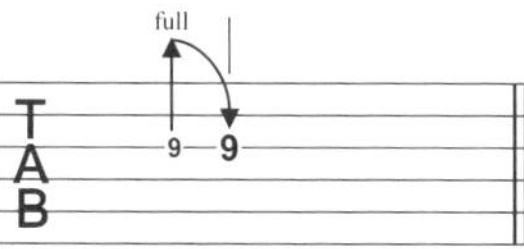

PRE-BEND & RELEASE: Bend the note as indicated. Strike it and release the note back to the original pitch.

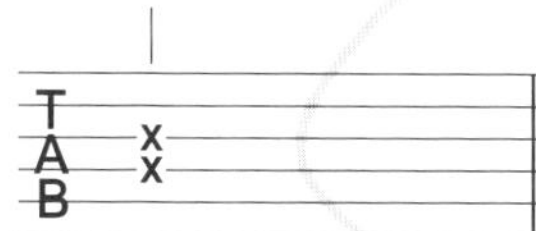

MUFFLED STRINGS: A percussive sound is produced by laying the first hand across the string(s) without depressing, and striking them with the pick hand.

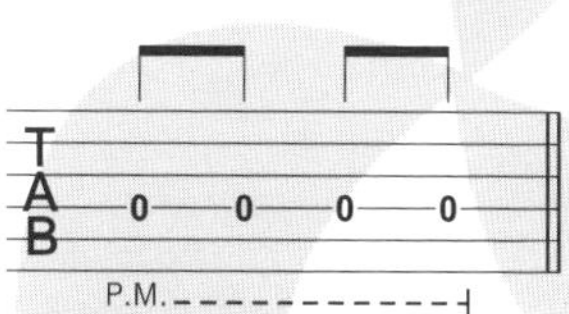

PALM MUTING: The note is partially muted by the pick hand lightly touching the string(s) just before the bridge.

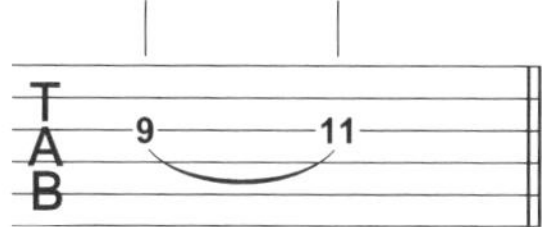

HAMMER-ON: Strike the first note with one finger, then sound the second note (on the same string) with another finger by fretting it without picking.

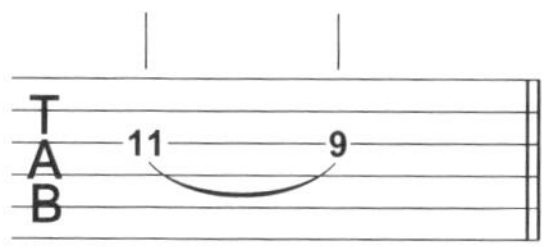

FLICK-OFF: Place both fingers on the note to be sounded, strike the first note and without picking, flick the finger off to sound the second note.

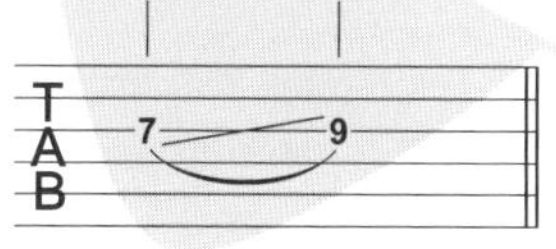

LEGATO SLIDE (GLISS): Strike the first note and then slide the same fret-hand finger up or down to the second note. The second note is not struck.

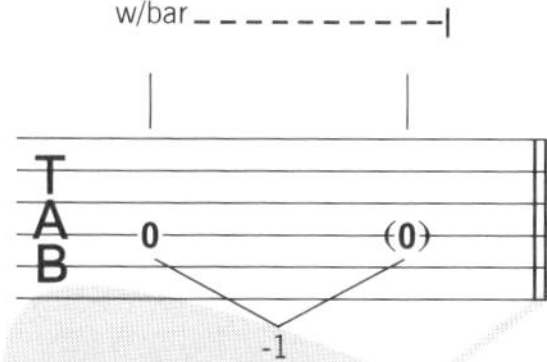

VIBRATO DIVE BAR AND RETURN: The pitch of the note or chord is dropped a specific number of steps (in rhythm) then returned to the original pitch.

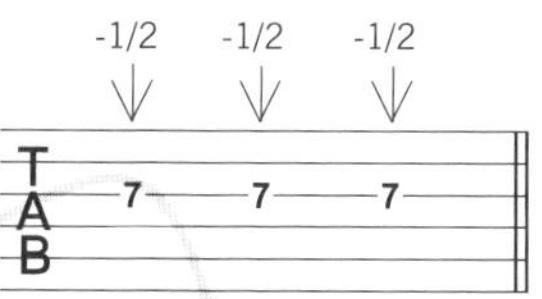

VIBRATO BAR DIP: Strike the note and then immediately drop a specific number of steps, then release back to the original pitch.

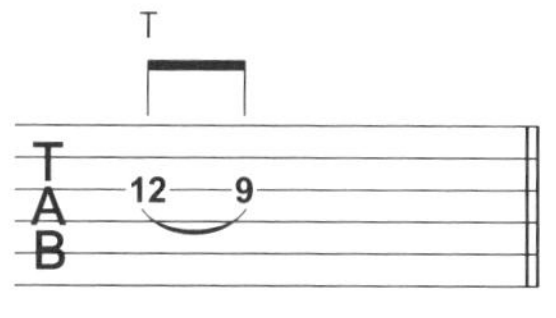

TAPPING: Hammer ('tap') the fret indicated with the pick-hand index or middle finger and flick-off to the note fretted by the fret hand.

TREMOLO PICKING: The note is picked as rapidly and continously as possible.

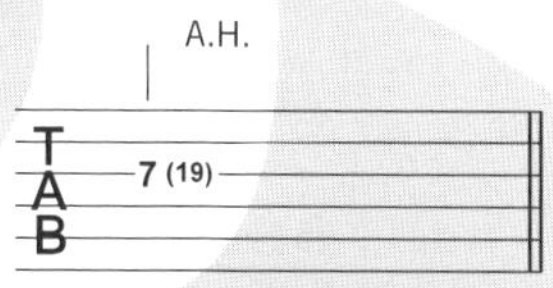

ARTIFICIAL HARMONIC: The note is fretted normally and a harmonic is produced by gently resting the pick hand's index finger directly above the indicated fret (in brackets) while plucking the appropriate string.

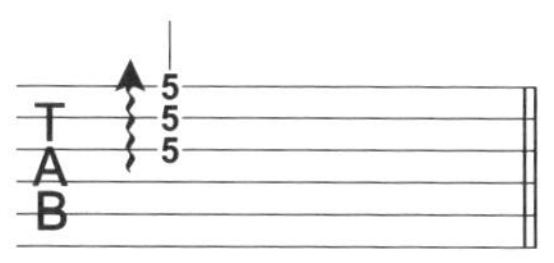

ARPEGGIATE: Play the notes of the chord indicated by quickly rolling them from bottom to top.

Every Breath You Take

Words & Music by Sting

Introduction

The Police's timeless record from 1983 is a seriously great pop song, which is built on a memorable and really enjoyable guitar part.

Section A

Don't worry if the opening chord riff to this song seems challenging initially. I remember the first time I tried to play this song and I was very disappointed that I couldn't even play the first chord! It really looks like you need super-long fingers and a big stretch to be able to play the chord, and you certainly will if you are going to hold all the notes down! So, what's the secret?

Playing a regular A barre chord (on the 5th fret) and then moving the little finger up two frets is pretty tricky, especially for anyone like me who has a very short little finger. Although I struggled with the chord for some time, I later gave up and resigned myself to playing the A chord in open position, even though it never quite sounded right. Then by chance I saw The Police playing this song on TV one day and noticed that Andy Summers wasn't making the stretch either—he was 'cheating' by playing the notes on the 3rd string with his first finger!

You can play these barre chord riffs using this big stretch if you have the dexterity to do so, but if not, play them using the following sequence of fretting hand fingers: 1 2 4 2 1 4 2 4. This same pattern can be used for the A and F♯m chords. Don't try to hold down the barre—just lift up and move your first finger between the thickest and 3rd strings, which you will find much easier!

The Dsus2 and Esus2 chords should be played as regular D and E barre chords (barring with your 3rd finger). Reach up with your 4th finger for the higher note (on the 3rd string). It's a little tricky but easily possible for most people, after a little practice.

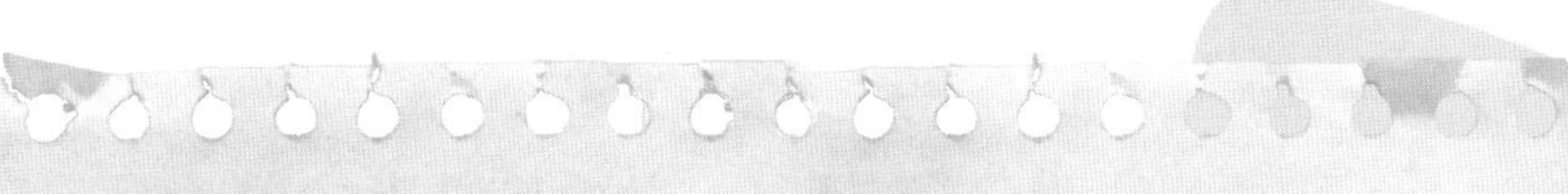

Section B

The guitar part here is a little unexpected, but follow along closely and you'll have it in no time. It's not hard—it just feels strange because it causes a break to the main pattern. The Badd9 coming up is just the same as the Aadd9 but up 2 frets, so this shouldn't present any problems. Take your time and get the notes right first time because it's harder to correct mistakes later than it is to learn a song correctly!

Section C

It's time to play some big chords and let them ring out. The trick here is to hit the chords 'positively' and not just thrash them. Give these sustained chords a definite strum and think about letting the chord ring out—this will help you make a good contact with the strings so that they ring out longer. Like everything else, it will take practice to perfect this technique, but how you approach playing, subconsciously, makes a difference to the sound that you make, so keep this in mind if you want these chords to sustain for a long time.

Every Breath You Take

Words & Music by Sting

A

Intro

♩ = 115

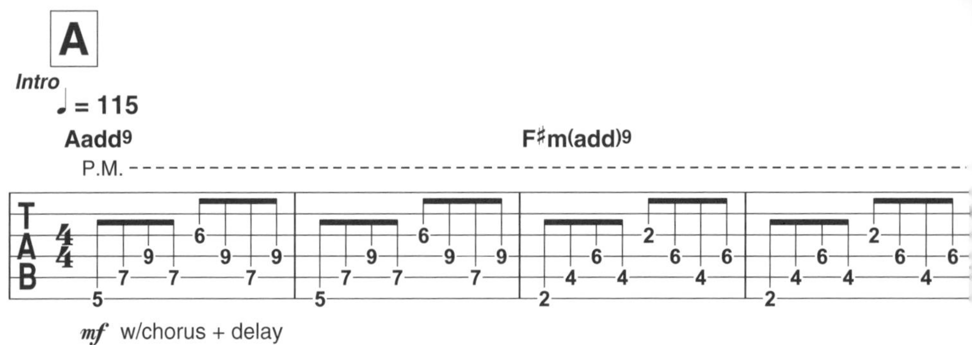
Aadd9
F♯m(add)9
P.M.
mf w/chorus + delay

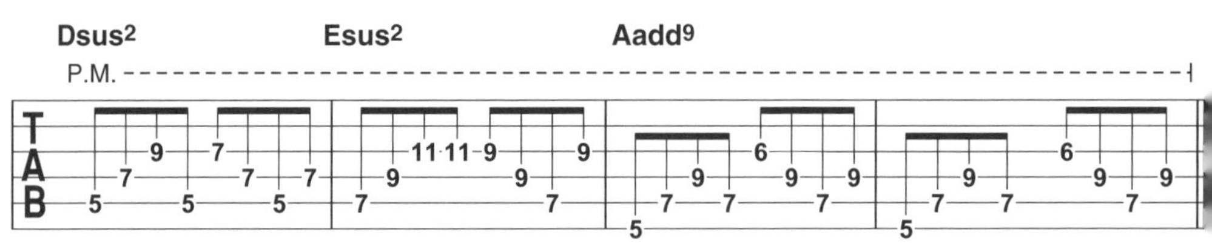
Dsus2
Esus2
Aadd9
P.M.
1. Ev'ry breath you_

Verse

Aadd9

P.M. *cont. sim.*

F♯m(add)9

take, ev-'ry move you_ make, ev-'ry bond you break,

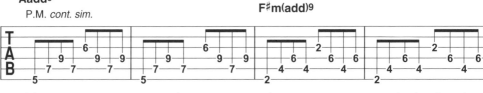

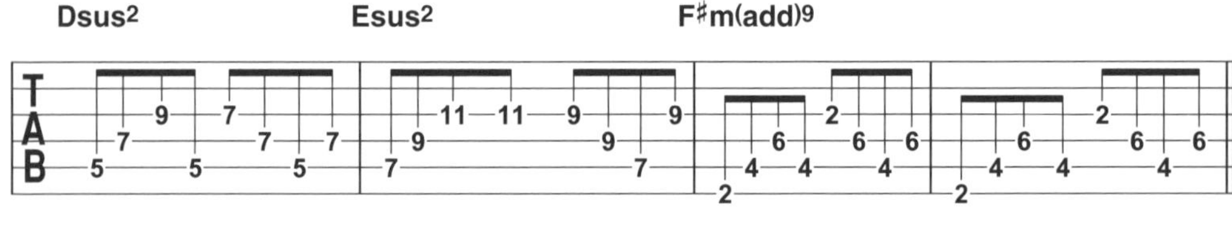
Dsus2
Esus2
F♯m(add)9
ev-'ry step you take, I'll be watch-ing you. 2. Ev'ry sin - gle_

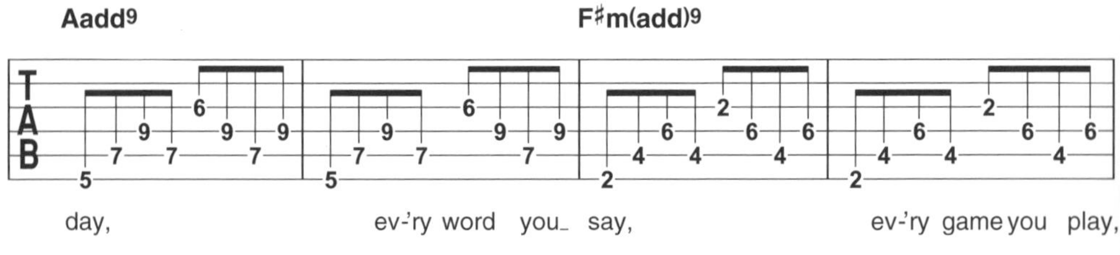
Aadd9
F♯m(add)9
day, ev-'ry word you_ say, ev-'ry game you play,

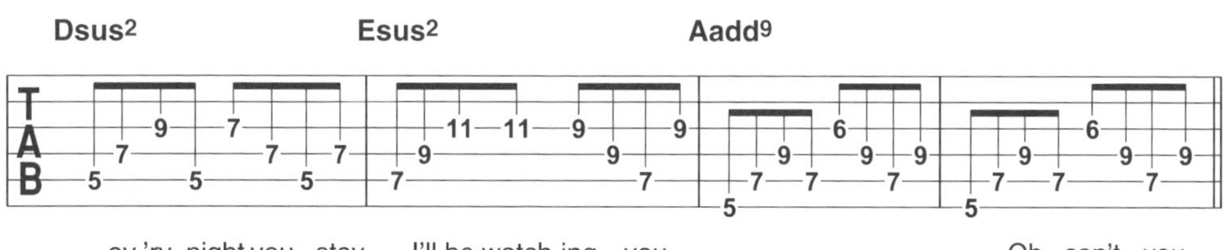
Dsus2 Esus2 Aadd9
ev-'ry night you stay, I'll be watch-ing you. Oh, can't you

B

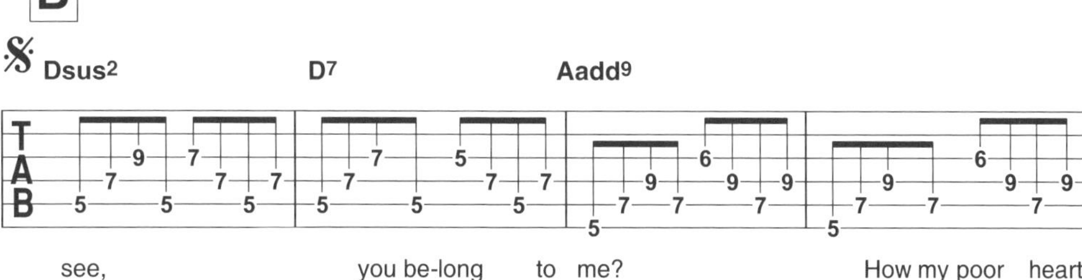
Dsus2 D7 Aadd9
see, you be-long to me? How my poor heart

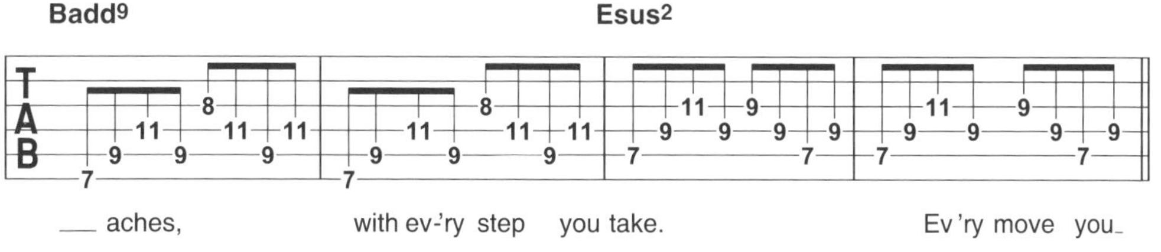
Badd9 Esus2
aches, with ev-'ry step you take. Ev'ry move you

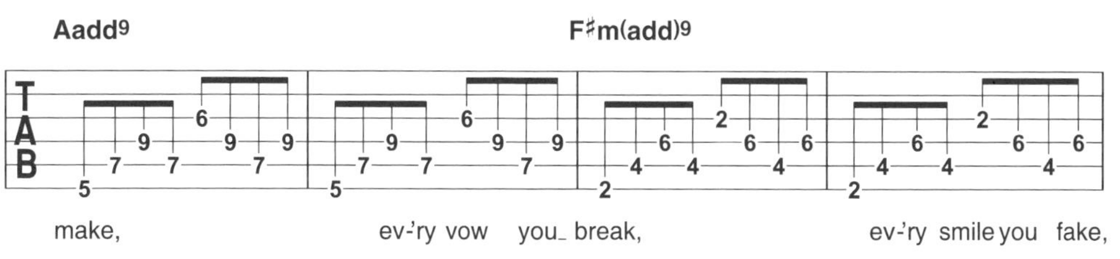
Aadd9 F♯m(add)9
make, ev-'ry vow you break, ev-'ry smile you fake,

To Coda ⊕

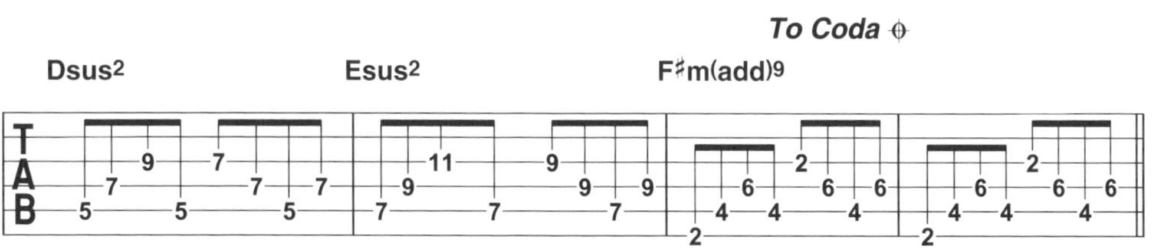
Dsus2 Esus2 F♯m(add)9
ev-'ry claim you stake, I'll be watch-ing you.

Beginner

Intermediate

Intermediate +

TAB

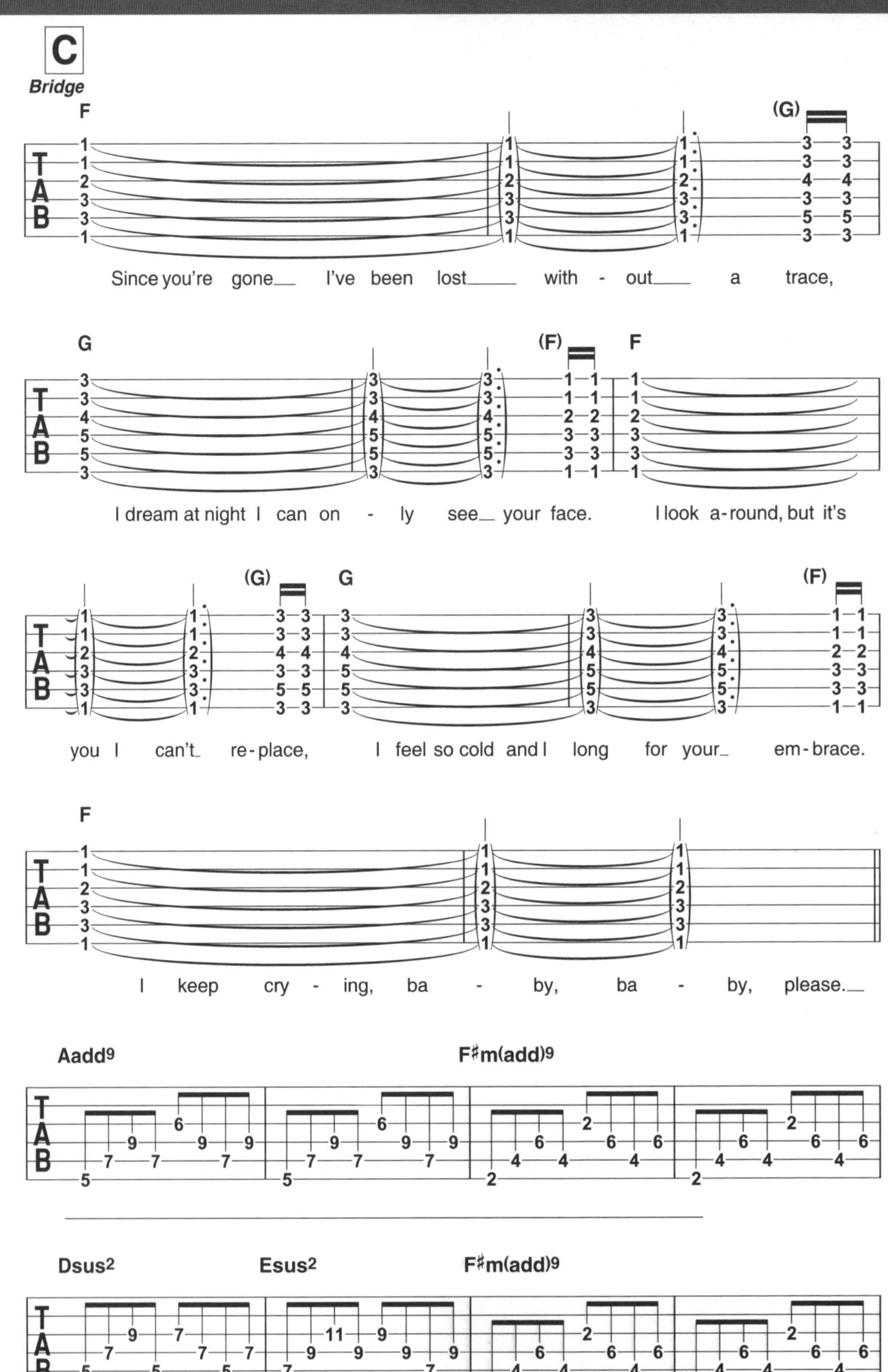

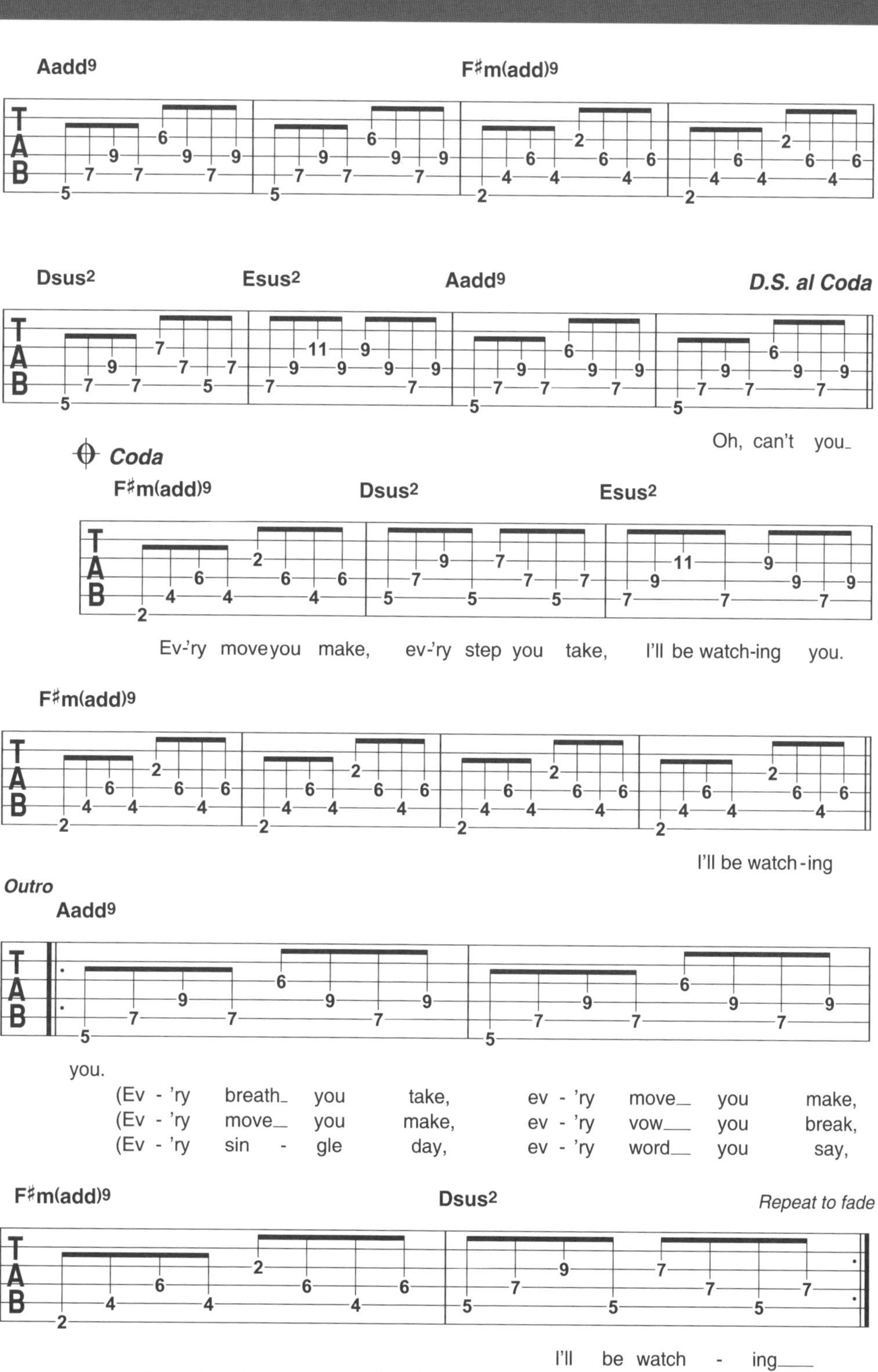
Aadd9
F♯m(add)9
Dsus2
Esus2
Aadd9
D.S. al Coda
Oh, can't you
Coda
F♯m(add)9
Dsus2
Esus2
Ev-'ry move you make, ev-'ry step you take, I'll be watch-ing you.
F♯m(add)9
I'll be watch-ing
Outro
Aadd9
you.
(Ev - 'ry breath you take, ev - 'ry move you make,
(Ev - 'ry move you make, ev - 'ry vow you break,
(Ev - 'ry sin - gle day, ev - 'ry word you say,
F♯m(add)9
Dsus2
Repeat to fade
I'll be watch - ing
ev - 'ry bond you break, ev - 'ry step you take.)
ev - 'ry smile you fake, ev - 'ry claim you stake.)
ev - 'ry game you play, ev - 'ry night you stay.)

Mr. Brightside

Words & Music by Brandon Flowers, Dave Keuning, Mark Stoermer & Ronnie Vannucci

Introduction

This song was a huge hit for The Killers in 2004. It features a super cool guitar riff which is not as hard as it sounds. Your mates will be really impressed!

Marker A

The main riff here is a humdinger, a proper classic guitar part that will live on! It's a little awkward but not technically difficult.

The fretting hand fingering for the first bar is 2 1 4 1 0 3 4 0 (with the 0 being open strings). The last open string is there to give you a chance to change the chord, so is nicely convenient. The second bar stays the same but you should use a small first-finger barre to hold down the two notes on the 16th fret. In the third bar, we reach over to the thickest string with our first finger on the15th fret, while the second finger takes over the note on the 16th fret of the 4th string.

There are a number of ways to pick this, so experiment a little and find out what works best for you. It appears (from watching some live clips of The Killers) that lead guitarist Dave Keuning plays alternate-picking, but starting with an up-pick, which I find next to impossible! I find using the pattern D D U D U U U U the easiest, but you need to experiment a bit and see what works best for you. However, don't be lazy and go for the first thing you play—if you explore some different picking patterns, it will help you to become a better player!

Marker B

Now we have ourselves some 'Killer' chords to deal with! There are some tricky chord changes and stretchy grips too and will take you some practice. Rather than trying to explain the fingering, I think some of the chord boxes will explain it better and more simply. Make sure you practice making the chord changes before you try to add all the picking in. A little time working out which finger will move where will save a lot of time later. Remember we humans can only focus on one thing at a time, so don't confuse yourself trying to learn more than one thing at a time.

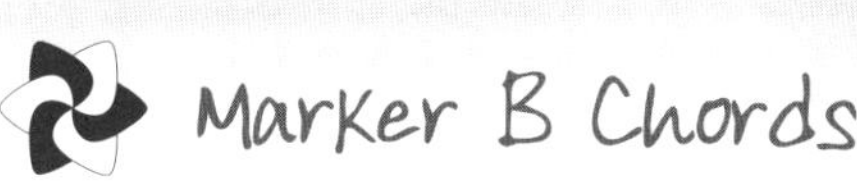

Marker B Chords

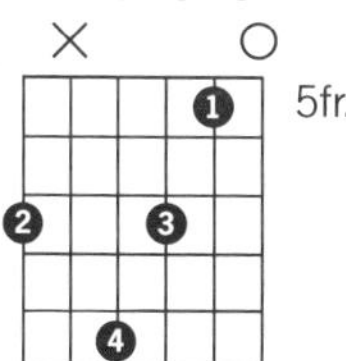

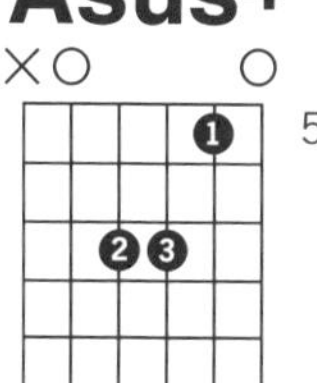

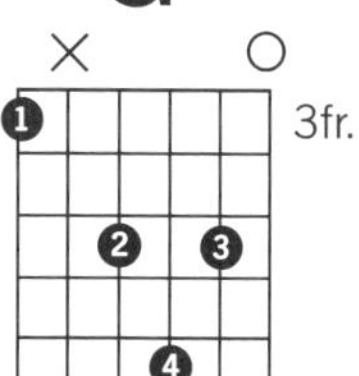

Marker C

Now we move on to a little diad (two note chord) riff. It's not too tricky—let the notes ring together and pick a little bit towards the bridge to keep the tone of the notes bright.

Marker D

Now another guitar part enters. When playing live, Keuning changes to this part, but listen closely to the recording and you can hear elements of the previous 8 bars sneaking through.

This guitar part consists of triad shapes, which are easy to play and sound great. At the very end of the four-bar sequence (on the chord A), I can hear the top triad which is shown, but when performing live, Keuning seems to play the descending line shown for the A chord at the first part of the chorus. You can choose which one to play.

Mr. Brightside

Words & Music by Brandon Flowers, Dave Keuning, Mark Stoermer & Ronnie Vannucci

Original key D♭ - tune all gtrs. down a semitone

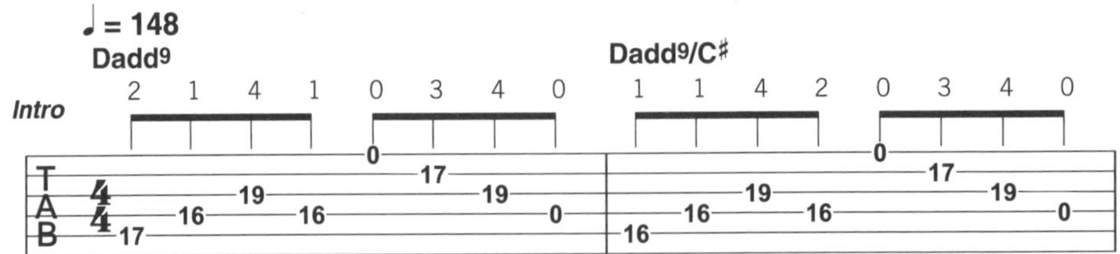

mf w/slight dist.

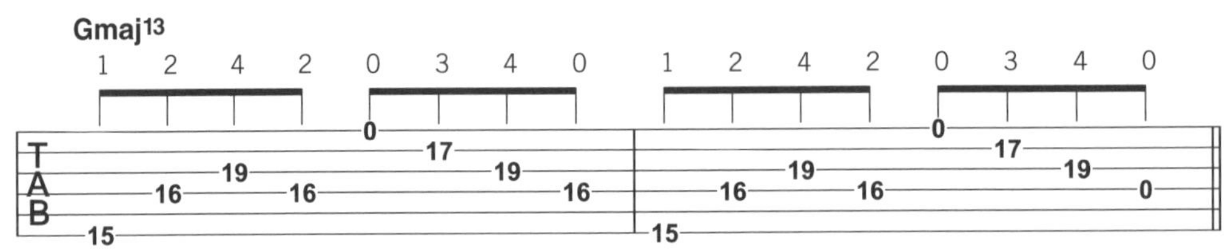

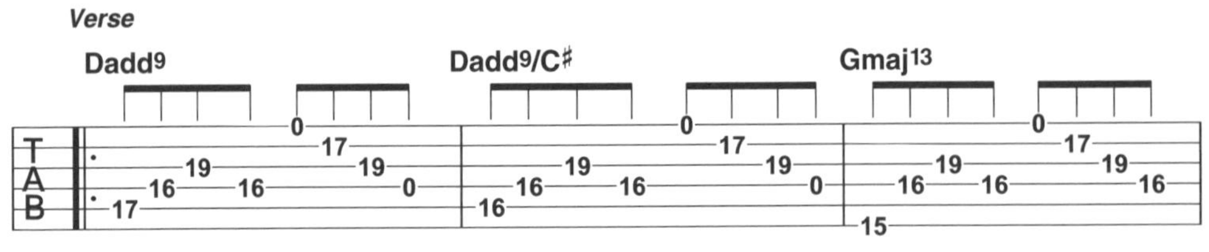

Com-ing out of my cage,__ and I've been do-ing just fine. Got-ta, got ta be down

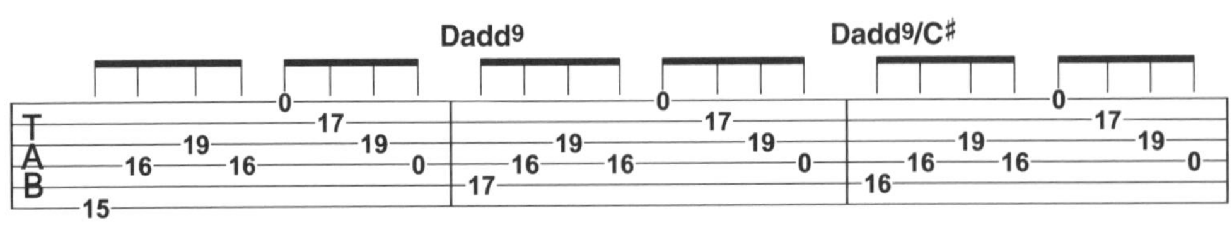

__ be-cause I want it all. It start-ed out with a kiss,__ how did it end up like

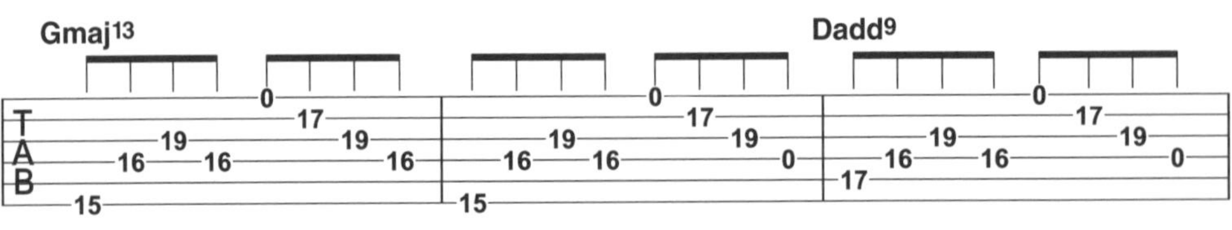

this? It was on-ly a kiss,__ it was on-ly a kiss. Now I'm fall-ing a - sleep

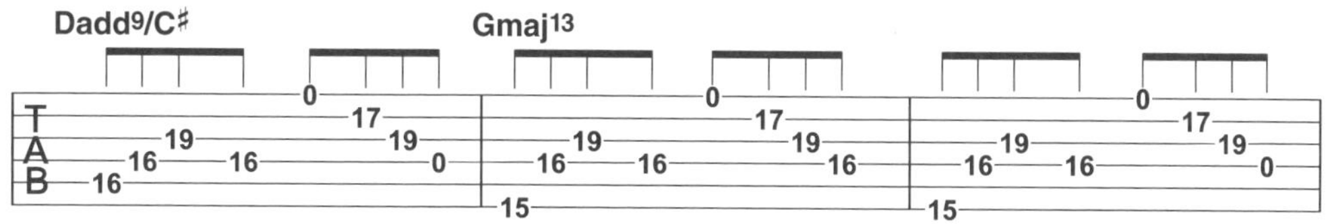

___ and she's call-ing a cab,___ while he's hav-ing a smoke,___ and she's tak-ing a drag.

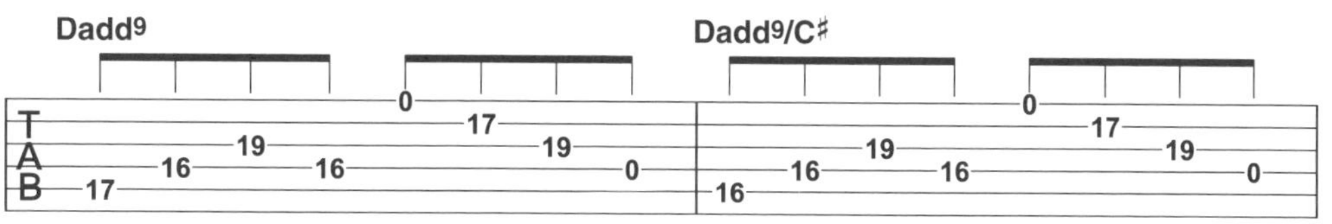

___ Now they're go - ing to bed___ and my sto-mach is sick,_

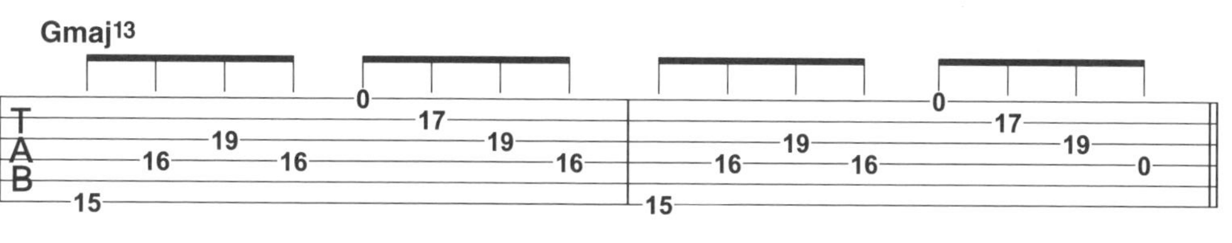

___ and it's all in his head___ but she's touch-ing his

B

Bridge

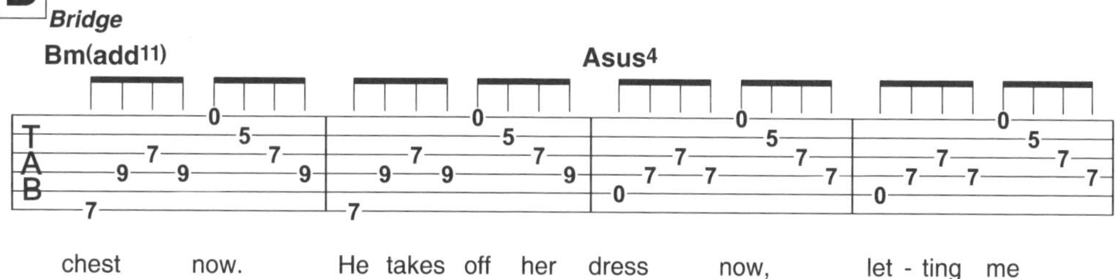

chest now. He takes off her dress now, let - ting me

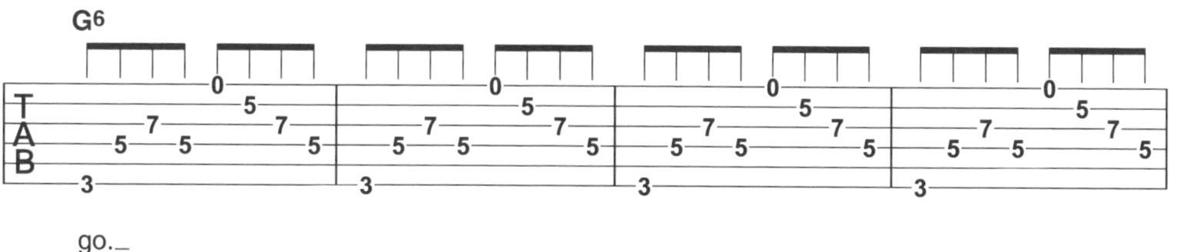

go._

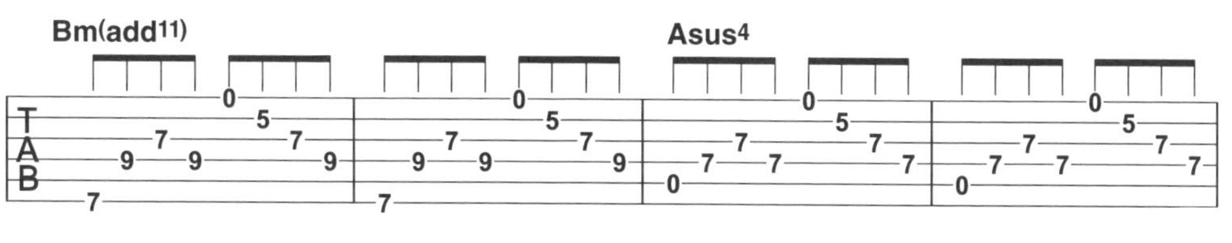

And I just can't look; it's kill - ing me and

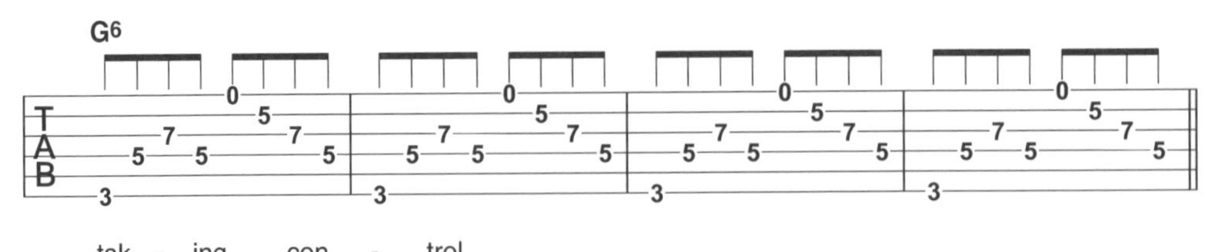

tak - ing_ con - trol.

C

Chorus

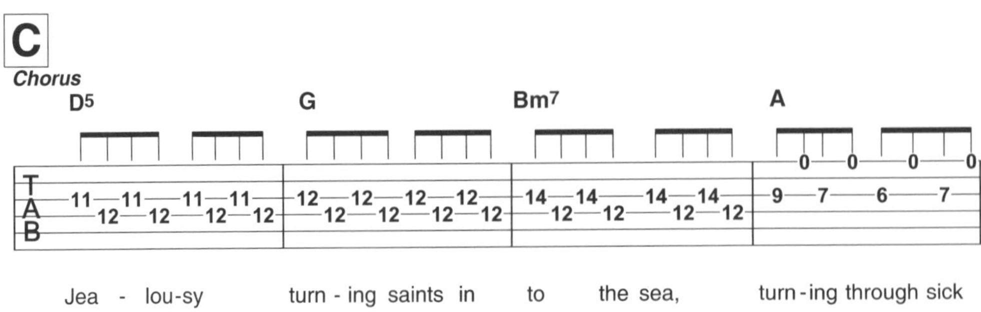

Jea - lou-sy turn - ing saints in to the sea, turn-ing through sick

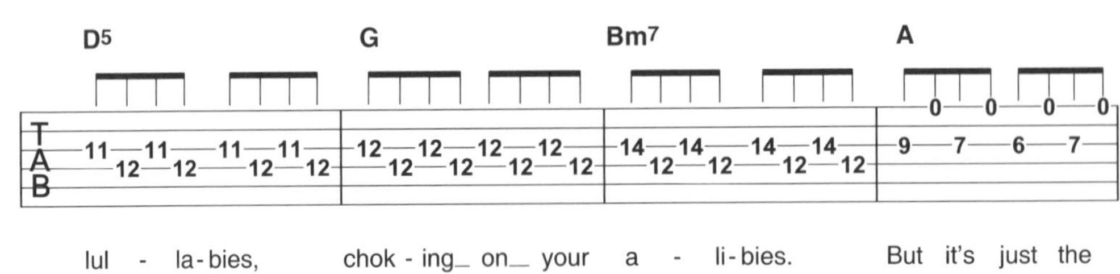

lul - la-bies, chok - ing_ on_ your a - li-bies. But it's just the

D

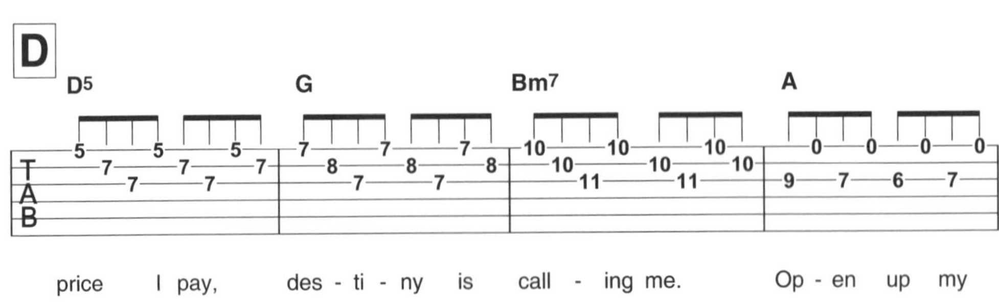

price I pay, des - ti - ny is call - ing me. Op - en up my

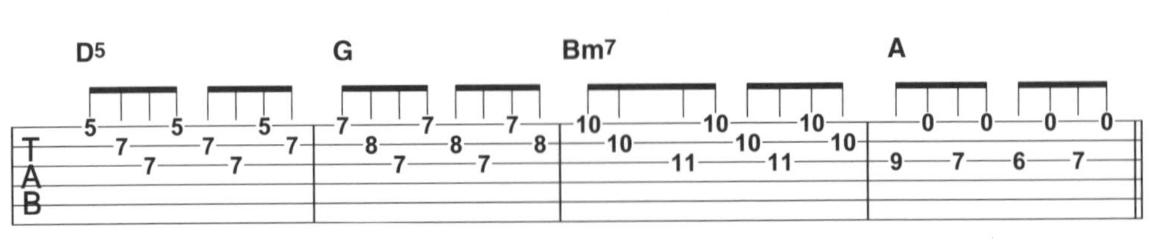

ea - ger_ eyes,_______ 'cause I'm Mis - ter Bright - side.

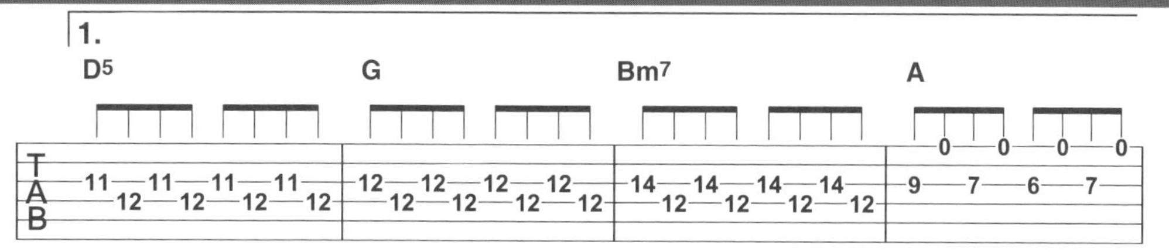

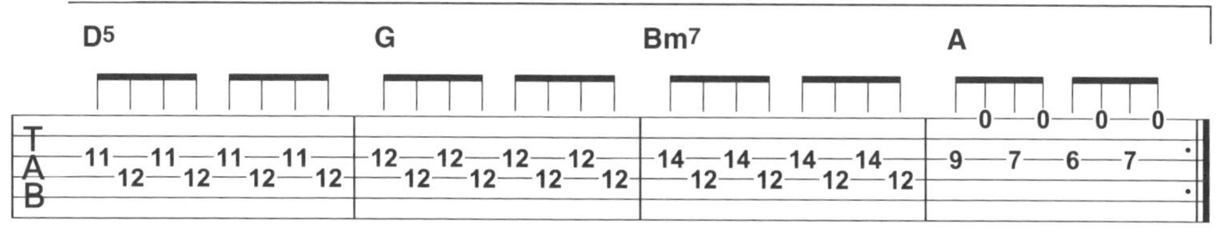

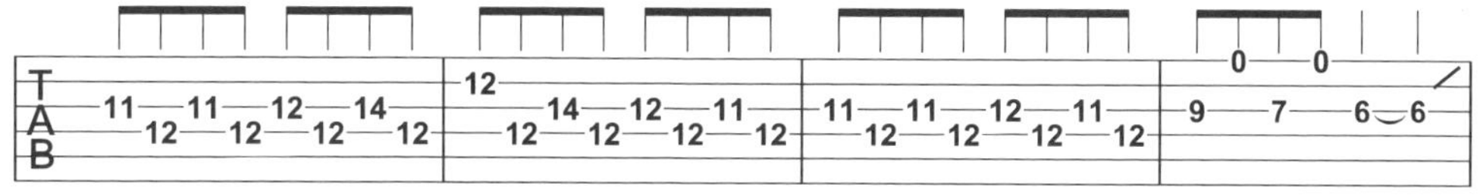

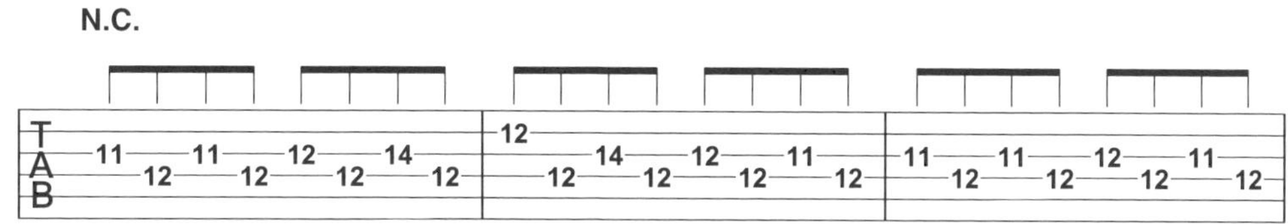

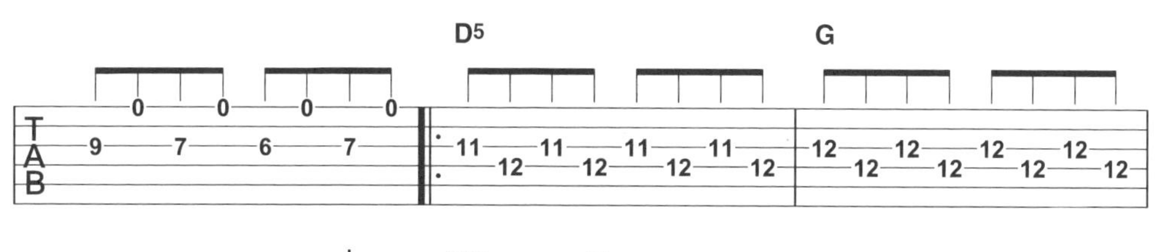

I nev - er.

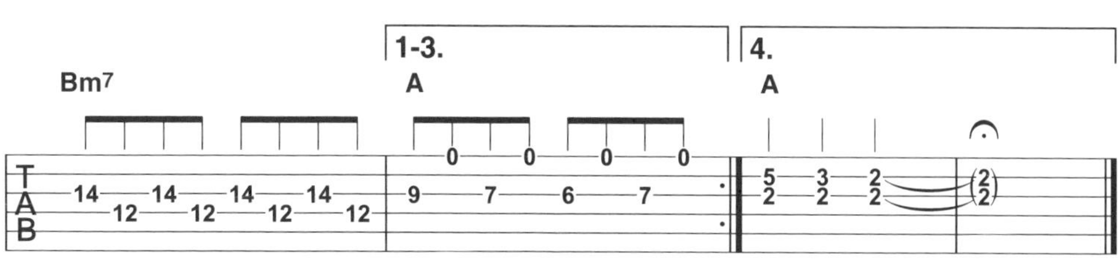

I

Day Tripper

Words & Music by John Lennon & Paul McCartney

Beginner

Intermediate

Intermediate +

TAB

Introduction

The Beatles' 'Day Tripper' features an all-time classic riff, which you'll have a lot of fun learning to play. For maximum enjoyment, I'd also recommend playing the riff along with the original record.

Marker A

The main riff to this song is very bluesy and much like some of the material covered in my '12-Bar Blues Variations' lesson in The Beginner's Course (BC-194). The correct fingering is shown in the TAB—notes on the 3rd fret will be played with your second finger; notes on the 4th fret will be played with your third finger and notes on the 2nd fret will be played with your first finger.

The rhythm is just as important here, so I have added the rhythm count under the first repeat of the main riff (it's exactly same as the first two bars). To get the rhythm right, I would recommend first working methodically on the notes and then once you are confident with them, starting to play the riff in time and in rhythm, but very slowly. Count along out loud and make sure that you are playing the rhythm absolutely correctly—once you are, you can start to speed up.

Also worth noting is the picking—the notes on the beat (1, 2, 3 or 4) will take down-picks and the notes on the ands (+) will take up-picks. Make sure you get this right, as it should help you once you start playing up to speed.

Marker B

Watch out for this little hammer-on—you aren't obliged to include it, but it will sound closer to the original if you do. I used to play the chorus using all down picks, but recent video evidence seems to show George Harrison using alternate-picking, which would explain why on the C♯7 and B7 chords, the chords played on the thickest 3 strings are down-strums and the others are played with an up-strum.

Marker C

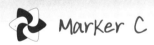

The start of the solo has the riff moved to a new key and there is some debate over where on the fretboard it was played. I have chosen to show you the easier position— for this, use your 3rd finger to slide up from the 5th to 6th fret on the fifth string, then use the 1st finger for the next two notes on the 4th fret, and then move your 1st finger back to the 2nd fret and let the 3rd finger take over duty on 4th fret notes.

There is some footage of George Harrison playing it further up the neck (around the 7th fret) which I think sounds a little closer to the recording, but it's quite a lot harder to play and essentially uses the same notes.

The short lead line solo starts a few bars later with a tone bend on the 5th fret, and you'll then have to hold it while you play the note on the thinnest string. I'd recommend bending with your 3rd finger and playing the note on the thinnest string with your little finger, although I believe that Harrison used his 2nd finger for the bend—it doesn't matter as long as you play the note in tune. For the next section, which is further up the neck, use your 1st and 3rd fingers—the precise fingering should be obvious.

Day Tripper

Words & Music by John Lennon & Paul McCartney

Beginner

Intermediate

Intermediate +

TAB

A

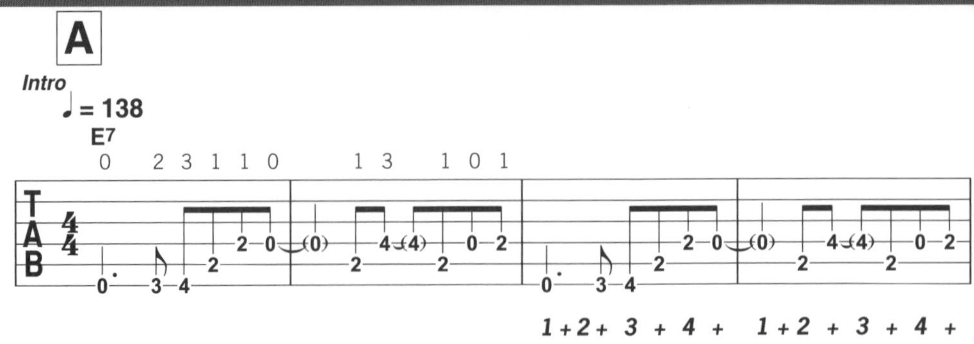

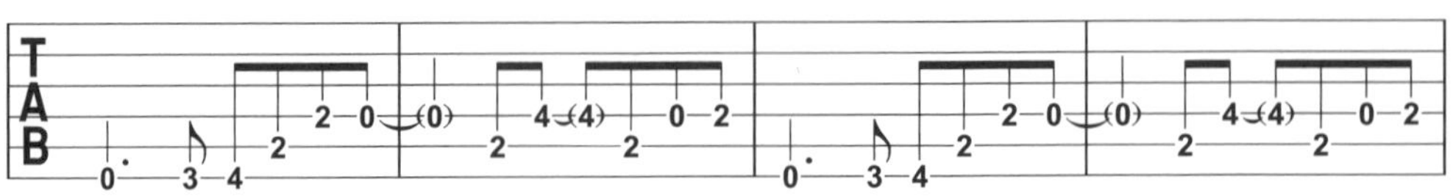

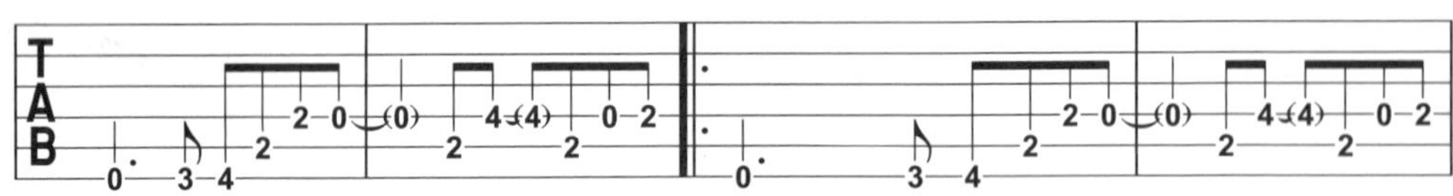

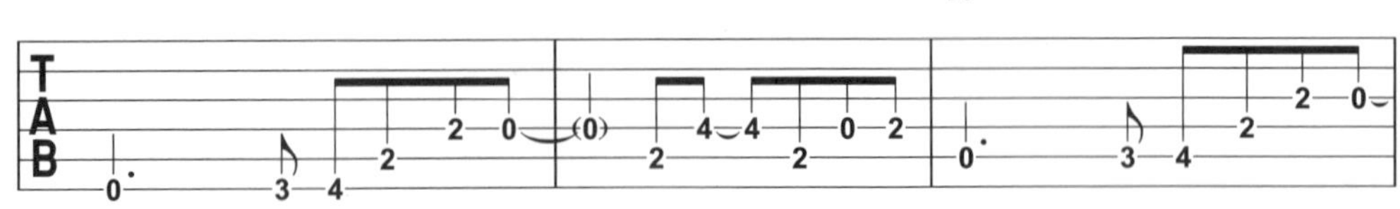

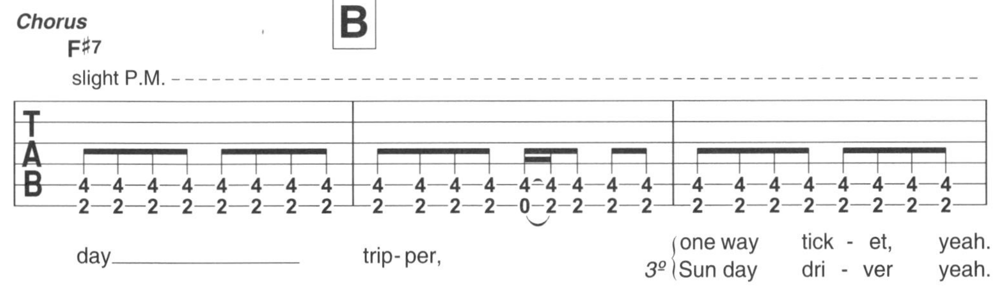
Chorus
B
F♯7
slight P.M.
day
trip-per,
one way tick - et, yeah.
3º Sun day dri - ver yeah.

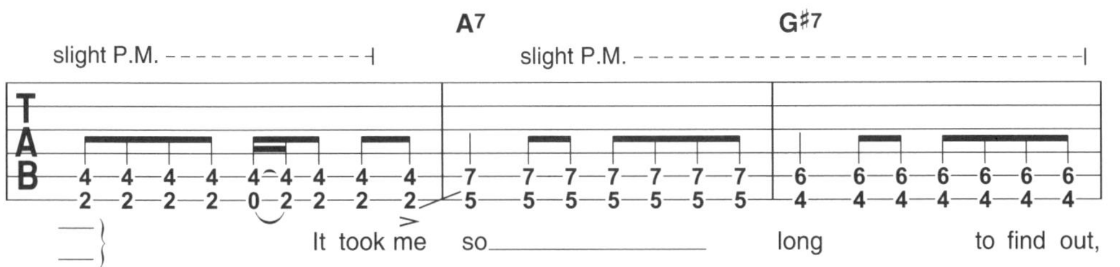
A7
G♯7
slight P.M.
slight P.M.
It took me so
long
to find out,

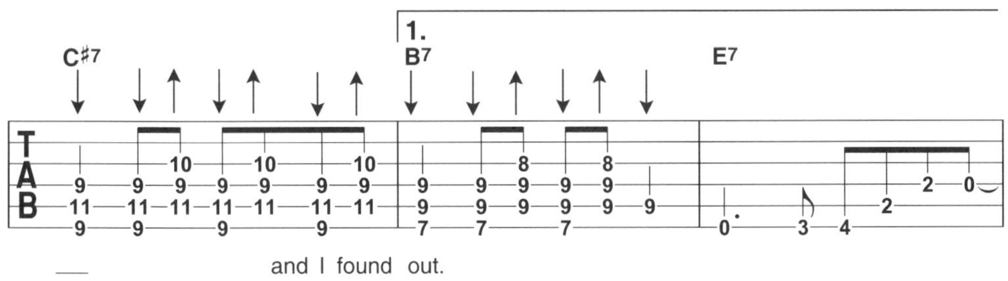
1.
C♯7
B7
E7
and I found out.

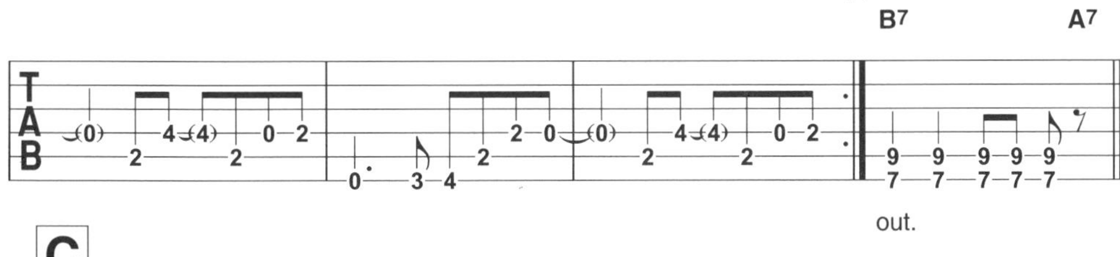
2.
B7
A7
out.

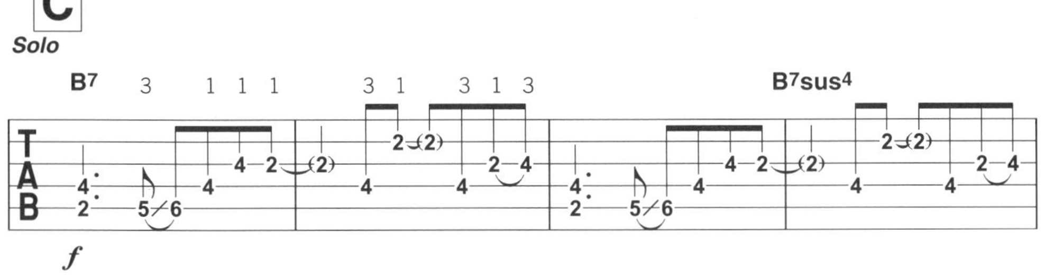
C
Solo
B7
B7sus4
f

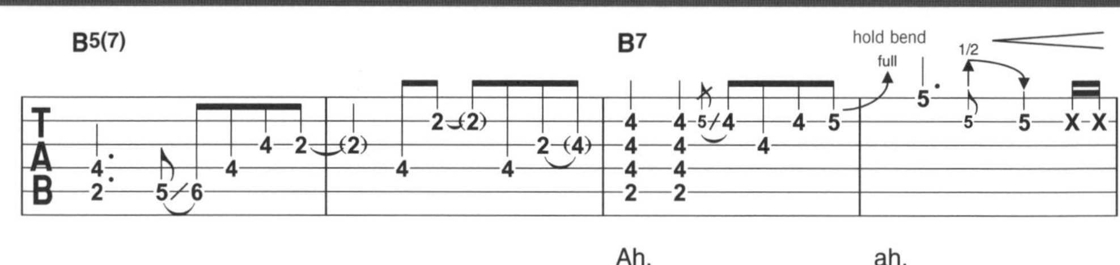
B5(7)
B7
hold bend
full
1/2
Ah,
ah,

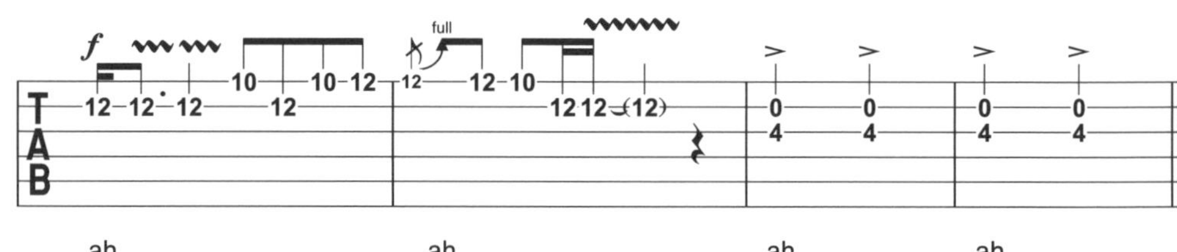
ah,
ah,
ah,
ah.

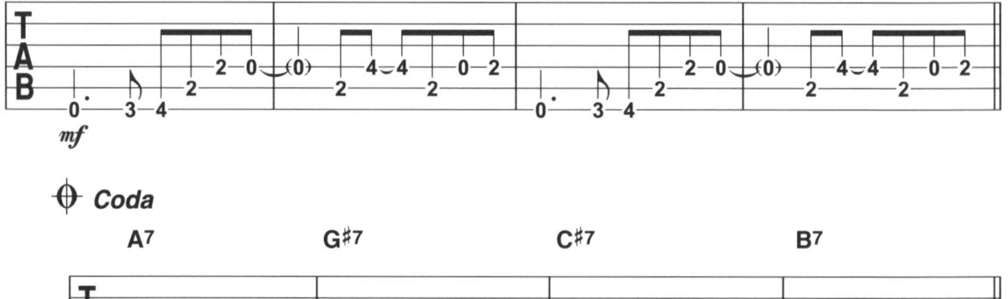
E7
D.S. al Coda
Coda
A7
G♯7
C♯7
B7
so
long
to find out,
and I found out.

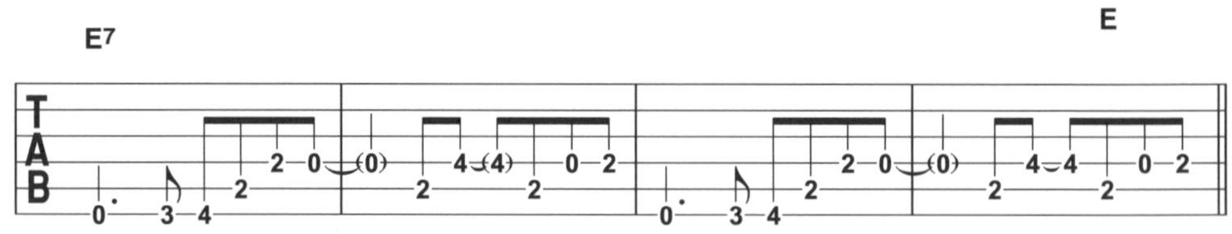
E7
E

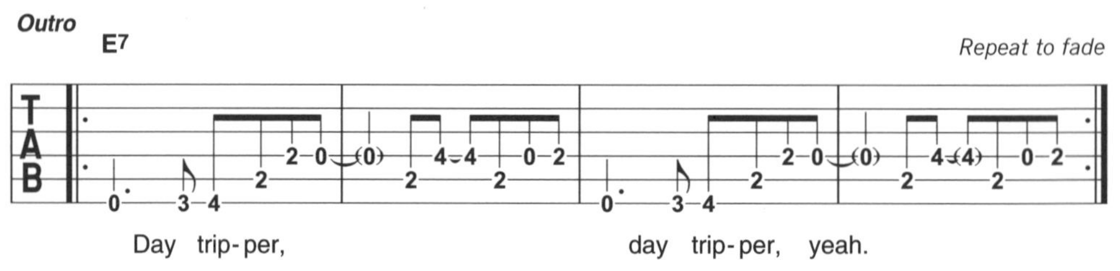
Outro
E7
Repeat to fade
Day trip-per,
day trip-per, yeah.

Someone Like You

Words & Music by Adele Adkins & Daniel Wilson

Introduction

Adele's signature song is a really big ballad, which works very well on guitar, even though it was originally written for piano accompaniment.

The Arrangement

What we've presented here is the original piano part arranged for guitar; the TAB displays pretty much exactly the notes that are played by the piano, with only a few minor alterations made in order to make the part playable on the guitar.

To play the TAB accurately you are going to have to play fingerstyle. That being said, we've also included chord symbols, in case you want to include some strumming.

Marker A

The main fingerstyle pattern is two bars long, although there are some minor variations to the part. Start by playing the first two notes together, using your thumb and index fingers (p & i), then middle, ring, middle (m, a, m). This pattern is repeated, and then repeated a further three times but without the thumb playing the low bass note. If you really struggle with this pattern, you might start by leaving out the thumb notes, and then adding them in later—but get the thumb notes in as soon as you can, as they will help with the flow of the pattern.

Marker B

As you work through the song, you will find that there are some awkward chord grips —some are hard because of the position of the fretting hand fingers, such as the D shown at Marker B, which is in fact a C-shape barre chord (below right).

Sometimes the chords are tricky because the fingers picking the strings have to skip over a string not played. These patterns aren't very instinctive, but because we're playing an arrangement of a piano part on guitar, we can expect a few challenges. If you really find these patterns hard, it's fine to simplify them and just play strings grouped together, as long as you are holding the correct chord notes with your fretting hand.

Feel free to experiment too. It's a great idea to make these arrangements your own and change them a bit—don't feel too tied to performing the exact arrangement.

Marker C

At this point we get some really 'stretchy' and tricky chords. Putting your 3rd finger up on the 4th fret of the Eadd9 and your 1st finger back on the 1st fret is a big stretch, but if you can do this, then you can leave that 3rd finger down for the whole 9-bar section. This will give you an anchor finger to help with the chord changes. But, it is a big stretch and if you can't reach it then you'll just have to jump quickly between chords!

Note that for that last Esus2/D (which only happens the second time) you can use one big barre and use your 2nd finger on the bass note, or keep your hand as it was for the D before it but slide your first finger up two frets—this will feel a little cramped but might be easier than jumping to the big barre. See what works for you.

Marker D

There are some very awkward jumps here between chords. If I was performing this song then I would almost certainly fiddle the arrangement to help it flow a little more, and quite possibly move the Bm barre chord lower, and instead use the A shape at the 2nd fret (see below) which means that some of the notes would change but it would make the chord changes easier and therefore help the guitar part become smoother and more comfortable to play.

After Marker D

This second last chorus is a breakdown, where the mood becomes far more mellow, before the song launches into the big final chorus, so play these chords delicately and don't grab at them. If you can, try to spread out the notes a bit—roll through them, playing thumb, index, middle and ring finger in quick succession.

The most important thing is to be aware of the dynamics—play the verses quietly so that you can build up to the choruses and make them big and powerful.

Chord Boxes

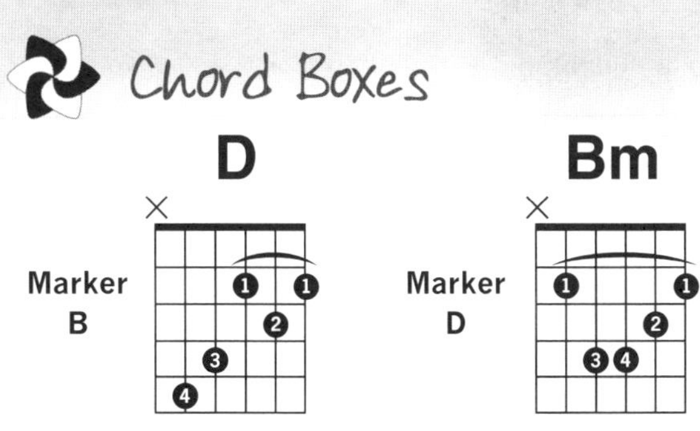

Someone Like You

Words & Music by Adele Adkins & Daniel Wilson

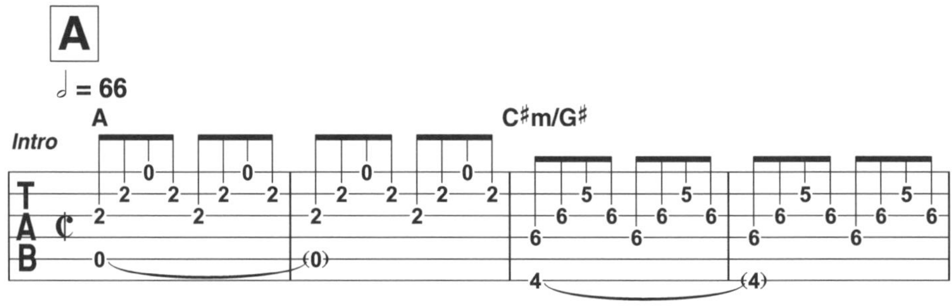
A
♩ = 66
Intro
A
C♯m/G♯

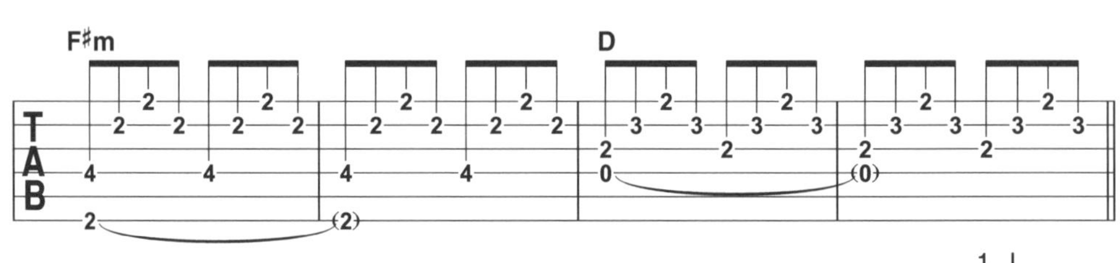
F♯m
D
1. I

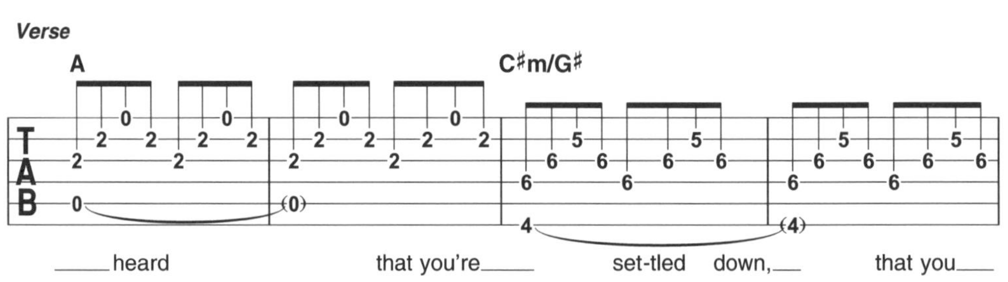
Verse
A
C♯m/G♯
heard that you're set-tled down, that you

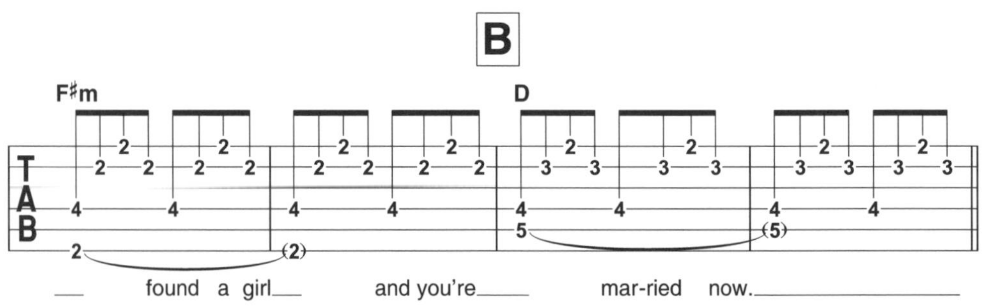
B
F♯m
D
found a girl and you're mar-ried now.

Beginner
Intermediate
Intermediate +
TAB

Verse

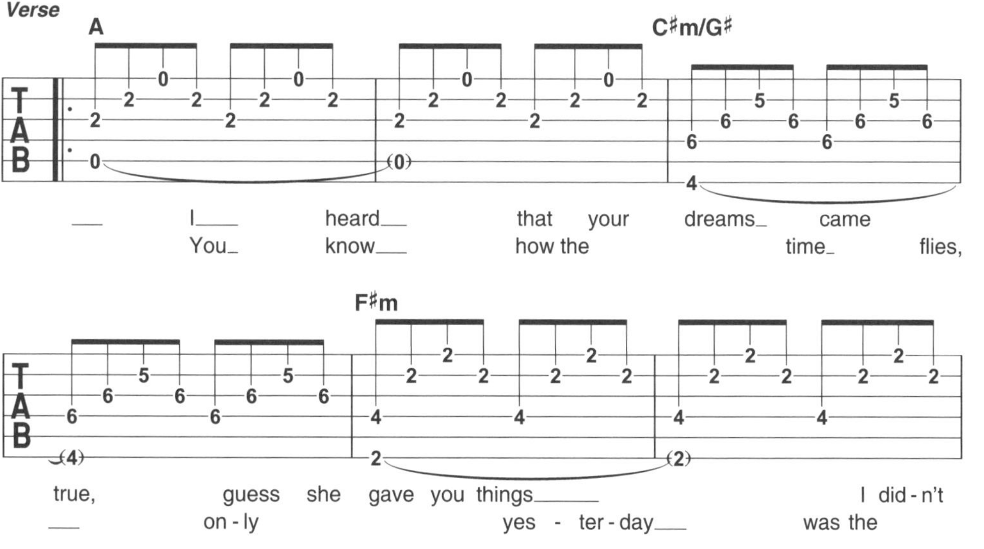
A
C♯m/G♯
T A B
I heard that your dreams came
You know how the time flies,
F♯m
true, guess she gave you things I did-n't
on-ly yes - ter-day was the

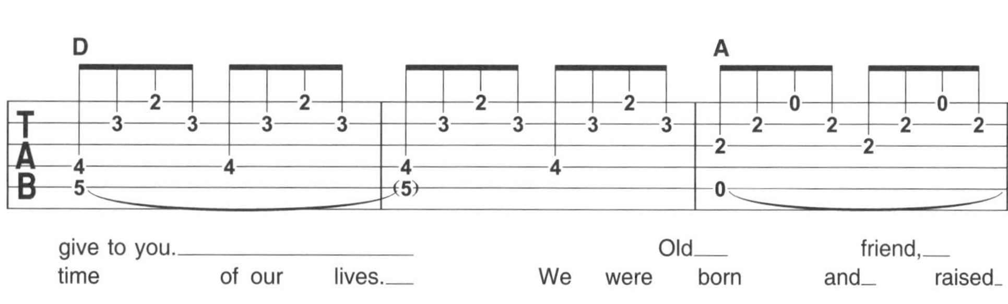
D
A
give to you. Old friend,
time of our lives. We were born and raised

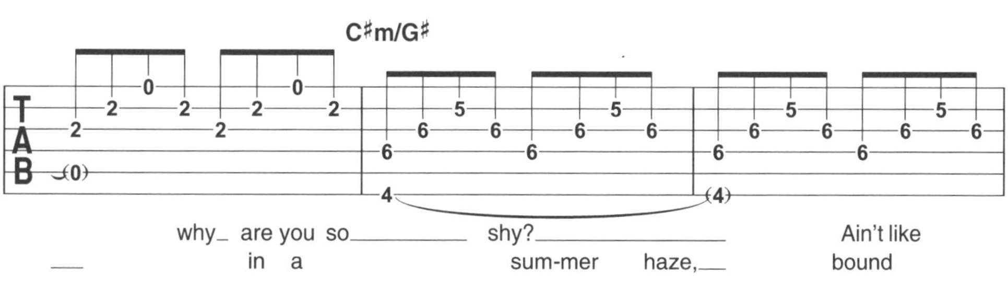
C♯m/G♯
why are you so shy? Ain't like
in a sum-mer haze, bound

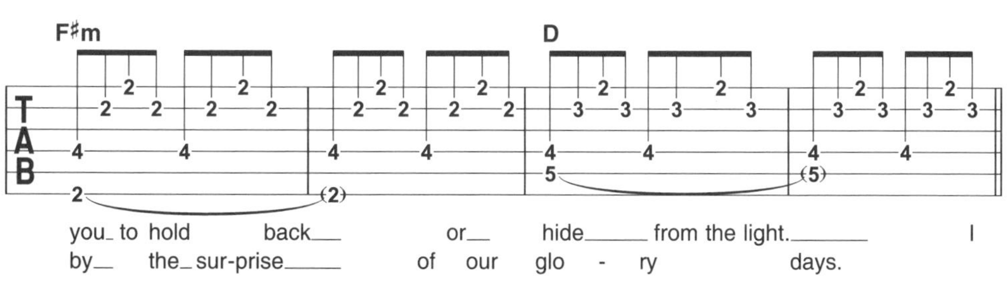
F♯m
D
you to hold back or hide from the light. I
by the sur-prise of our glo - ry days.

C

Pre Chorus

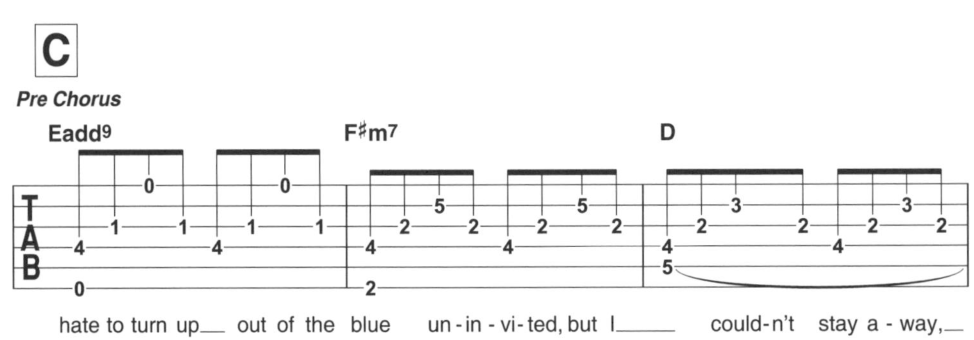
Eadd9
F♯m7
D
hate to turn up out of the blue un-in-vi-ted, but I could-n't stay a-way,

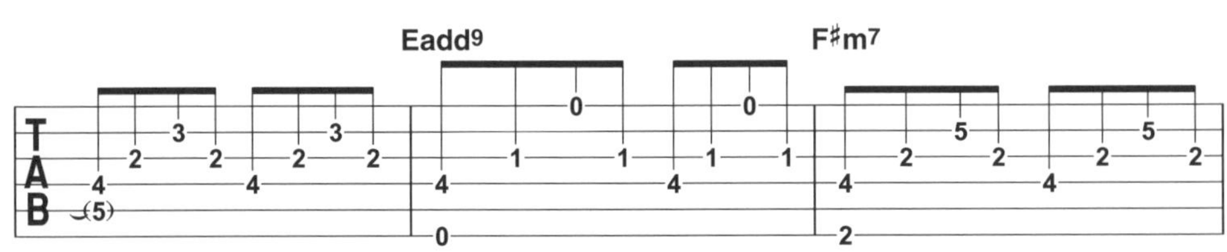
Eadd9
F♯m7
I could-n't fight it. I had hoped you'd see my face and that you'd be re-mind-ed that for

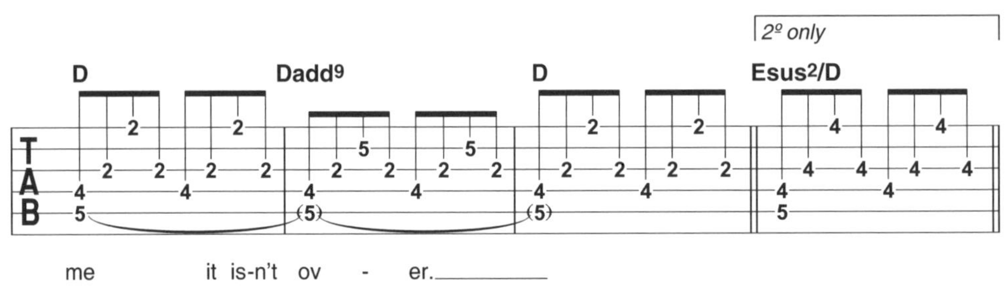
2º only
D
Dadd9
D
Esus2/D
me it is-n't ov - er.

Chorus

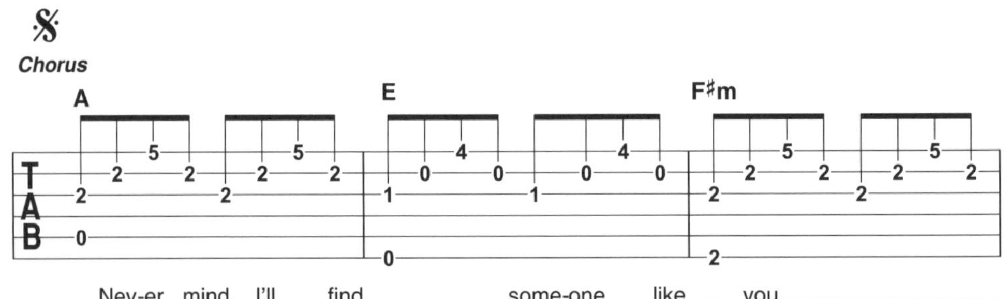
A
E
F♯m
Nev-er mind, I'll find some-one like you,

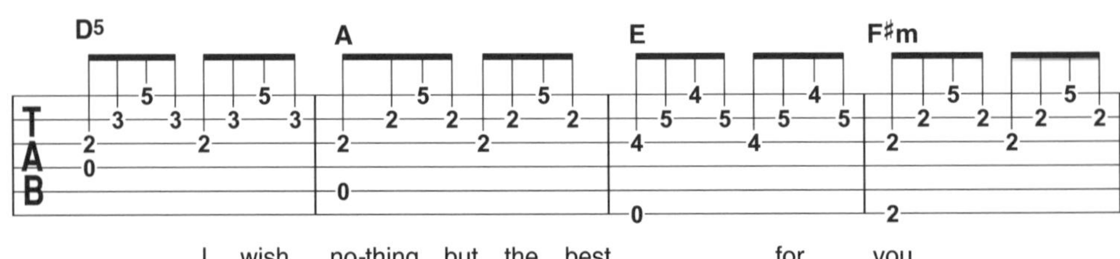
D5
A
E
F♯m
I wish no-thing but the best for you

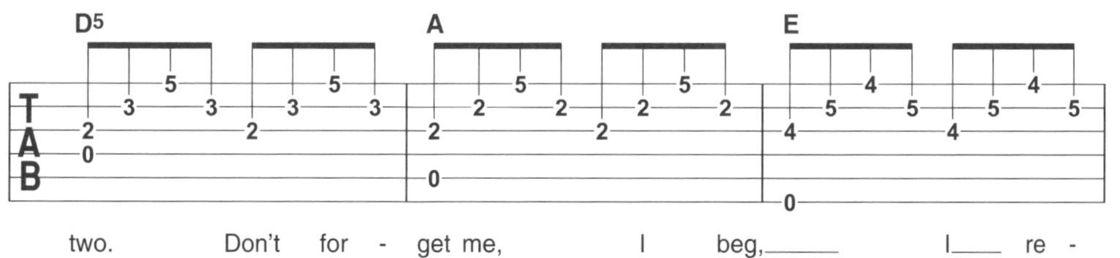
D5 A E
two. Don't for - get me, I beg,___ I___ re -

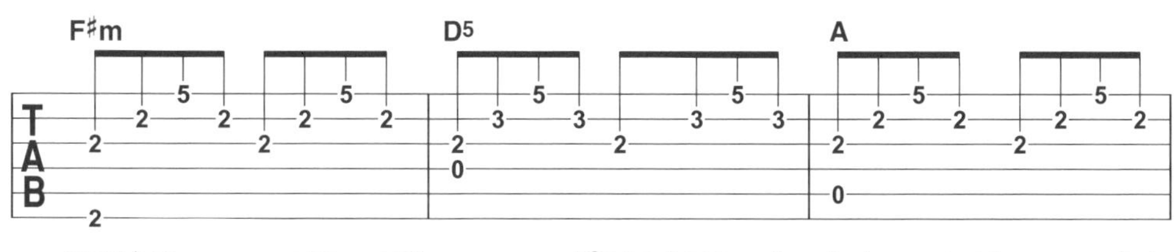
F♯m D5 A
-mem-ber_______ you_ said,__ "Some-times it lasts___ and loves, but

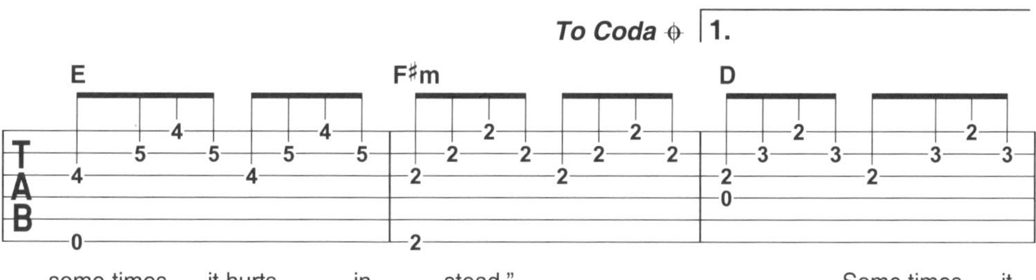
To Coda
1.
E F♯m D
some-times it hurts in - stead."________________ Some-times it

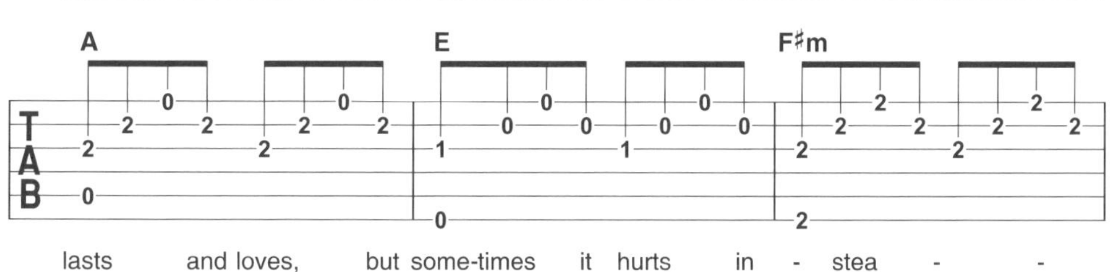
A E F♯m
lasts and loves, but some-times it hurts in - stea - -

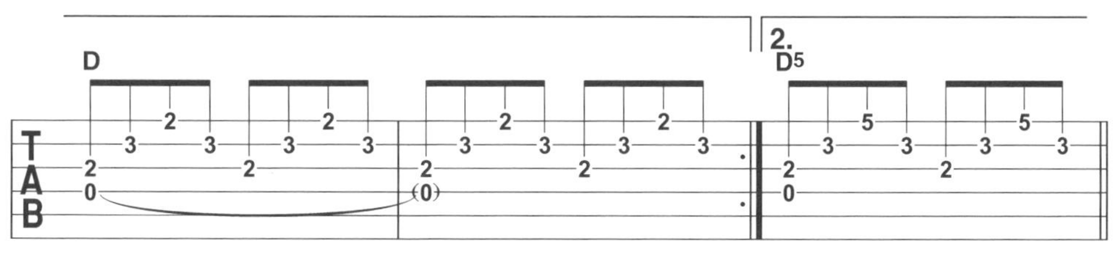
2.
D D5
- ead.

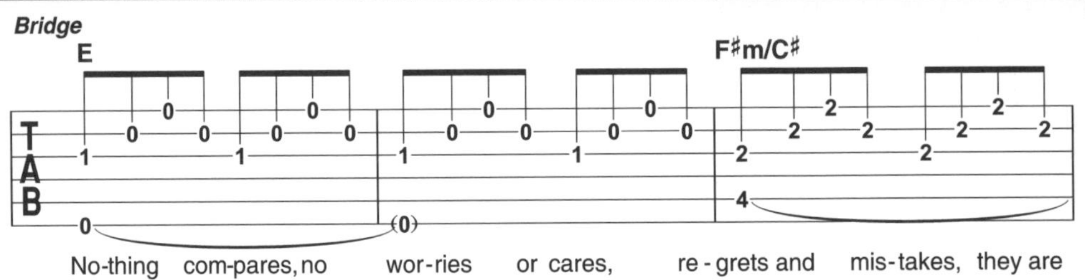
Bridge
E
F♯m/C♯
TAB
No-thing com-pares, no wor-ries or cares, re - grets and mis-takes, they are

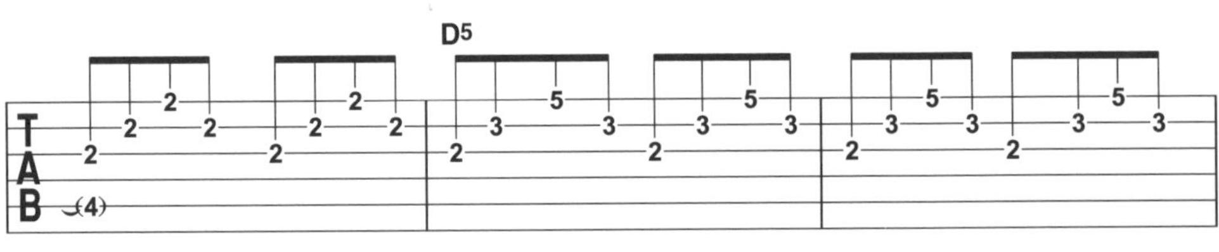
D5
TAB
me - mo-ries made. Who would have known how bit-ter - sweet

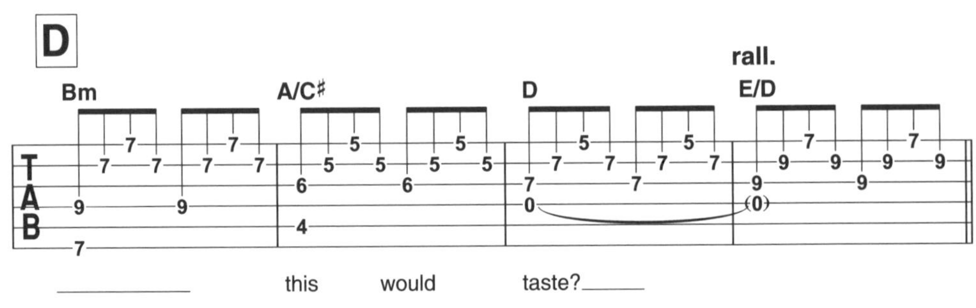
D
rall.
Bm
A/C♯
D
E/D
TAB
this would taste?

Chorus

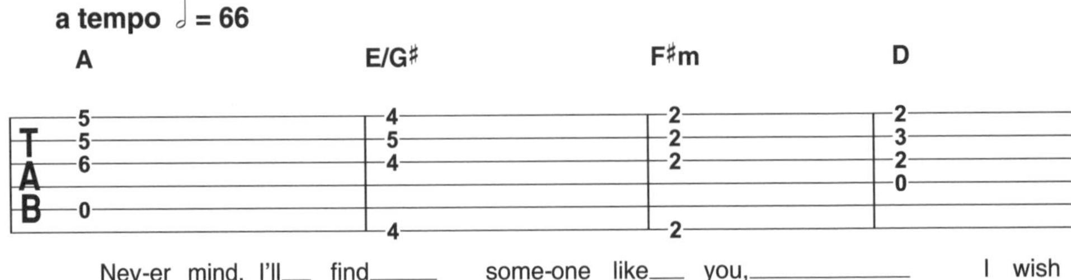
a tempo 𝅗𝅥 = 66
A
E/G♯
F♯m
D
TAB
Nev-er mind, I'll find some-one like you, I wish

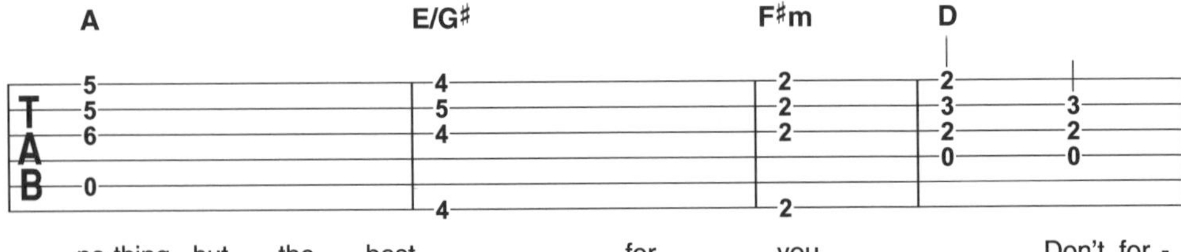
A
E/G♯
F♯m
D
TAB
no-thing but the best for you. Don't for -

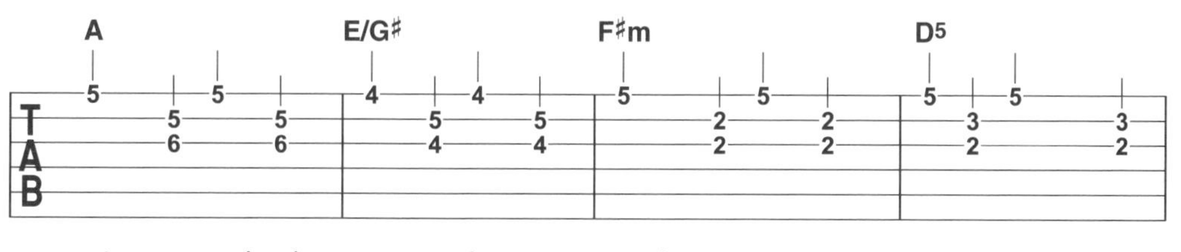

-get me, I beg,____ I__ re - mem-ber____ you_ said,__ "Some-times it

D.S. al Coda

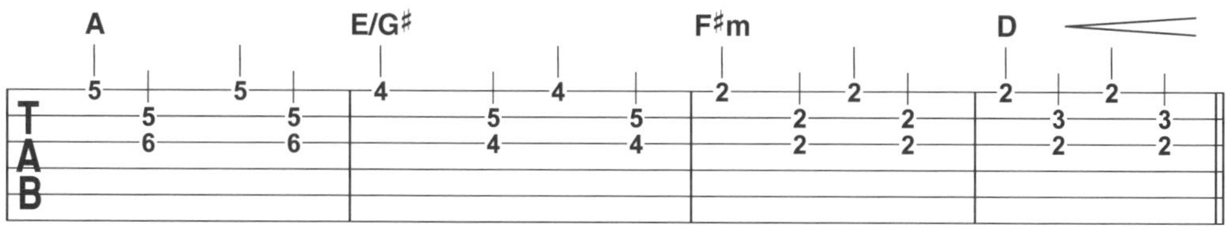

lasts and loves, but some-times it hurts in - stead."________

Coda

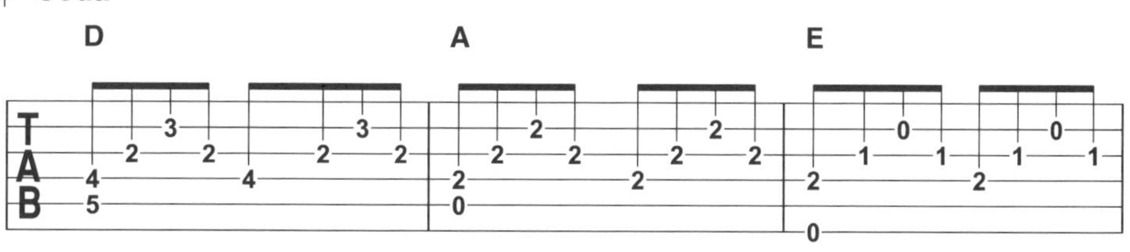

Some-times it lasts and loves, but some-times it hurts in-

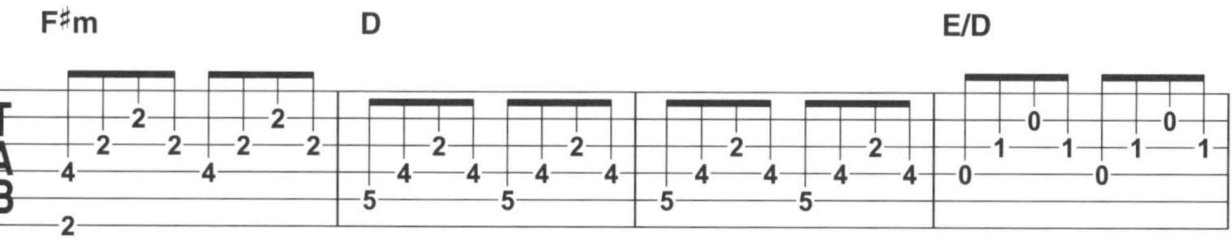

- stead.____________

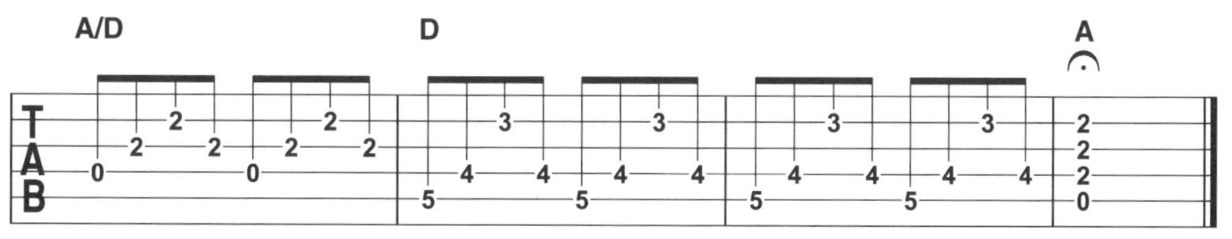

Beat It

Words & Music by Michael Jackson

Beginner

Intermediate

Intermediate +

TAB

Introduction

Featuring not one, but two 80s guitar gods on the original recording, Michael Jackson's 'Beat It' was one of the huge-selling singles off *Thriller* (1984).

Where To Start?

Not only is this song a true pop hit, but it also features some awesome guitar playing and a solo by Eddie Van Halen! The majority of the song is not too tricky, but the solo is properly challenging, using finger tapping, tapped harmonics and other rock techniques. Steve Lukather (of Toto fame, and one of the greatest session guitarists of all time) did much of the rhythm guitar playing on the track, which explains why it's so fantastic!

Probably the hardest thing about the solo is the rhythm. The rhythm is 'loose but in time' which is a trademark of Eddie Van Halen's style of playing. Getting some of the stretches and complex passages under your fingers is difficult, but playing with the right time feel is the hardest part for most people.

It is most important to break down the song, looking at it bit by bit. There are many techniques to explore and master, so take your time and enjoy the ride!

Marker A

Figure 1 is the main riff—there is nothing too tricky about it, but make sure you get the rhythm tight. To get the right feel you really need to listen and play along with the original recording. Make sure you keep the staccato notes (shown with a dot above the note) tight and short.

Marker B

While the main part continues to play the riff, there is an overdubbed guitar part that plays a very cool little diad (two note) riff. Note the muted parts, which work with the main riff to create a great groove. Once you get to the verse, you have three R5 power chords (E5, D5 and C5) followed by a simple palm-muted riff.

Marker C

Please bear in mind that this solo was improvised, therefore playing this solo exactly note-for-note is going to be pretty tricky and I doubt that Van Halen played it exactly the same way twice anyway! There are many techniques used in this song and I won't have space here to describe each in detail, but most of the techniques have lessons on the main website.

The solo starts with the whammy bar depressed until the strings are slack and slowly returned to pitch as you place your finger on the 4th fret. I use my 2nd finger to fret the note with the 1st finger behind to mute the rest of the strings, otherwise you get a whole lot of unwanted noise.

You then have two tapped harmonics, where you will tap on the 24th fret—you have to tap accurately, hard and fast to get the harmonic ringing out, and plenty of distortion and volume will help too!

Marker D

Now we get to our first finger tapping lick. Make sure you play this very slowly to get the pattern under your fingers correctly, and be sure to identify the note sequences which will help you remember it. There are lessons on tapping on the website (Lesson RO-001) which explain the technique in full.

Marker E

This next section requires a big stretch—it's right at my limit and I struggle, but it'll be easy for people with long or dexterous digits! Again you must practise this slowly and carefully, getting it right and then slowly working it up to tempo. There is another pattern in the middle, so it's worth working on that too, over and over, then joining it with the entry and exit!

Marker F

Next up we have some bluesy licks followed by another Van Halen trademark, the 'Tap 'n' Slide' where he taps the 15th fret and slides it up the neck, flicking it off at the end of the fretboard back to the note he started on (now played by the 3rd finger). It's a super cool trick and one you should explore more because it sounds great! There is also a 'Dive Bomb' at the end, playing the open G string and then lowering the whammy bar until the string is slack—this became a very popular 90s rock technique.

Marker G

Now we have an Artificial Harmonic (AH), commonly called Pinch Harmonic or 'Squealy' (this is covered on the website, in Lesson TE-012). It's played with a bend and followed by a flick off (pull-off) and then a whammy bar dip. This lick sounds great and is well worth practising on its own, as you're sure to use it in your own improvisations!

Marker H

This lick uses a series of whammy bar dips followed by an artificial harmonic squeal. I've often seen this played with a 3rd fret bend rather than the whammy dips at the 5th fret, and it might be right, but I'm pretty sure it's the whammy bar dips...either can sound right, so you might like to try using 3rd fret bends if the whammy technique doesn't work for you.

Marker I

Blues rock licks ahoy! Here we have some pretty classic E minor pentatonic licks with a rock tilt that sound awesome. It will take you some practice to get it just like the record but it's not too tricky!

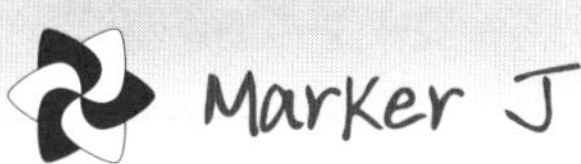

Marker J

We have another monster tapping lick here. Like the last tapping lick, you just have to take your time, playing it very slowly over and over to get the muscle memory working and then gradually speeding it up. There is no 'trick' for this kind of stuff, just slow and careful practice!

Marker K

The solo finishes with some tremolo picking, which is very fast picking on one note. The solo starts with a unison bend, but then rips into a run up the thinnest string, picking each note as fast as possible until the big climax bend, before doing a pick slide down the thickest string to join the rhythm part again! Van Halen played the tremolo picking in quite a unique way (I seem to recall him calling it 'butterfly picking') so it's worth watching some videos of him doing this (he also uses the technique in 'Eruption' and there are many videos around of him playing that) but I've found that technique awkward so I just pick as fast as I can and it usually sounds right!

Beat It

Words & Music by Michael Jackson

Beginner
Intermediate
Intermediate +
TAB

Moderately fast (♩ = 136)

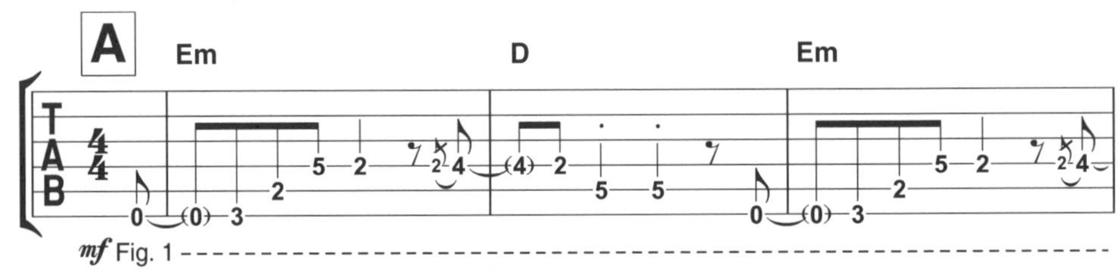
A
Em
D
Em
TAB
mf Fig. 1

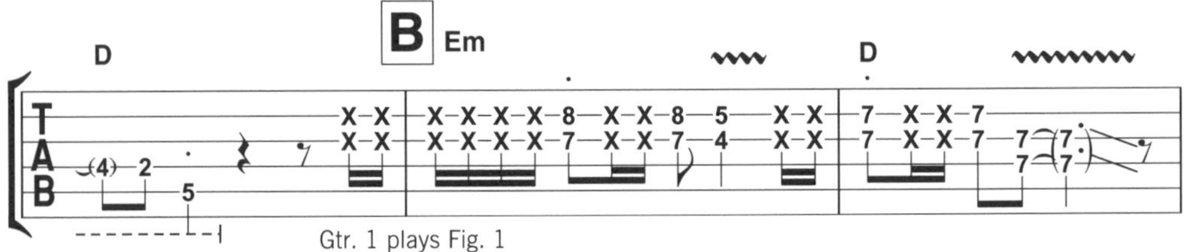
D
B
Em
D
TAB
Gtr. 1 plays Fig. 1

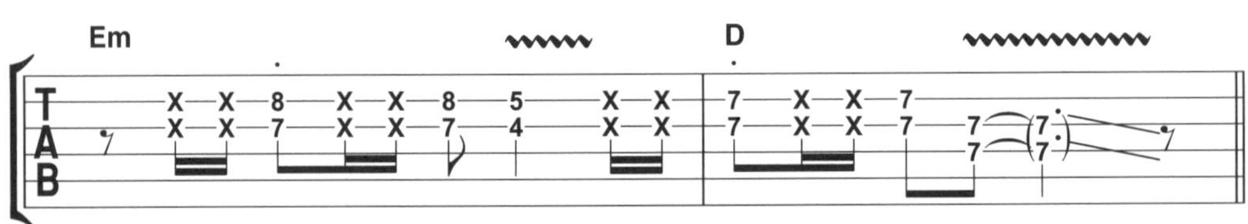
Em
D
TAB

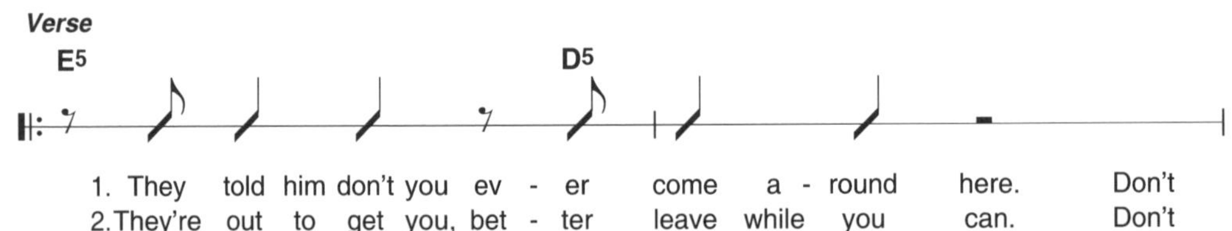
Verse
E5
D5
1. They told him don't you ev - er come a - round here. Don't
2. They're out to get you, bet - ter leave while you can. Don't

E5
D5
C5
D5

wan-na see your face, you bet-ter dis-ap-pear. The fi-re's in their eyes and their
wan-na be a boy, you wan-na be a man. You wan-na stay a - live, bet - ter

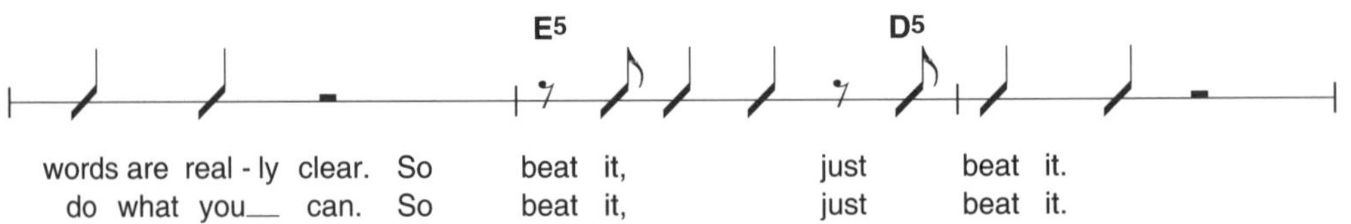
E5
D5
words are real - ly clear. So beat it, just beat it.
do what you__ can. So beat it, just beat it.

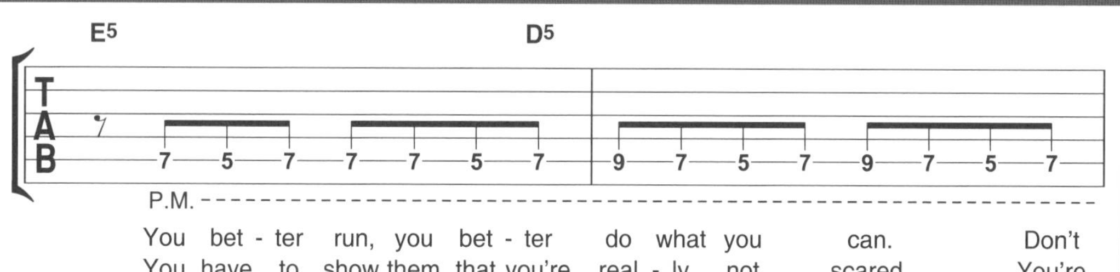
E5
D5
P.M.
You bet - ter run, you bet - ter do what you can. Don't
You have to show them that you're real - ly not scared. You're

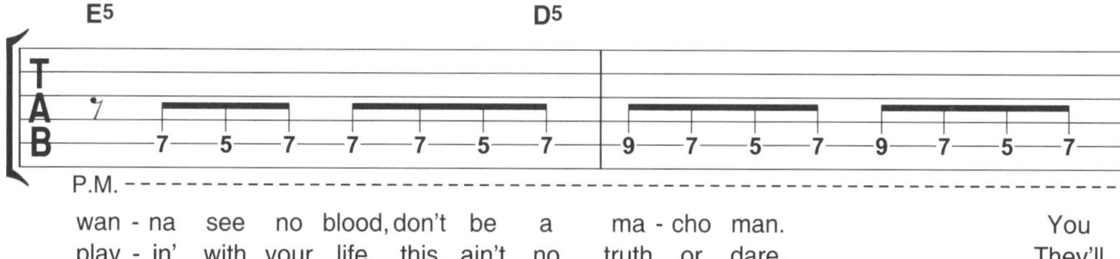
E5
D5
P.M.
wan - na see no blood, don't be a ma - cho man. You
play - in' with your life, this ain't no truth or dare. They'll

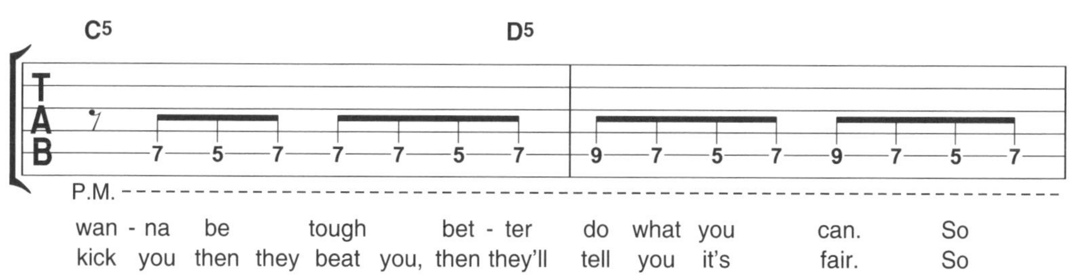
C5
D5
P.M.
wan - na be tough bet - ter do what you can. So
kick you then they beat you, then they'll tell you it's fair. So

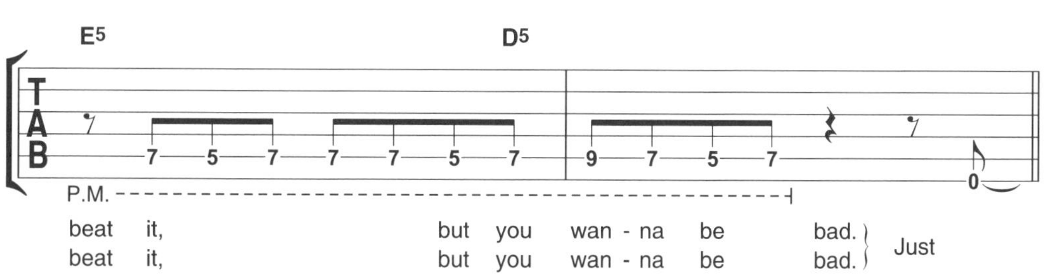
E5
D5
P.M.
beat it, but you wan - na be bad.
beat it, but you wan - na be bad.
Just

Chorus

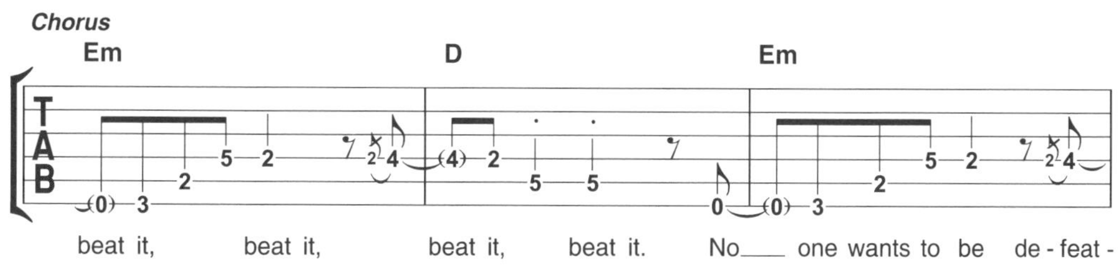
Em
D
Em
beat it, beat it, beat it, beat it. No___ one wants to be de - feat -

Beginner

Intermediate

Intermediate +

TAB

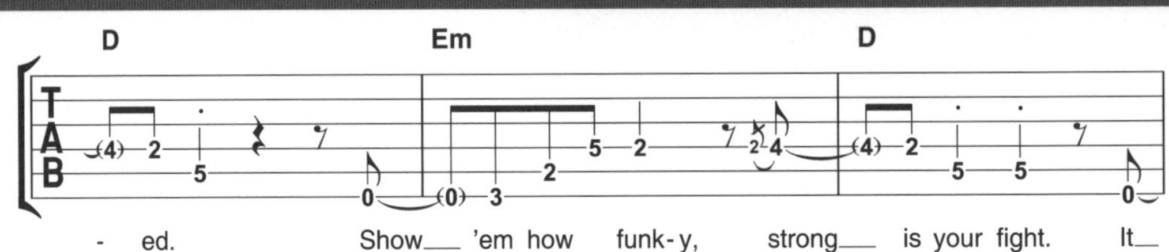
D
Em
D
T
A
B
- ed. Show 'em how funk-y, strong is your fight. It

1.
Em
D
Em
does-n't mat-ter, who's wrong or right. Just beat it, beat it. Just

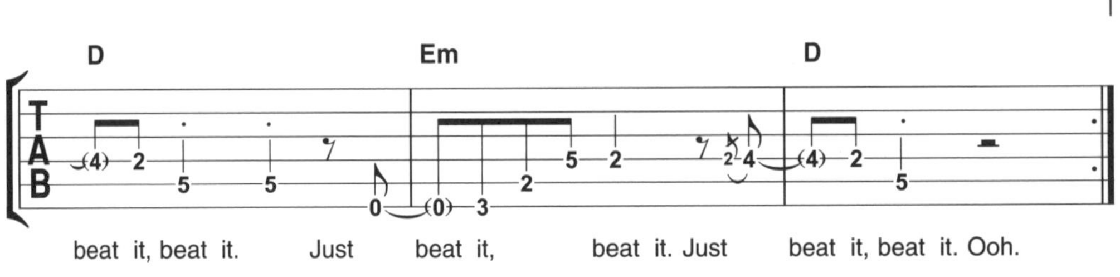
D
Em
D
beat it, beat it. Just beat it, beat it. Just beat it, beat it. Ooh.

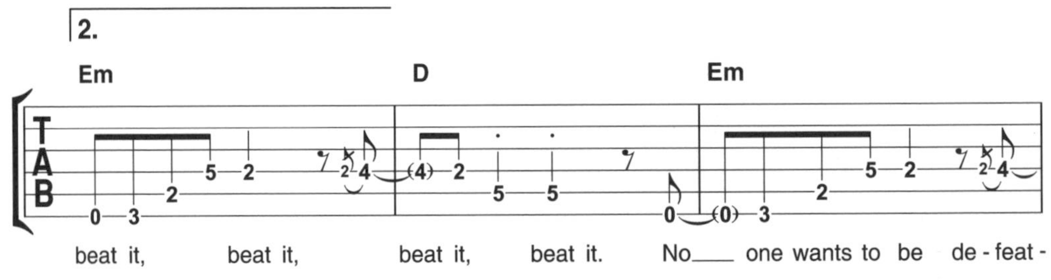
2.
Em
D
Em
beat it, beat it, beat it, beat it. No one wants to be de-feat-

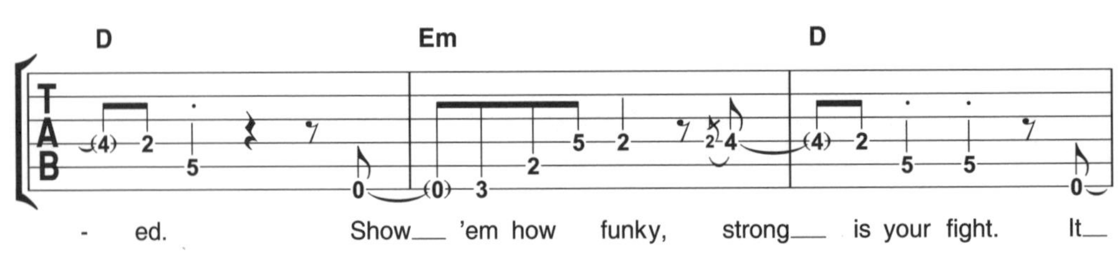
D
Em
D
- ed. Show 'em how funky, strong is your fight. It

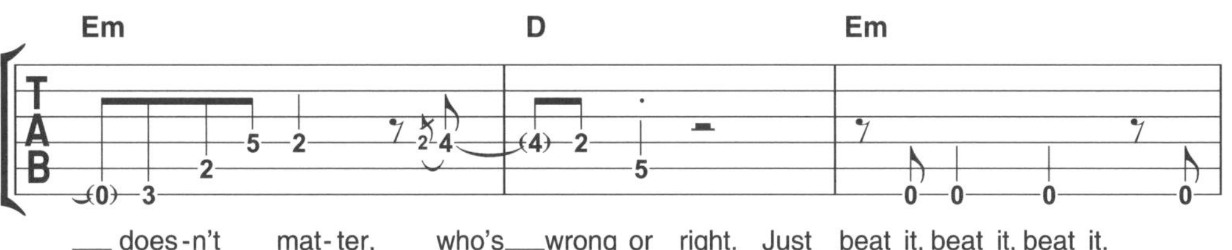
Em
D
Em
T
A
B
___ does-n't mat-ter, who's___wrong or right. Just beat it, beat it, beat it.

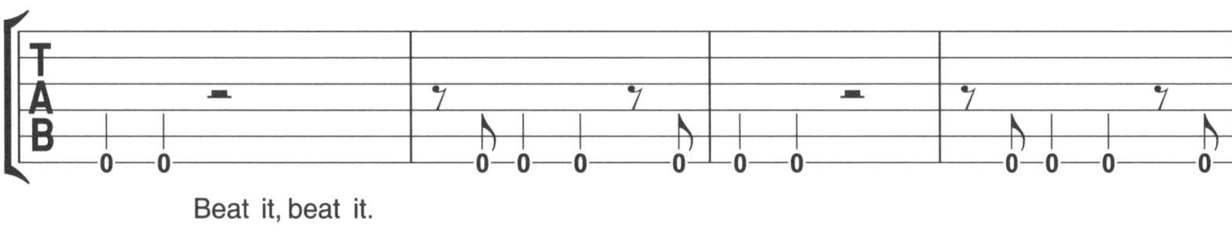
T
A
B
Beat it, beat it.

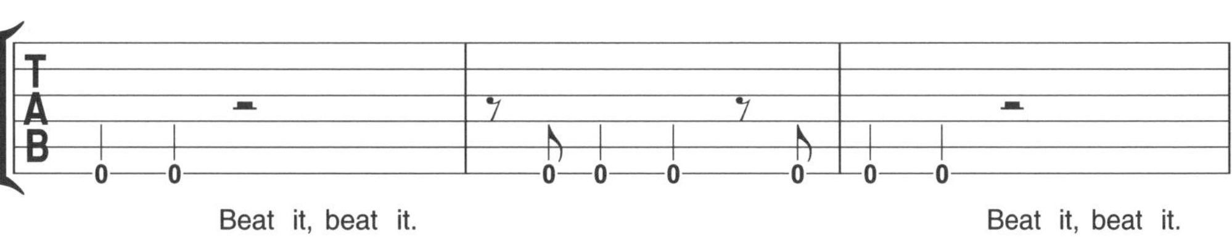
T
A
B
Beat it, beat it.
Beat it, beat it.

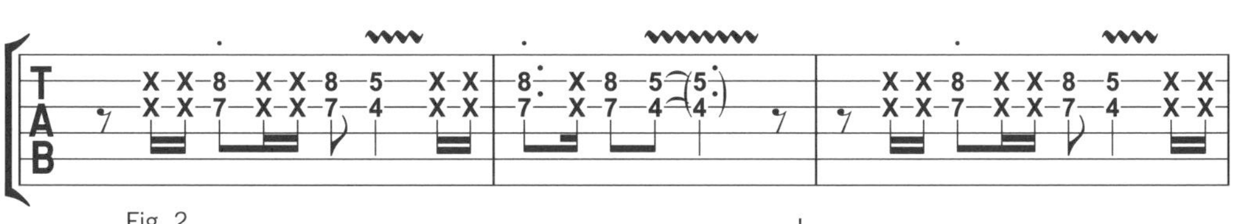
T
A
B
Fig. 2

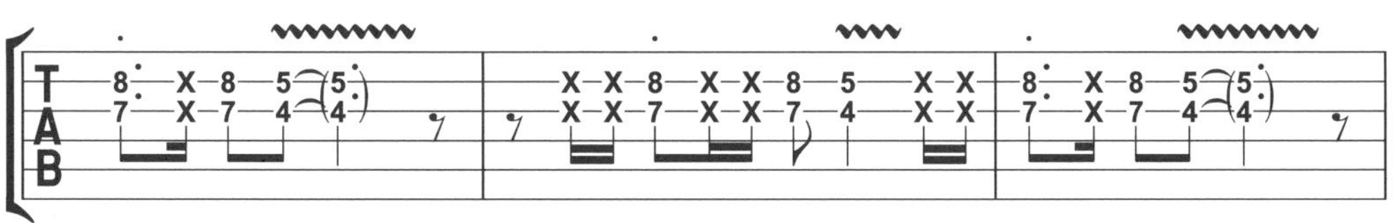
T
A
B

Beginner

Intermediate

Intermediate +

TAB

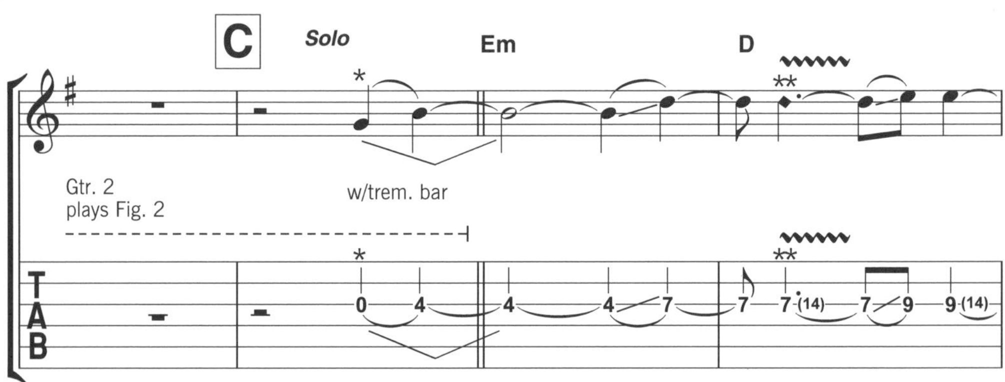

* Depress bar to slack, strike note and gradually release bar, then slide up to D note.

** While holding note with L.H. tap fret 14 w/index finger of R.H. right above fret wire and immediately pull finger away.

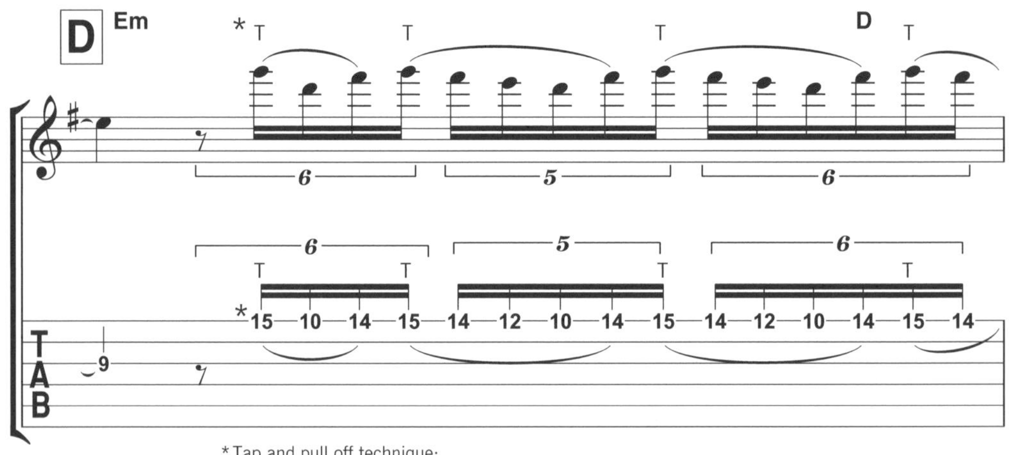

* Tap and pull off technique:
Tap first note in group (T), pull off (P) to 2nd note and then slur remaining notes in group.

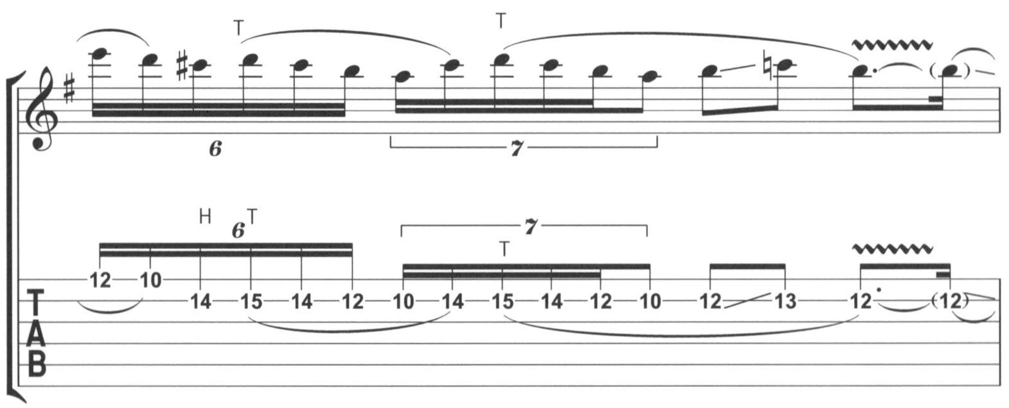

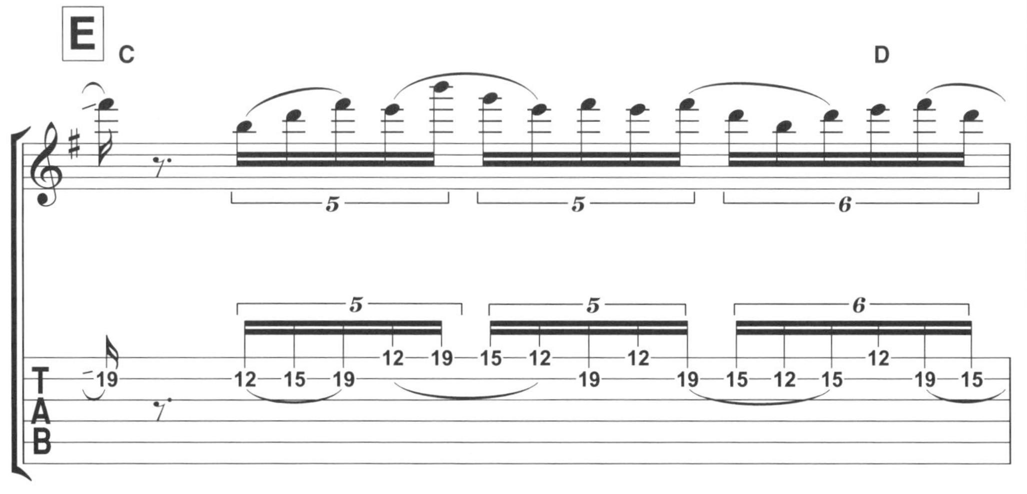
E
C
D
5
5
6
TAB

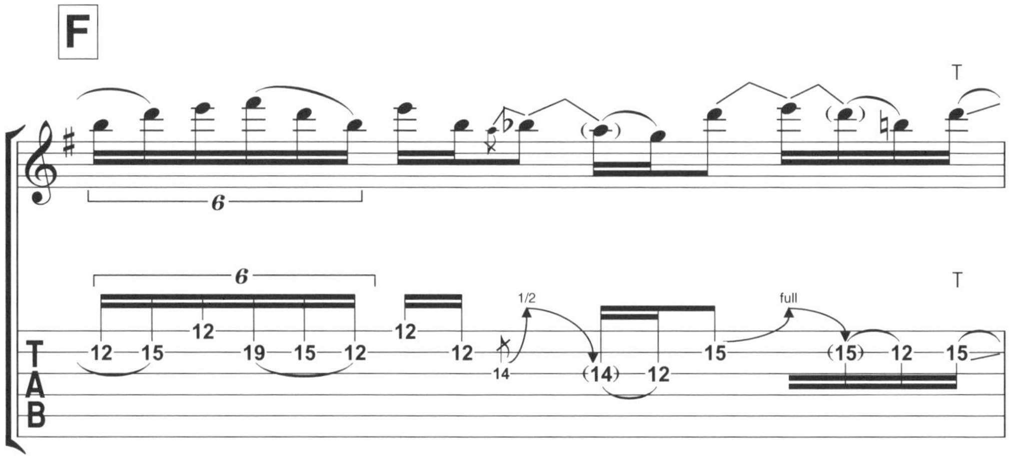
F
6
T
1/2
full
TAB

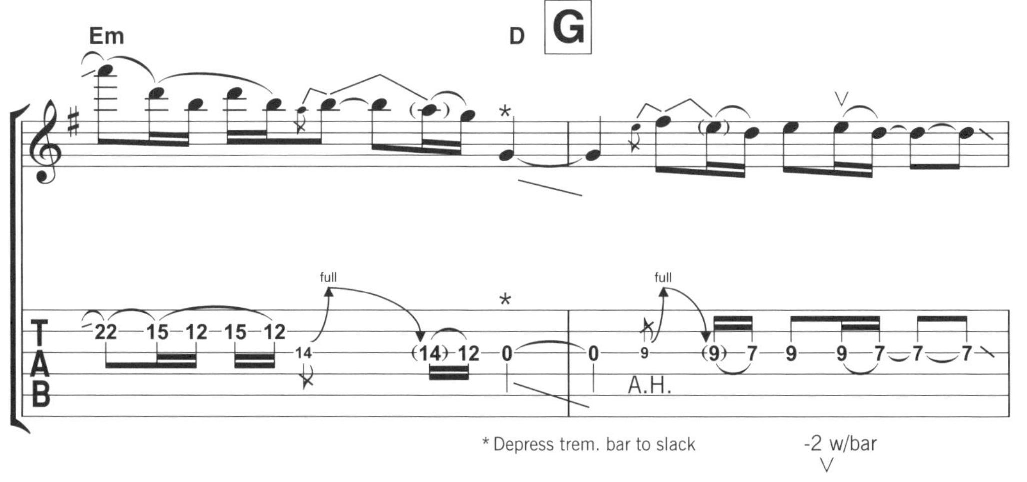
Em
D
G
full
full
A.H.
TAB
* Depress trem. bar to slack
-2 w/bar

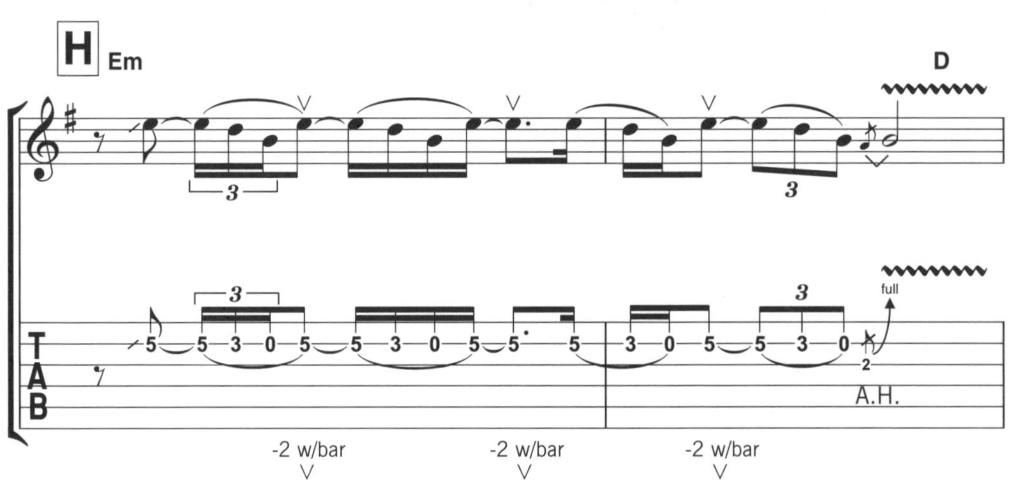
H
Em
D
3
full
A.H.
-2 w/bar
-2 w/bar
-2 w/bar

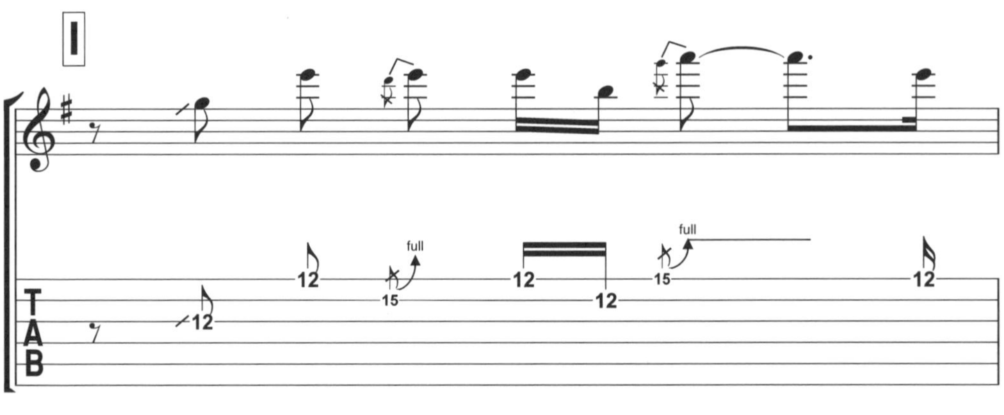
I
full
full

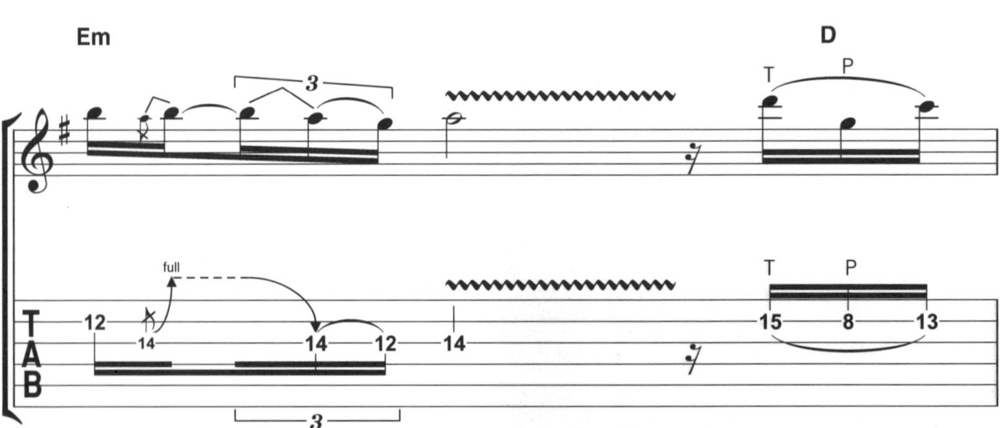
Em
D
T
P
3
full

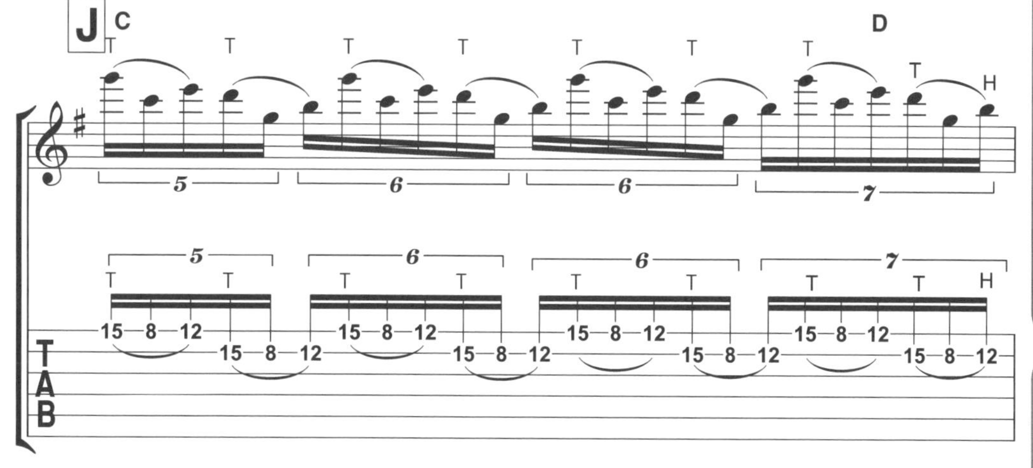
J
C
D
T
H
5
6
7
15
8
12

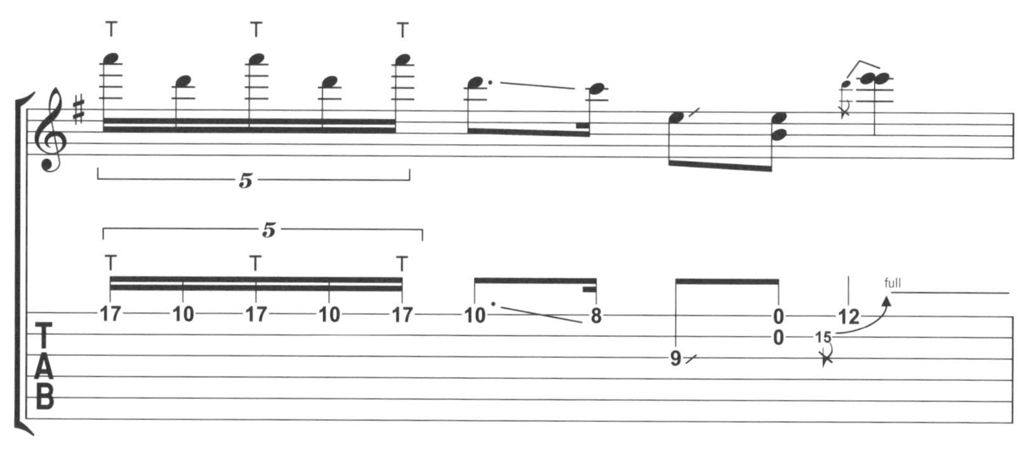
T
5
17
10
8
0
9
12
15
full

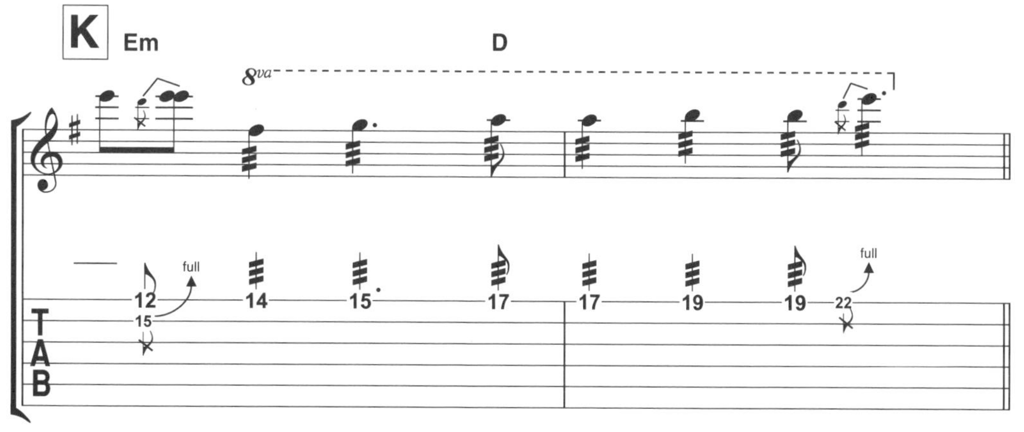
K
Em
D
8va
full
12
15
14
17
19
22

On repeats play Fig. 1 throughout Outro

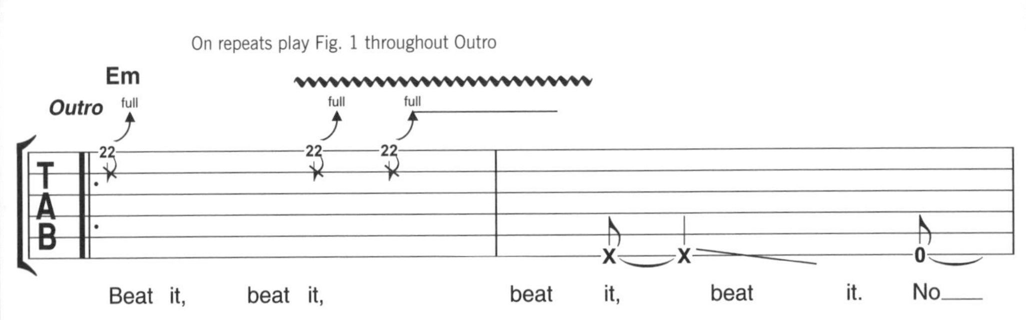

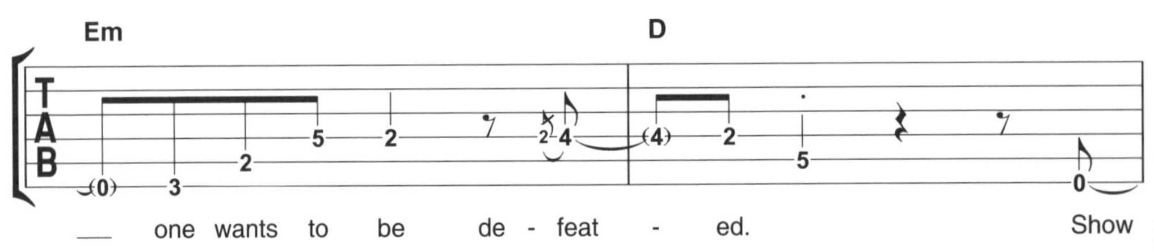

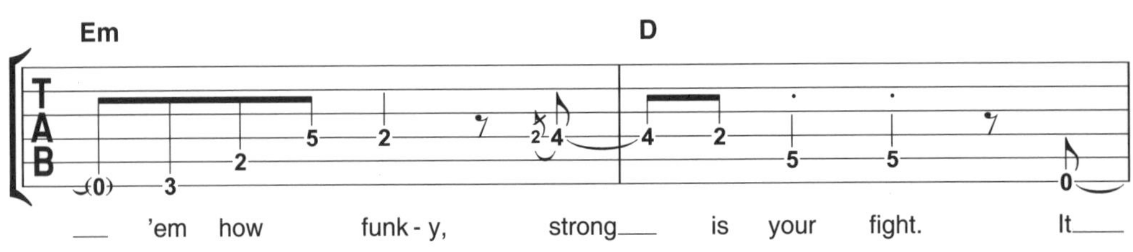

(Repeat to fade)

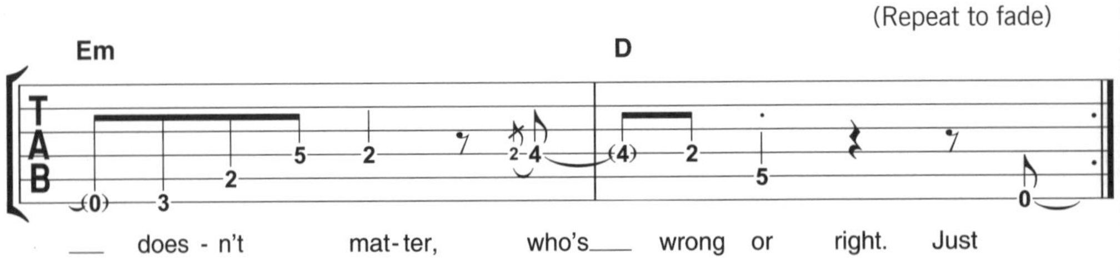

Kinman HX

CHORD GLOSSARY

Open Chords You'll Need

This is where you'll find all the chords you need for strumming through any of the songs featured in this book. Although you'll find chord boxes for some specific chords in many of the songs' tutorial sections, here are some more standard chords, alongside some less familiar Minor 7th, sus, 'add' and 'slash' chords.

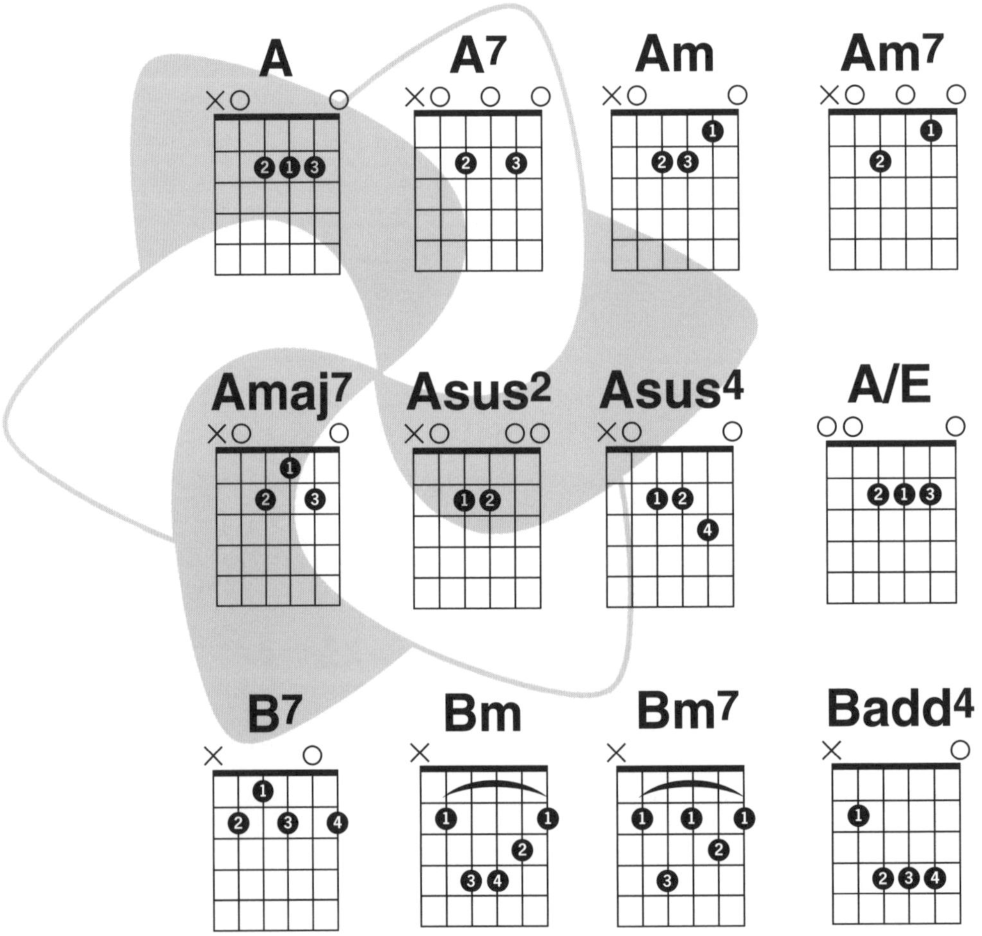

A

A7

Am

Am7

Amaj7

Asus2

Asus4

A/E

B7

Bm

Bm7

Badd4

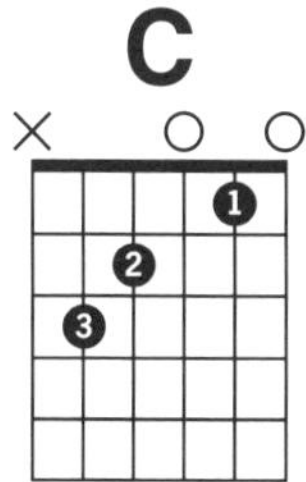
C

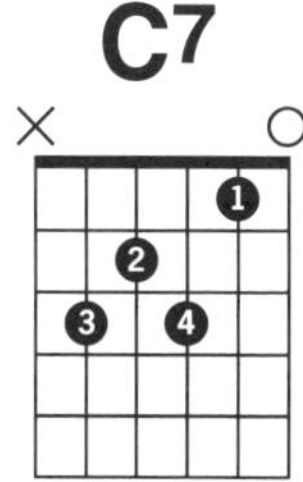
C7

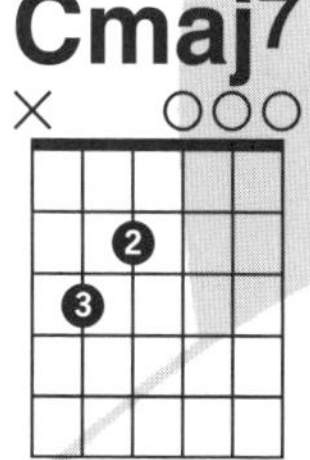
Cmaj7

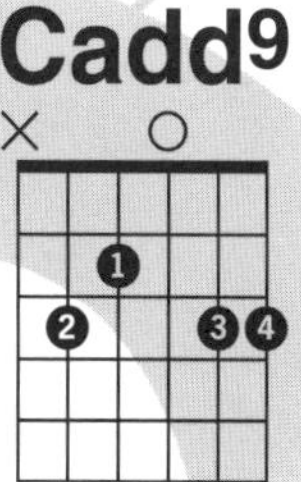
Cadd9

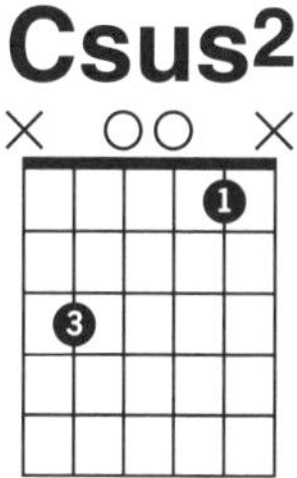
Csus2

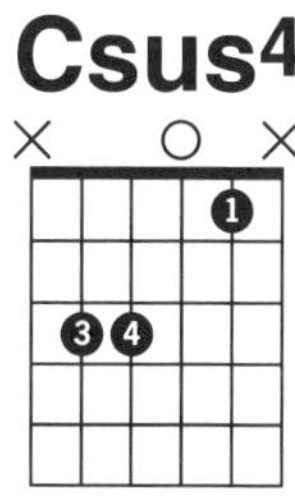
Csus4

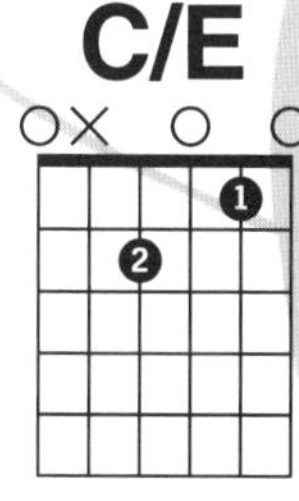
C/E

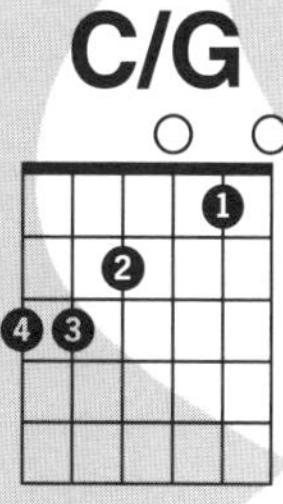
C/G

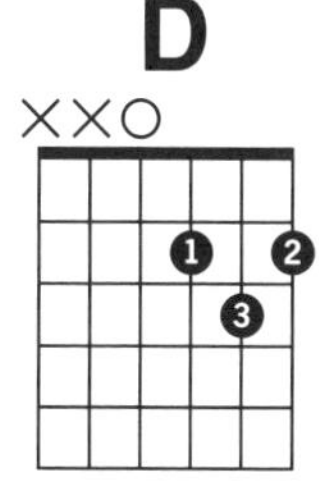
D

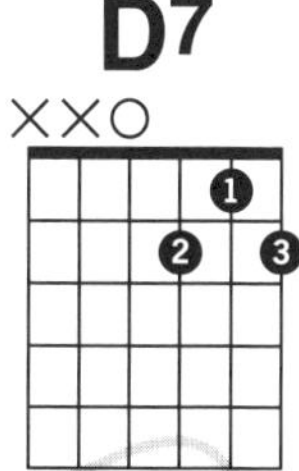
D7

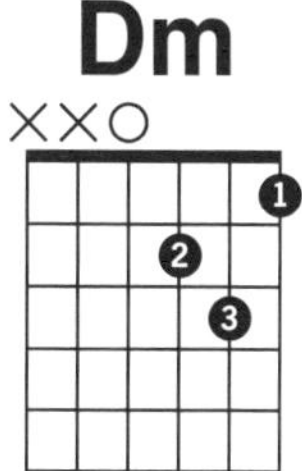
Dm

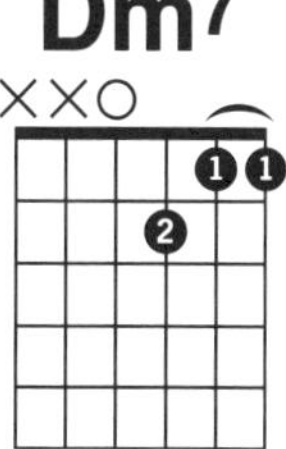
Dm7

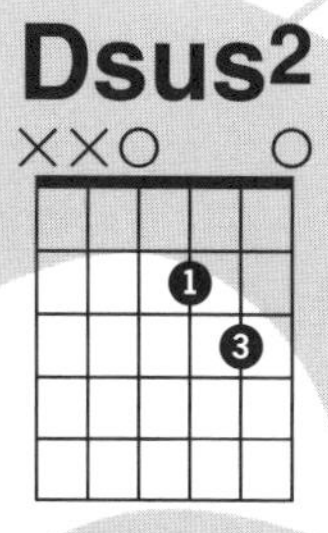
Dsus2

Dsus4

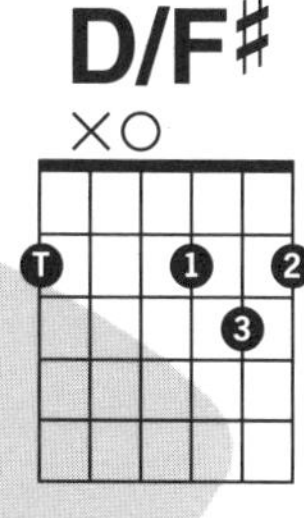
D/F♯

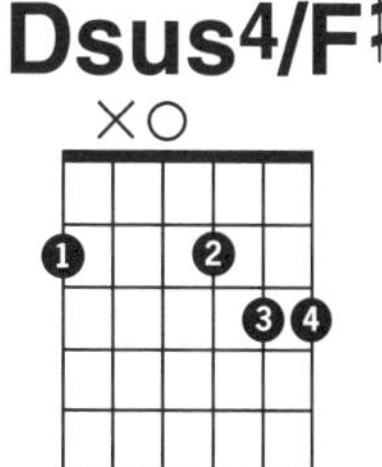
Dsus4/F♯

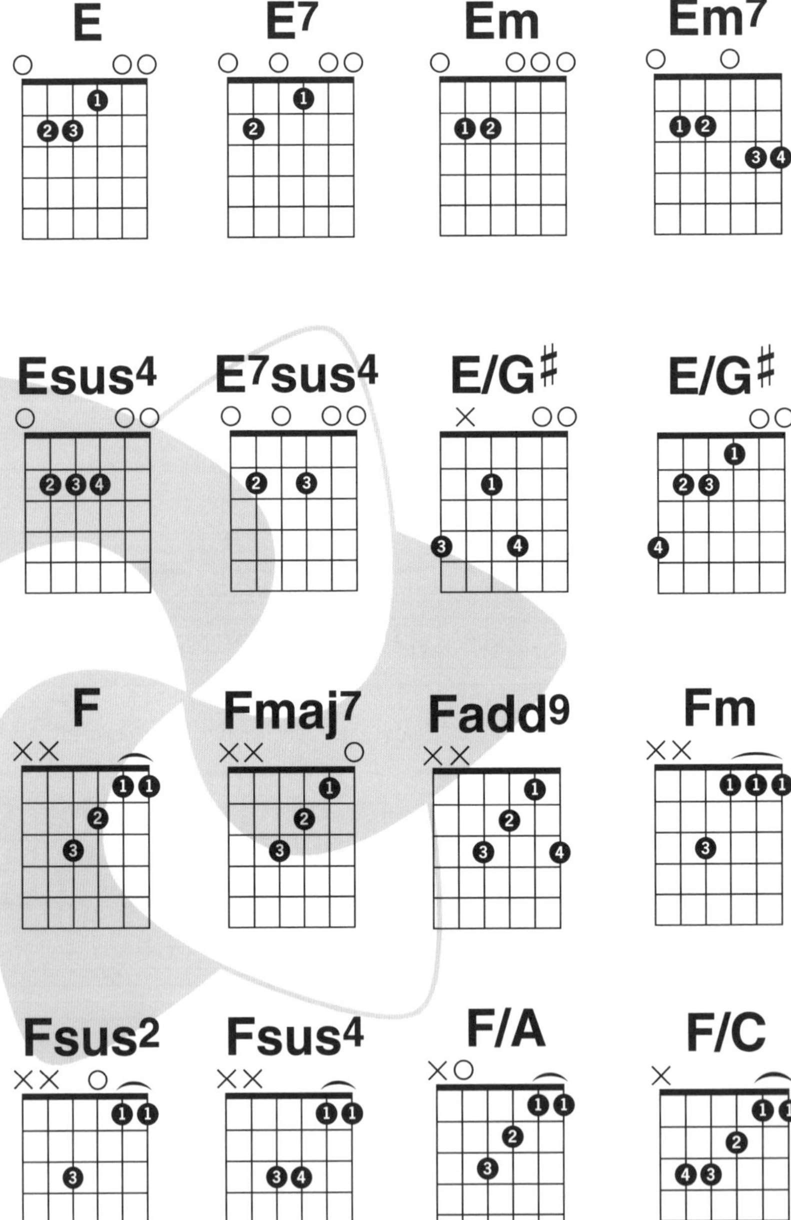
E
E7
Em
Em7
Esus4
E7sus4
E/G♯
E/G♯
F
Fmaj7
Fadd9
Fm
Fsus2
Fsus4
F/A
F/C

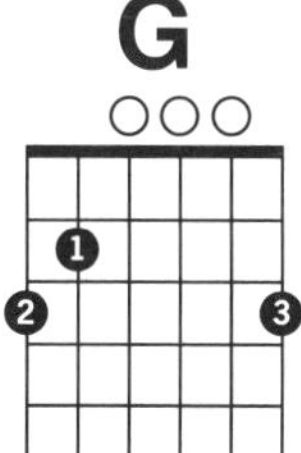
G

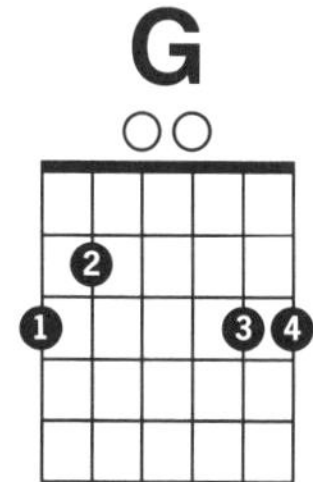
G

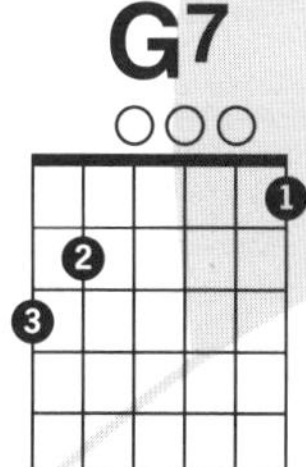
G7

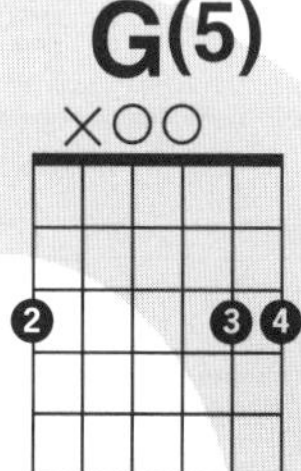
G(5)

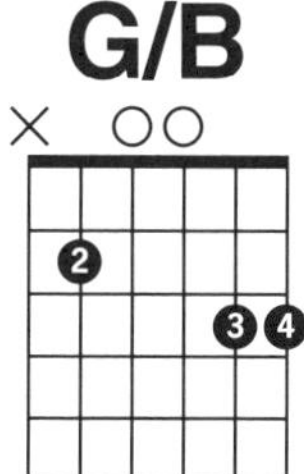
G/B

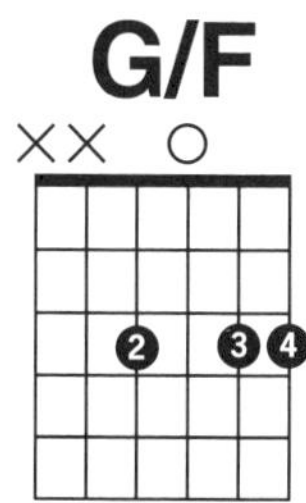
G/F

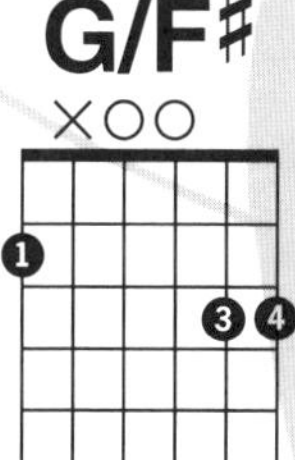
G/F♯

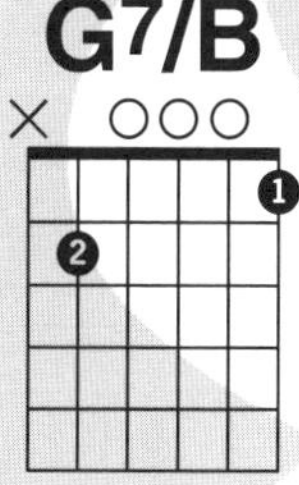
G7/B

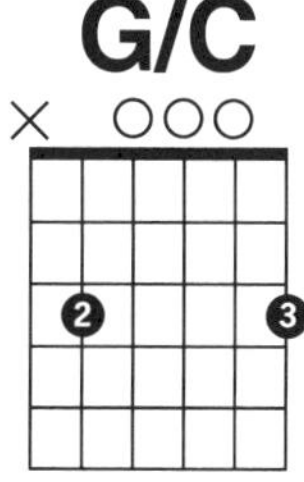
G/C

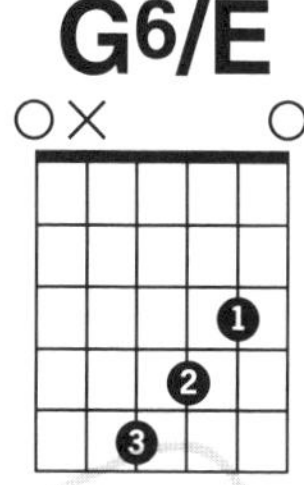
G6/E

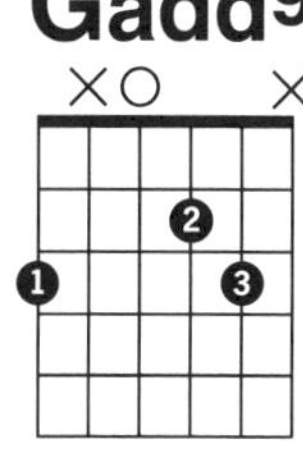
Gadd9

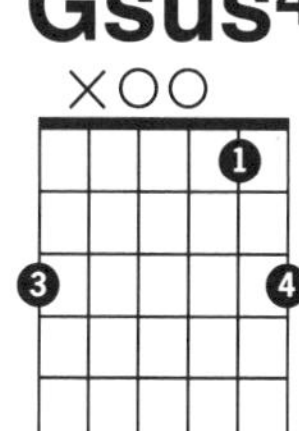
Gsus4

justinguitar.com

Collect the series ...

Justinguitar.com
Beginner's Course
AM1001440R

Justinguitar.com
Beginner's Songbook
AM1005334

Justinguitar.com
Vintage Songbook
AM1005169

Justinguitar.com
Acoustic Songbook
AM1005147R

Justinguitar.com
Rock Songbook
AM1005180

Justinguitar.com
Australian Songbook
AM1005191

- Refresh your beginner skills with the comprehensive ***Justinguitar.com Beginner's Course*** and the accompanying *Beginner's Songbook*.
- Collect the other songbooks in the series. In each of the Acoustic, Vintage, Rock and Australian songbooks, you'll find 50 more songs specially chosen for guitarists who are looking to progress beyond beginner level.